MONOGRAPHS ON BIOCHEMISTRY

EDITED BY

R. H. A. PLIMMER, D.Sc.

AND

F. G. HOPKINS, M.A., M.B., D.Sc., F.R.S.

MONOGRAPHS ON BIOCHEMISTRY

EDITED BY

R. H. A. PLIMMER, D.Sc.

AND

F. G. HOPKINS, M.A., M.B., D.Sc., F.R.S.

THE NATURE OF ENZYME ACTION. By Sir W. M. BAYLISS, D.Sc., F.R.S. 8s. net.

ALCOHOLIC FERMENTATION. By ARTHUR HARDEN, Ph.D., D.Sc., F.R.S.

THE CHEMICAL CONSTITUTION OF THE PROTEINS. By R. H. A. PLIMMER, D.Sc. Part I., Analysis. 7s. net.

THE PHYSIOLOGY OF PROTEIN METABOLISM. By E. P. CATHCART, M.D., D.Sc., F.R.S. 12s. 6d. net.

THE SIMPLE CARBOHYDRATES AND THE GLUCOSIDES. By E. FRANKLAND ARMSTRONG, D.Sc., Ph.D., F.R.S. 13s. net.

OXIDATIONS AND REDUCTIONS IN THE ANIMAL BODY. By H. D. DAKIN, D.Sc., F.I.C., F.R.S. 6s. net.

THE RESPIRATORY EXCHANGE OF ANIMALS AND MAN. By AUGUST KROGH, Ph.D. 9s. net.

LECITHIN AND ALLIED SUBSTANCES. THE LIPINS. By HUGH MACLEAN, M.D., D.Sc. 8s. 6d. net.

NUCLEIC ACIDS. Their Chemical Properties and Physiological Conduct. By WALTER JONES, Ph.D. 9s. net.

———

LONGMANS, GREEN AND CO.,

London, New York, Toronto, Bombay, Calcutta and Madras.

THE
CHEMISTRY OF UREA

THE THEORY OF ITS CONSTITUTION, AND OF THE ORIGIN
AND MODE OF ITS FORMATION IN LIVING ORGANISMS

BY

EMIL A. WERNER, M.A., Sc.D., F.I.C.

PROFESSOR OF APPLIED CHEMISTRY IN THE UNIVERSITY OF DUBLIN

LONGMANS, GREEN AND CO.

39 PATERNOSTER ROW, LONDON, E.C.4
NEW YORK, TORONTO
BOMBAY, CALCUTTA AND MADRAS
1923

Made in Great Britain

GENERAL PREFACE.

THE subject of Physiological Chemistry, or Biochemistry, is enlarging its borders to such an extent at the present time, that no single text-book upon the subject, without being cumbrous, can adequately deal with it as a whole, so as to give both a general and a detailed account of its present position. It is, moreover, difficult, in the case of the larger text-books, to keep abreast of so rapidly growing a science by means of new editions, and such volumes are therefore issued when much of their contents has become obsolete.

For this reason, an attempt is being made to place this branch of science in a more accessible position by issuing a series of monographs upon the various chapters of the subject, each independent of and yet dependent upon the others, so that from time to time, as new material and the demand therefor necessitate, a new edition of each monograph can be issued without re-issuing the whole series. In this way, both the expenses of publication and the expense to the purchaser will be diminished, and by a moderate outlay it will be possible to obtain a full account of any particular subject as nearly current as possible.

The editors of these monographs have kept two objects in view : firstly, that each author should be himself working at the subject with which he deals ; and, secondly, that a *Bibliography*, as complete as possible, should be included, in order to avoid cross references, which are apt to be wrongly cited, and in order that each monograph may yield full and independent information of the work which has been done upon the subject.

It has been decided as a general scheme that the volumes

v

first issued shall deal with the pure chemistry of physiological products and with certain general aspects of the subject. Subsequent monographs will be devoted to such questions as the chemistry of special tissues and particular aspects of metabolism. So the series, if continued, will proceed from physiological chemistry to what may be now more properly termed chemical physiology. This will depend upon the success which the first series achieves, and upon the divisions of the subject which may be of interest at the time.

R. H. A. P.
F. G. H.

PREFACE.

THE results of researches commenced about ten years ago led the writer to doubt the validity of the carbamide formula, so universally accepted by chemists to represent the constitution of urea.

A new formula, which was in much better agreement with the facts, was suggested.

To those unfamiliar with the chemical history of urea, an attempt to refute such a long-standing conception as the carbamide formula would appear no doubt superfluous. The "conclusive" evidence reiterated in the literature, and handed down from text-book to text-book appears sufficient to disarm all further criticism on the subject.

To confirm the original doubt, to test the merits of the new formula, and above all to arrive at the truth has necessitated a reinvestigation of the chief decompositions of urea, and of all the methods which have been devised for its synthesis. The results have surprised no one more than the writer himself.

In this book an attempt has been made to give a comprehensive account of the chemistry of urea, from the date of its isolation to the present time, including all the experimental and theoretical evidence which it is hoped will convince others that an erroneous conception has undoubtedly prevailed amongst chemists in assuming urea to be carbamide.

Considering the simple composition of urea, the existence of a misconception as regards its molecular structure is all the more remarkable. Whilst the reason for the fact may be unique, it is easy to explain.

The production of carbon dioxide and ammonia by the natural fermentation of urea, and by its artificial hydrolysis, led to an early conclusion that urea was carbonate of ammonia from which the elements of water have been abstracted.

The suggestion of the carbamide formula soon followed. That this formula should have received *apparent* confirmation from a succession of peculiarly deceptive syntheses of urea was an unfortunate coincidence.

In this particular respect the chemistry of urea is without a parallel amongst the multitude of carbon compounds.

The results appeared so convincing, and the explanations so straightforward that, so far as an attack on the carbamide formula was concerned, it seemed almost futile to inquire any further into the mechanism of the reactions.

The effect was inevitable. In spite of numerous "anomalies" in the syntheses and decompositions of urea which were never explained, it has been generally assumed that in all its reactions urea behaves in accordance with the requirements of the carbamide formula.

One of the main objects of this book is to prove the fallacy in this assumption, and to show that in the light of the new cyclic formula disagreements between facts and theory no longer prevail in the chemistry of urea.

Modern researches, especially the investigations of M. Fosse, have revealed a much wider distribution of urea in living matter than was previously supposed. Whilst the formation of urea in the higher animals throughout their existence has been long since recognised, there is no doubt it plays an important part in nitrogen metabolism in all forms of animal and plant life, even the very lowest, at some period or other of their existence.

To physiologists, and biologists in general, the constitution of urea is a matter of considerable interest, since a proper appreciation of the mode of its formation in Nature depends on a correct knowledge of its molecular structure.

The writer hopes that the arguments which are put forward in the discussion of this subject in Chapter XII. will help to a clearer understanding of the origin and mode of formation of urea in the animal body.

All syntheses of free urea are similar in their final mechanism.   They are similar, in fact, to Wöhler's historic synthesis, namely, the union of ammonia with cyanic acid in the keto-form.

That serious consideration must be given to the chemistry of cyanic acid in its relation to protein building, and protein degradation in plants, and in animals respectively, is an obvious consequence of this fact.

It is no exaggeration to say that the persisting belief in the carbamide formula has proved a serious barrier to the advancement of our knowledge of this interesting subject.   One ventures to claim that this barrier has now been removed.

The cyclic formula brings the constitution of urea into intimate relation with that of the salts of ammonia.   Since the subject is one of much interest in connection with the chemistry of urea a special chapter is devoted to its discussion.

It is no wonder that the text-books have perpetuated the practice of dealing with urea as an immediate derivative of carbonic acid.   The chemistry of cyanic acid, curiously enough, has always been given minor consideration in its relation to the structure of urea.   This, of course, is wrong.   In the hope of remedying this defect a series of simple lecture experiments are described to demonstrate the properties and constitution of urea on the basis of the cyclic formula.

To make this book of value in the laboratory, as well as of interest in the study, a detailed account is given of all the up-to-date methods in use for the detection and estimation of urea, whilst the older methods have also received due attention. These will be found in Appendix I., which is specially intended for students of medicine.

The fixation of nitrogen in the form of urea is an important problem which has recently been receiving much attention.   A brief reference to the results which have been obtained so far is contained in Appendix II.   It is not unlikely that the efforts to solve this problem will be more successful when the true mechanism of the formation of urea from carbon dioxide and ammonia, via cyanic acid, is more generally appreciated.

The chemistry of substituted derivatives of urea is outside the scope of this work which is restricted to the consideration of the constitution of urea itself.   Hence they are referred to only in connection with the theoretical evidence which they supply in support of the main question. On the other hand, every care has been taken to include a reference to all the theoretical and experimental work which has been contributed to the chemistry of urea proper, since the discovery of the latter just 150 years ago. This has been no light task, and the writer hopes that no serious omission has occurred.

An extensive bibliography of the chemistry of urea, and cyanic acid, and of all the work more or less directly concerned therewith, is given in chronological order. Repetition is thus avoided.

On consulting the bibliographical list under the date, given in brackets, after each name a reference to the work quoted will be found.

It may be well to point out that whilst a good deal of the experimental work for which the writer is responsible has appeared in a series of papers published in the "Transactions of the Chemical Society" over a period of several years, much new matter, particularly on the theoretical side, is presented in this book for the first time.

To his friend and former pupil, Dr. W. R. Fearon, F.T.C.D., the writer tenders his best thanks for several useful suggestions, particularly in that part of the subject which belongs to biological chemistry.

E. A. W.

TRINITY COLLEGE,
    DUBLIN, *April*, 1922.

CONTENTS.

CONTENTS

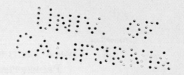

CHAPTER I.

INTRODUCTORY.

The History of Urea to the end of the 19th Century.

IF the importance of a subject can be measured by the amount of work which has been devoted to its study, then assuredly the chemistry of urea can lay claim to a high position in this respect.

Urea was discovered nearly one hundred and fifty years ago, and ever since it has been the subject of numerous investigations, the most interesting of which, from a theoretical point of view, are those concerning the constitution of its molecule.

In the following synopsis of its history it will be seen that, in spite of the comparatively simple composition of urea, much doubt has all along prevailed regarding the question of its molecular constitution.

Although urea is contained in normal human urine to the extent, roughly speaking, of 22 grams per litre, its separation in a pure state is a very tedious operation, and considering the several steps which are involved in the process it is no wonder that the isolation of urea, in a crystalline form, was delayed until the very end of the eighteenth century.

Whilst such chemists as Boerhaave, Marggraf (1709-1783), and Scheele (1742-1786), amongst others, had drawn attention to the presence of "a particular nitrogenous substance" in urine, it was apparently left to Rouelle cadet to make the first attempt to separate it.

In November, 1773, Rouelle, by extracting with alcohol the residue left after the evaporation of urine over a cautiously heated sand-bath, obtained a "substance savoneuse" which gave by analysis much more than half of its weight of "volatile alkali." Rouelle did little more than show that the impure product so obtained was rich in nitrogen, and gave, on fermentation, carbonic acid and ammonia.

To Fourcroy and Vauquelin must be given the credit for having obtained urea in a crystalline form for the first time. In a remarkably comprehensive investigation, the results of which are contained in three memoirs (1798-1799), these careful observers show that, whereas fresh

I

concentrated urine becomes a crystalline mass [1] on the addition of strong nitric acid, a similar phenomenon does not occur with concentrated urine which has previously undergone putrefaction. It is, they said, "this special matter of the urine, which we now call urea (urée), which gives rise to the carbonate of ammonia which replaces it in the putrefaction."

They proved that the crystals formed were a definite compound of urea with nitric acid, a fact which led them to look upon urea as a truly remarkable body, since no other animal substance then known behaved in this way.

Fourcroy and Vauquelin did not succeed in obtaining urea in a state of purity from the nitrate; the removal of the colouring matter was apparently an insurmountable problem at that period. Nevertheless, they studied its decomposition by heat and by acids and alkalis respectively, and the interesting and accurate observations which they made in connection with these reactions will be referred to in their proper place later on.

When we consider the rate of progress of experimental chemistry at the present time, it seems remarkable that a period of over twenty years should elapse between the work of Fourcroy and Vauquelin and the preparation of urea in the pure state. This was accomplished in 1820 by Proust. By decomposing urea nitrate with carbonate of lead he was successful in removing nearly all of the colouring matter, and obtained, as he stated, almost colourless crystals.

Prout, in 1824, made the first accurate analysis of urea, and determined its correct empirical formula.

The following results of Prout's analyses leave no doubt as regards the purity of the material which he prepared :—

	Per Cent.	Atomic Proportions.		
Carbon	19·97	1·66	1	
Hydrogen	6·67	6·67	4	(CH_4N_2O)
Nitrogen	46·65	3·33	2	
Oxygen	26·65	1·66	1	

99·94

The composition of natural urea was thus definitely established when Wöhler in 1828 proclaimed to the chemical world the preparation of urea by artificial means. This was the outcome of a simple attempt to combine ammonia with cyanic acid.

Whilst Wöhler's discovery was undoubtedly one of the first magnitude in the history of chemistry, it was hardly possible to estimate

---

[1] They state, "this property we had noticed two years previously in our investigations on the urine of different animals." It is very well known that dogs' urine is occasionally very rich in urea content.

its full importance at the time, since ammonium cyanate was still unknown, and the phenomenon of isomerism had not yet been observed.

The blow which it gave to the theory of the "vital principle," so strongly upheld by Berzelius, was a strong but not a shattering one. Even twenty years afterwards Organic Chemistry was defined by Berzelius as the chemistry of compounds formed under the influence of life.

In May, 1830, Dumas prepared the first acid amide, namely, oxamide,[1] which he obtained by the action of heat on ammonium oxalate. He studied the hydrolysis of the amide by acids and by alkalis respectively, and pointed out the simple relation which existed between the ammonium salt and the amide produced from it. He threw out the suggestion at this stage that perhaps urea and ammonium cyanate were related, as oxamide to ammonium oxalate.

Later in the same year Dumas studied the decomposition of urea by strong sulphuric acid and by potassium hydroxide, and from a comparison of his results with those obtained from oxamide, he concluded that "urea is to carbonate of ammonia as oxamide is to oxalate of ammonia." He predicted the possible formation of urea from carbonate of ammonia by a reaction similar to that by which he had obtained oxamide from oxalate of ammonia.

Dumas made no attempt to introduce any type of structural formulæ to illustrate the above relationships, and though the temptation was evidently there, he judiciously refrained from suggesting the word "carbamide" as an alternative term for urea.

After a lapse of nearly three years Liebig and Wöhler (1832-33) had completed their brilliant researches on the "benzoyl" radicle, with the result that "rational" or "structural" formulæ were now being freely used to represent the molecular constitution of many organic compounds.

In the meantime Liebig and Wöhler (1830) prepared cyanic acid and cyanate of ammonia, and showed from a study of its properties that the latter compound was quite different from urea, thereby correcting a false impression, prevalent at the time, that urea and cyanate (or cyanite) of ammonia were possibly one and the same substance. In the early part of the same year (1830) Berzelius published the results of his investigations of racemic and tartaric acids. He showed that the two acids had the same composition, and drew the general

---

[1] This was originally obtained in 1817 by Bauhof, by the action of aqueous ammonia on ethyl oxalate, but its nature was not defined.

attention of chemists to the recognition of this phenomenon in organic nature for which he proposed the term "isomerism." Curiously enough, whilst he cited grape sugar and milk sugar (which Prout had recently shown to have the same composition) and fulminic and cyanic acids as further examples of isomeric bodies, Berzelius made no reference to the probable isomerism of urea and cyanate of ammonia.

There is evidence, however, to prove that they were very soon recognised as isomeric compounds.[1]

It was only natural to expect that an early attempt would now be made to solve the problem of the constitution of such a comparatively simple compound as urea.

In 1838 V. Regnault, influenced no doubt by the suggestion of Dumas, sought to prepare urea by the interaction of phosgene and ammonia. It was assumed that the reaction product should be a mixture of *carbamide* and sal ammoniac ($CON_2H_4 + 2NH_3 . HCl$) and, quotes Regnault, " d'après la manière de voir la plus généralement adoptée l'urée est précisement cette carbamide." He failed to obtain urea, or even to recognise its presence, but concluded from evidence of a peculiar character (see Chapter VII.) " qu'il se forme un mélange de sel ammoniac et de carbamide, laquelle carbamide n'est pas l'urée." The difference he explained by assigning to carbamide the formula $(CO)N_2H_4$, whilst the expression $(C_2O_2)N_4H_8$ was proposed for urea.

Whilst Regnault's paper is of historical interest, since here we find for the first time the introduction of the name "carbamide," his experiment failed in its main object.

In 1842 Dumas and Cahours, in a paper on nitrogen metabolism, speaking of the nitrogen taken as food by man, remark, " Ainsi il sort de l'animal, l'acide carbonique, l'eau, l'acide cyanique, l'oxyde d'ammonium, ces deux derniers combinés et modifiés produisent, comme M. Wöhler nous a montré, de l' urée. Il reste à se demander ce que c'est que cette urée."

In 1850 Hofmann prepared carbanilid, or di-phenylurea, from the interaction of phosgene and aniline, and pointed out that since the reaction was obviously of the same type as that employed by Regnault in the production (?) of " carbamide," it afforded a striking confirmation of the latter's original explanation of the phenomenon, " if," remarked Hofmann, " we recollect that carbamide is actually a submultiple of urea ; that is, urea is dicarbamide."

---

[1] In a paper read before the French Academy in December, 1830, on " Matiéres organiques azotées " by Henry and Plisson, these chemists refer to urea and " cyanite " of ammonia as " exemples bien sensibles de corps isômères."

It seems, therefore, quite clear that, at this period of its history urea was believed to be a substance quite distinct from carbamide, and whilst the constitution of the latter was considered as proved, that of urea remained still obscure.

A truly singular conclusion, bearing in mind that the supposed carbamide had not been isolated. This erroneous conception prevailed apparently for several years; it was abandoned only in 1856 when Natanson proved that urea was formed from the interaction of phosgene and ammonia (thus succeeding where Regnault had failed), and also when ethyl carbonate was heated at 180° with excess of ammonia solution.

The direct synthesis (as it was assumed) of urea from two immediate derivatives of carbonic acid, in accordance with what were now recognised as general methods for the production of acid amides, appeared to leave no doubt as regards its constitution, and the names "carbamide" and "urea" now became synonymous terms.

The formation of urea from oxamide, noticed by Williamson in 1847, helped, no doubt, to support confidence in the carbamide formula.

In 1868 Basarov announced the synthesis of urea by the action of heat on ammonium carbamate (and ammonium carbonate) under pressure, thus giving practical effect to the suggestion put forward nearly forty years previously by Dumas. This attracted more than ordinary attention since it was believed to supply the final proof required to establish the validity of the "carbamide" formula. The synthesis was supposed to arise from a simple loss of water from the ammonium salt, viz. :—

$$CO . (NH_2) . O . NH_4 \rightarrow CO(NH_2)_2 + H_2O.$$

This, however, was not quite the view held by Kolbé, in whose laboratory Basarov carried out his experiments. While expressing his conviction that urea is not carbamide, Kolbé was disposed to represent the change as follows :—

$$\left. \begin{array}{c} CO . H_2N \\ H_4N \end{array} \right\} O = \left. \begin{array}{c} CO . H_2N \\ H_2 \end{array} \right\} N + H_2O.$$

Whilst all the syntheses of urea, with the exception of Wöhler's, appeared to uphold the symmetrical "diamide" formula, several of the properties and decompositions of urea were found to be at variance with this conception.

Wanklyn and Gamgee (1868) studied the decomposition of urea by potassium permanganate in strongly alkaline solution; their results

led them to conclude that (1) "the two nitrogen atoms are not combined in the same manner in the urea molecule," and (2) "urea is not
resolved into ammonia and carbonic acid with anything like sufficient
ease to admit of its being carbamide."

They proposed the modified formula $H_2N . C(NH) . OH$. It was
perhaps an unfortunate coincidence that this formula should have been
put forward almost at the same time as the announcement of Basarov's
synthesis, as it does not appear to have received the general attention
which it deserved.

In the following year (1869) Heintz suggested the formula
$CO : NH_2 . NH_2$, in which the central nitrogen atom is represented as
pentavalent, a difference in the function of the two nitrogen atoms
being one of the chief features displayed. This formula is such a
radical departure from the carbamide structure that it was never given
any serious consideration. It is in the main similar to that advocated
by Kolbé. In spite of the synthetic evidence, investigations relating
to the chemistry of urea in the succeeding years show that there was
still certain hesitation in accepting the " carbamide " formula.

Fenton, in 1879, decided in favour of Wanklyn and Gamgee's
formula in explaining the decomposition of urea by a hypochlorite in
alkaline solution, whereby only one atomic proportion of nitrogen was
set free.

In 1882 Griess, in discussing the respective merits of the " carbamide " and Wanklyn formula, arrived at the conclusion that, whilst the
latter represents a urea capable of combining with either acids or
bases, the former represents an unknown substance.

In discussing the constitution of cyanuric acid in 1885, Hofmann
remarked, "its formation from carbamide does not prove it to have the
constitution commonly assigned to it, since the constitution of carbamide itself has not been definitely established." Thus, nearly sixty
years after Wöhler's synthesis, it was conceded by one of the most
eminent authorities of the time that the structure of the urea molecule
still remained obscure. With the exception of the production of urea
by the action of ammonia on phenyl carbonate (Hentschel, 1884) and
on guaiacol carbonate (Cazeneuve, 1896), reactions which are but ex-
tensions of Natanson's synthesis from ethyl carbonate, no new evidence
has been discovered to support the carbamide formula since Basarov's
experiments. Whilst it is clearly evident that a certain distrust in this
formula persisted up to about the date last mentioned, its universal
acceptance in modern times is a prominent feature in the history of
urea. All the available methods for solving the problem had ap-

parently been exhausted.   There was seemingly no alternative but to
accept the "carbamide" formula, and it must be admitted once again
that the synthetic evidence appeared to point conclusively towards
this decision.   Indeed, the belief in the validity of the carbamide
formula had become so strongly rooted, that the present-day literature
leaves the student no reason to think that the molecular constitution
of urea was ever a matter of any doubt.

In 1913 the writer, for reasons which are fully detailed in the
succeeding chapters, suggested the cyclic formula

$$\text{HN} : \text{C} \Big\langle \begin{array}{c} \diagup \text{NH}_3 \\ | \\ \diagdown \text{O} \end{array}$$

to represent the constitution of urea in the static condition or when
present in a neutral solvent.   The defence of this formula has necessitated
an investigation into the mechanism of all the principal syntheses and
decompositions of urea.   The results obtained, after eight years, have
brought to light the peculiarly delusive nature of the different syntheses, and have proved conclusively, he ventures to hope, that the
"carbamide" formula is quite untenable.

Chemists are left to judge if the numerous facts, old and new,
attaching to the chemistry of urea (many of them have hitherto
remained obscure) have been properly explained by the theories
put forward by the writer.

In presenting this sketch of the history of urea, only those facts
and incidents which bear directly on the vexed question of the constitution of urea have been selected.

CHAPTER II.

THE MECHANISM OF WÖHLER'S SYNTHESIS.

THE outstanding event in the history of urea is unquestionably Wöhler's synthesis, which has made the year 1828 a memorable one in the annals of chemistry.

Like many epoch-making discoveries, it may be said to have come before its time, since nearly twenty years passed before the next synthesis of a carbon compound (acetic acid, Kolbé 1845) was recorded ; after which many syntheses followed in rapid succession. The following account [1] of the artificial production of urea, as described by Wöhler, throws an interesting light on the origin of his discovery : " J'ai annoncé que par l'action du cyanogène sur l'ammoniaque liquide, il se forme de l'acide oxalique et une substance blanche cristalline, que l'on obtient aussi toutes les fois que l'on cherche à combiner l'acide cyanique avec l'ammoniaque par double décomposition.

" J'ai obtenue la même substance blanche plus facilement en décomposant le cyanate de plomb par l'ammoniaque liquide. Comme j'ai trouvé qu'il ne se formait aucun autre produit, et que l'oxide de plomb etait separé pur, j'imaginai qu'il pouvait se former, par la combinaison de l'acide cyanique avec l'ammoniaque, une substance organique et peut-être un principe semblable à une base salifiable végétale. J'ai fait quelques recherches, sur l'action des acides sur le corps cristallisé ; 'mais il se comporte avec eux d'une manière indifférente, a l'exception de l'acide nitrique, qui forme aussitôt dans la dissolution concentrée un précipité en écailles brillantes.

" Ces cristaux purifiés montraient un caractère très-acide ; et j'étais déjà porté à les prendre pour un acide particulier, lorsque j'ai trouvé que par la neutralisation avec les bases ils donnaient des nitrates. Cette similitude de resultats avec ceux que donne l'urée m'engagea à faire des essais comparatifs sur l'urée pure séparée de l'urine ; il en est résulté de la manière la plus évidente que l'urée et ce corps cristallin, ou le cyanate d'ammoniaque, si on peut l'appeler ainsi, sont des matières absolument identiques."

Urea was therefore originally obtained by Wöhler (1822) by the hydrolytic decomposition of cyanogen (in the presence of ammonia), a

---

[1] Communicated to the " Annales de Chimie et de Physique," in 1828.

reaction which was investigated by Vauquelin in 1818, who obtained the ammonium salt of an acid to which he gave the name "acide cyanique."

Whilst it may be justly argued that Wöhler's discovery[1] was not the first synthesis of an organic compound, it was certainly the first recorded example of an "isomeric transformation," and herein lay its great distinction.

Assuming urea to be carbamide, it is the custom to represent the change merely as

$$NH_4.OCN = CO(NH_2)_2$$

with the not uncommon remark that carbamide is produced as the result of a "simple" molecular rearrangement of ammonium cyanate.

When the thoughtful student endeavours to form a mental picture of the remarkable rearrangement of atoms required by such a change, the complexity of the phenomenon is at once apparent, and it is certainly not made any easier of comprehension by the occasional use, in text-books and elsewhere, of such formulæ as NH_4NCO and NH_4CNO, to represent ammonium cyanate.

The first experiments on the mechanism of Wöhler's synthesis were made in 1895 by Walker and Hambly, and later by Walker and Kay (1897), and by Walker and Wood (1900).

The following interesting facts were established :—

1. The transformation of ammonium cyanate into urea is a bimolecular reaction.

2. In a decinormal aqueous solution the change is appreciable at 25°, and the velocity of the action increases rapidly with rise of temperature. Whilst at 80° half of the ammonium cyanate is transformed in from ten to twelve minutes, at 25° three days are required to produce the same effect.

3. At 100° an equilibrium is attained which corresponds to a mixture of approximately 95·5 parts of urea and 4·5 parts of ammonium cyanate. A similar condition is reached by heating a solution of urea at 100°. The change is therefore reversible under this condition.

[1] Had urea not been a substance produced in the animal body, its synthesis would certainly not have attracted the attention which it did. Hennell's synthesis of alcohol, for example (1828), passed almost unnoticed. Ethylene, the starting-point of Hennell's experiment, was an organic compound, which, it is true, had not been synthesised, but Wöhler also started with an organic compound, viz. cyanic acid, which had been "synthesised" by Berthollet in 1787.

There is little doubt that Vauquelin must have obtained urea, as well as ammonium cyanate, but failed to recognise its presence. It was not until 1830 that Wöhler definitely proved that urea was formed when cyanogen was decomposed in aqueous solution.

4. Whilst the presence of ammonium sulphate and of potassium cyanate respectively increased the velocity of the transformation, free ammonia (N/10) had a slight retarding effect.

5. The presence of alcohol increased the velocity of the transformation in a marked manner; thus in 90 per cent alcohol the rate of change was 30 times greater than in pure water.

6. Pure solid ammonium cyanate was rapidly changed to urea at 70° to 80°. The presence of moisture is an important factor in promoting the transformation even at the ordinary temperature. In an atmosphere dried by means of phosphorus pentoxide, the cyanate showed little sign of alteration even after several months.

The formation of urea from ammonium cyanate was studied by Walker and his co-workers from a purely physico-chemical standpoint, and they concluded that the ions $NH_4^{\cdot}$ and CNO' were the active agents concerned in the change, which they represent as taking place in two stages, namely :—

$$NH_4CNO \rightarrow NH_4^{\cdot} + CNO' \rightarrow CO(NH_2)_2.$$

Whilst no doubt certain of the facts observed (such as 2, 3, 4) were apparently in favour of an ionic theory of the change, the great acceleration of the change produced by the presence of a high concentration of alcohol was certainly not to be expected.

Moreover, several other neutral substances examined by Walker and Kay were found to have a still greater accelerating effect than alcohol on the change. In the following table are given the values which they found with decinormal solutions of ammonium cyanate which contained in each case 10 per cent. by volume of the neutral substance :—

	Velocity Constant $(K \times 100)$.	Percentage Increase on Rate of Change.
Pure water	0·595	—
Glycerol	0·763	28·2
Ethyl alcohol	0·777	30·6
Cane-sugar	0·810	36·1
Glycol	0·819	37·7
Methyl alcohol	0·871	46·4
Acetone	0·882	48·2

In order to eliminate a needless number of zeros, the values for K (as given by Walker) have been multiplied a hundredfold.

The accelerating influence of acetone, it will be seen, is nearly 18 per cent. greater than that of ethylic alcohol. Whilst they state, " To what this acceleration may be due, we have at present no means of ascertaining," it was suggested, so far as ethylic alcohol is concerned, that, by altering the nature of the solvent it so increases the rate of interaction of the ions $NH_4^{\cdot}$ and CNO' that the effect more than counterbalances the diminution in the velocity of the change which should result from the diminished concentration of the ions produced by its presence.

If this be so, then the effects of the other neutral substances must presumably be due to the same cause.   The results are certainly not of an order that could be claimed to support an ionic theory of the change.   The effect of ammonium sulphate in promoting the rate of the transformation of ammonium cyanate is assumed to be due to the increase of the active mass of the $NH_4^{\cdot}$ ion, the $SO_4^{\prime}$ ion remaining a disinterested spectator of the change.

This is quite in harmony with the electrolytic dissociation theory and with the views commonly held as regards the constitution of salts of ammonia; on the other hand, free ammonia in solution with the cyanate retards the reaction, and this effect has also been assumed to uphold the above theory of the change.   Now in such a solution there are, *according to this theory*, $NH_4^{\cdot}$ and $OH^{\prime}$ ions, relatively small in number no doubt, and hence, since there is a small increase of the active mass of the former ion, one would scarcely expect to find a retardation of the change in this case.

Whilst full praise must be granted to the interesting and valuable observations recorded by Walker and his co-workers, the fact remains that the fundamental question arising out of Wöhler's synthesis has been left untouched by their investigations, namely—"How is urea formed in this transformation of ammonium cyanate?"   Assuming, for a moment, that the ions $NH_4^{\cdot}$ and $CNO^{\prime}$ have a real existence, what is the next step whereby "carbamide" is produced from them?

The ionic theory of the change has failed to throw any real light on the main question, and in consequence it has been largely abandoned in recent years.

Liebig and Wöhler (1831) showed that ammonium cyanate contained in a vessel loosely covered with paper was almost entirely converted into urea after two days' exposure at ordinary temperature, *whilst it continually gave off ammonia*.   When the salt was left in an atmosphere of ammonia, enclosed in a bell-jar standing over mercury, it was found to be unchanged after eight days.

There are, as we shall see, three phases involved in the transformation of ammonium cyanate into urea.

In the above experiments of Liebig and Wöhler we find the key to the explanation of the first phase.   Strange that it should have required nearly a hundred years to find the explanation of the two remaining phases.

All ammonium salts are characterised by the ease with which they are dissociated,[1] by heat, into ammonia and the particular acid from which they are derived. If the salt is derived from a weak acid, such as carbonic, carbamic, or cyanic acid, it suffers dissociation even at the ordinary temperature. It is this dissociation of ammonium cyanate into ammonia and cyanic acid that gives rise to its spontaneous transformation into urea.

It is the first phase in Wöhler's synthesis.

When dissociation is prevented, as in Liebig and Wöhler's second experiment, urea is not formed.

The presence of water, as is well known, is a necessary factor in promoting dissociation of ammonium salts, according to the change $NH_4X = NH_3 + HX$, hence dry ammonium cyanate, as Walker has shown, is not changed to urea at the ordinary temperature.

A full discussion on the constitution of ammonium salts in their relation to the present subject is properly deferred until all the facts connected with the constitution of urea have been considered.

In the meantime, the writer ventures to remark that the strong belief in the ionisation of ammonium salts in solution, to the exclusion of their possible "hydrolytic" dissociation according to above equation, has been, to a great measure, responsible for the failure to appreciate and explain the chemical relations of ammonium cyanate and urea.

While the writer was engaged in the investigation of this question, Chattaway (1912) put forward the following scheme to explain the probable change which occurs in Wöhler's synthesis, viz. :—

$$H_4N.N:C:O \rightleftarrows HN:C:O + NH_3 \rightleftarrows HN:C{\overset{OH}{\underset{NH_2}{\big<}}} \rightleftarrows H_2N.CO.NH_2$$

(Ammonium cyanate.)　　　　　　　　　　　　　　　　　　　（" Carbamide."）

Whilst the dissociation of the ammonium salt is correctly considered to be the first phase in the change, the view taken of its constitution leads at once to an insurmountable difficulty in understanding the progress of the reaction from left to right. Since all the changes are represented as reversible, if cyanic acid is considered to be $HN:C:O$ only, then why should we have on the one hand the reaction

$$NH_3 + HN:C:O = H_4N.N:C:O$$

---

[1] The term dissociation is used throughout the following pages to denote all changes corresponding to that mentioned above. The tendency, so common at present, to use the single word "dissociation" when electrolytic or "ionic" dissociation is meant is, to say the least of it, misleading. The term was introduced into chemical phraseology for a special purpose long before the ionic theory was suggested. There is no reason why a term to describe a fact should be usurped in order to denote a condition which is theoretical.

and on the other hand the reaction

$$NH_3 + HN:C:O = HN:C\begin{cases} NH_2 \\ OH \end{cases}$$

Either one or the other of the two isomerides has apparently no right of existence according to this scheme.

The same objection applies to an explanation suggested by Hill and Wheeler (1912); thus ammonium cyanate breaks up with heat into HNCO and NH_3, and then the NH_3 adds itself, as follows :—

$$\begin{array}{ccc} HN:C:O & & H_2N.CO \\ \uparrow + \uparrow & = & | \\ H.NH_2 & & NH_2 \end{array}$$

Both schemes fail to give an insight of the full mechanism of the change, and they take a wrong view of the nature of the first phase.

Now, ammonium cyanate dissociates into ammonia and cyanic acid only, and since the former is not known to exist in an isomeric form, a change in the constitution of the latter must be responsible for the production, from these two substances, of a compound different from the original ammonium cyanate.

If a change in the configuration of the cyanic acid molecule from $HO.C:N$ to $HN:C:O$ with rise of temperature be admitted, then all phenomena connected with the transformation of ammonium cyanate into urea can be explained in a simple manner.

The following scheme, proposed by the writer in 1913, gives a clear conception of the progress of the change :—

$$\begin{array}{ccccc} & & NH_3 & & \\ & & \diagup\ \diagdown & & \\ H_4N.O.CN \rightleftarrows & & + & & \rightleftarrows HN:C\begin{cases} NH_3 \\ O \end{cases} \\ & \downarrow & & \downarrow & \\ \text{Ammonium cyanate.} & H.O.CN & \rightleftarrows & HN:C:O & \text{Urea.} \\ & \text{(Enol-form.)}^1 & & \text{(Keto-form.)} & \end{array}$$

There are thus three distinct phases in the synthesis, namely :—

Phase 1. Dissociation of ammonium cyanate giving ammonia and cyanic acid in the enol-form.

Phase 2. Change of cyanic acid from the enol to the keto-form as an effort to attain greater stability.

Phase 3. Reunion of ammonia with cyanic acid in the altered form to produce urea of constitution quite different from " carbamide ".

---

[1] Since the group ·HN·CO· shows great analogy in its behaviour to the group ·CH$_2$·CO·, the distinctive terms " enol " and " keto " are equally well applicable to the former group, and are used here in preference to the usual unsuitable terms " normal " and "*iso*" for the two forms of cyanic acid.

It will be seen, therefore, that as soon as phase I is in progress the production of urea is dependent on the migration of a single atom of hydrogen, in cyanic acid, from oxygen to nitrogen. No further migration of atoms, nor an obscure atomic rearrangement, such as is demanded by the change $NH_4OCN \rightarrow CO(NH_2)_2$ is necessary to form urea from the cyanate.

The ease with which the change takes place, and the small heat effect by which it is accompanied, are indicative of a small atomic disturbance during the reaction. A close similarity in structure between the two isomerides seems a natural consequence thereof.

The partial reversion of urea to ammonium cyanate in aqueous or in alcoholic solution, at a temperature much below that at which urea is known to change otherwise, is an interesting fact which was scarcely to be expected with the "carbamide" formula in mind.

For this reason, no doubt, the phenomenon remained for such a long time unnoticed.

Since the difference between the two isomerides is no more than the difference between the union of ammonia with each of the two forms of cyanic acid, not only is the simple mechanism by which one is changed to the other explained by the above scheme, but the limitations of, and conditions necessary for, the reversion from right to left are fairly well predicted.

As ammonium cyanate is dissociated by heat, so is urea. The temperature at which the latter is affected is relatively high; it will vary with the nature of the solvent, but the dissociation point of urea must be reached before it can show reversion.

No theory to explain the mechanism of Wöhler's synthesis can be expected to claim general acceptance until it has received the full support of experimental evidence. It is obvious that in the foregoing explanation of the change, the conception that cyanic acid may be represented by two different molecular forms in equilibrium requires such support. The whole success of the scheme may be said to pivot upon this point.

The constitution of cyanic acid is therefore a question of paramount importance in solving the problem of the relation which exists between the two isomerides, urea and ammonium cyanate. It must, therefore, be given full consideration before the main question, i.e. the constitution of urea itself, can be logically dealt with.

CHAPTER III.

THE CONSTITUTION OF CYANIC ACID. ITS POLYMERISATION AND HYDROLYSIS.

IN 1824 Wöhler determined the composition of certain metallic cyanates, and deduced therefrom the composition of the free acid, which at the time was only recognisable in aqueous solution by its pungent odour. His results were received with grave doubt, since they gave the same composition for the acid as that found for fulminic acid by Liebig and Gay Lussac (1824). Since the two substances were very different, the salts of one exploding and of the other not, these investigators remarked : " Il faudrait, pour expliquer cette différence, admettre entre leurs élémens un mode de combinaison différent ? "

In 1826 Liebig analysed the acid and concluded that it contained less oxygen than Wöhler had found, and proposed the name " cyanous acid."

All doubt was set at rest in 1830, when Wöhler prepared anhydrous liquid cyanic acid by the distillation of cyanuric acid, which he had previously obtained by the action of heat on urea.

The phenomenon of isomerism had in the meantime become an established fact.

In the same year Liebig and Wöhler, working together, made a careful investigation of the acid. They showed how the liquid changed, even at 0°, spontaneously, and with explosive violence, into a white insoluble substance, which they named "insoluble cyanuric acid," and later, cyamelide.

Their observations on the behaviour of the acid in the presence of water are of special interest. They remark : " One part reacts with water to form carbonate of ammonia, which is then decomposed by another part into carbonic acid and *urea*, while a third part changes alone into the white insoluble substance " (cyamelide).

Liebig and Wöhler noticed also the formation of some cyamelide during the spontaneous transformation of ammonium cyanate into

15

urea, and Walker likewise observed its formation in small amount during the slow transformation of the cyanate in aqueous solution at low temperatures.

This is the result of a "secondary" reaction,[1] which has been considered of little or no importance.

(a) Polymerisation of Cyanic Acid.

Much uncertainty has always prevailed as to the constitution of cyanic acid; is it to be regarded as HOCN or HNCO? In its enolic form it may be considered as the nitril of carbonic acid, and the hydrolysis of the alkali cyanates goes to show that the salts are derived from this form of the acid. Thus, in the case of ammonium cyanate, which yields more or less ammonium carbonate during its conversion into urea in aqueous solution, the change is evidently as follows :—

$$H_4N . O . CN + H_2O \rightarrow H_4N . O . CO . NH_2$$
$$+ H_2O \rightarrow H_4N . O . CO . O . NH_4,$$

ammonium carbamate being an intermediate product. Assuming the formula $H_4N . N : C : O$, the change would be by no means easy to follow, even admitting the existence of the ions NH'_4 and NCO' in solution.

Now, cyanic acid represents an unstable group of four atoms, which, in virtue of the closely related electro-chemical nature of three of them (C, N, and O), is not capable of assuming a simple molecular configuration which can give rise to a condition of electrostatic equilibrium. This end is attained by polymerisation to a six-membered ring, the most stable form of cyclic molecules.

Two different polymerides are formed from cyanic acid, which are believed to be correctly represented by the following structural formulæ :

Cyamelide $HN : C \Big\langle \begin{matrix} O . C(NH) \\ O . C(NH) \end{matrix} \Big\rangle O$ Cyanuric acid $HO . C \Big\langle \begin{matrix} N . C(OH) \\ N . C(OH) \end{matrix} \Big\rangle N$

(Hantzsch's formula.)   (Enol-form.)

Cyamelide is formed only when polymerisation is effected at a low temperature; cyanuric acid is formed exclusively at a high temperature,

---

[1] The whole chemistry of urea abounds in secondary reactions, nearly all of which have been lightly passed over as of no consequence so far as the main reaction is concerned. Secondary reactions are almost invariably the beacons which light up the path to the proper understanding of the mechanism of the main reaction. Failure to appreciate this fact has been largely responsible for the many erroneous interpretations of the decompositions and reactions of urea.

but is also produced in considerable quantity at a low temperature. It is obvious there must be a definite reason for the formation of the two polymerides.

The following theory of the polymerisation, put forward by the writer (1913), based on the existence of two forms of cyanic acid in equilibrium, gives a simple and satisfactory explanation of the phenomenon. The enol-form of the acid is the less stable, and will tend to attain greater stability by changing to the more stable keto-form, thus :—

Enol.   Phase (a).   Phase (b).   Keto.

Since an interval of time must elapse, while the hydrogen atom has migrated from oxygen to nitrogen, either a valency of the oxygen atom becomes momentarily free (a), followed immediately by a momentary liberation of a carbon valency (b) when the hydrogen atom unites with nitrogen, or when the hydrogen atom has attained a position as represented in (a) a simultaneous liberation of the respective valencies occurs, their union within the molecule giving rise to the keto-form of the acid. Since this is also an unstable configuration, it is natural to conclude that the chief result will be the formation of cyamelide by the union of three molecules when in the state represented by phase (b), the free valency of the oxygen atom of one molecule uniting with the free valency of the carbon atom of another, thus :—

Three molecules in phase (b).   Cyamelide (Hantzsch's formula).

When cyanic acid is generated at a high temperature, as during the decomposition of urea by heat, it is liberated solely in the keto-form, which then polymerises at once to cyanuric acid as follows :—

Keto-form.   Intermediate phase (a).   Enol-form.

Whilst the enol-form, HOCN, cannot exist free at the temperature, the tendency of HNCO to co-exist in equilibrium with it would still persist, and it is from this cause that the polymerisation takes effect. Hence, since it cannot be formed by union of the momentary free valencies of the carbon and nitrogen atoms within the molecule itself,

a state of stable equilibrium is attained by the union of three molecules in phase (a) to form cyanuric acid the moment the hydrogen atom
has entered into union with oxygen, thus :—

$$HO.C\underset{N==C(OH)}{\overset{N\to\gets C(OH)}{\diagdown\diagup}}N \quad \to \quad HO.C\underset{N:C(OH)}{\overset{N.C(OH)}{\diagdown\diagup}}N.$$

Cyanuric acid (enol form).

It is obvious that cyamelide cannot be formed in the above reaction.

It was formerly supposed that when cyanic acid polymerised
spontaneously at $0°$, the product was cyamelide only. Senier and Walsh
(1902) showed as the result of a single experiment, in which no particular effort was made to control the temperature, that the product
contained in round numbers 70 per cent of cyanuric acid and 30 per
cent of cyamelide.

If this theory of the polymerisation of cyanic acid is sound, it follows
that the proportions of the respective isomerides formed must be a
function of the temperature at which polymerisation takes effect.

Hence, if cyanic acid exists as an equilibrium mixture which is
represented thus,

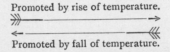

HO . CN (enol-form).   Promoted by rise of temperature.   HN : C : O (keto-form).
Stable only at low   Stable at high
temperature.   Promoted by fall of temperature.   temperature.

its composition at any particular temperature should be revealed by the
relative proportions of the two polymerides formed.

This suggestion has been recently put to the test by Werner and
Fearon (1920); the results, which are given below, verify the theoretical
deduction :—

TABLE I.

Temperature of Polymerisation (Approximate).	Weight of Polymeride.	Cyanuric Acid Found.	Percentage Composition of Polymeride.	
			Cyamelide.	Cyanuric Acid.
$0°$	0·53 gram.	0·216 gram.	59·25	40·75
5	0·42 ,,	0·174 ,,	58·58	41·42
10	0·105 ,,	0·045 ,,	57·27	42·73
20	0·24 ,,	0·136 ,,	42·92	57·08

Whilst accurate control of the temperature at which polymerisation
takes place is practically impossible on account of the heat developed
during the change, sufficient evidence was obtained to show that at $0°$,

for example, the equilibrium mixture had approximately the composition 60 per cent HOCN and 40 per cent HNCO.

The formation of cyamelide, but of no cyanuric acid, during the transformation of ammonium cyanate at low temperature, confirms therefore the view that cyanic acid in the form HOCN results from the dissociation of the ammonium salt.

(b) Hydrolysis of Cyanic Acid.

The formation of urea, when cyanic acid is decomposed by water, which was so clearly pointed out by Liebig and Wöhler, is a very interesting fact in connection with the foregoing view of the nature of cyanic acid. The statement, if taken literally, would appear to indicate that they believed urea could be formed from the direct union of cyanic acid and ammonia. Even if this interpretation of their view was not intended, it is nevertheless true.

The formation of urea during the hydrolysis of cyanic acid at 0°, i.e. at a temperature much below that at which ammonium cyanate is known to undergo transformation, has been proved beyond question by Werner and Fearon (1920). Not less than six consecutive changes are involved when cyanic acid is decomposed in the presence of water. These are conveniently divided into two groups :—

Primary changes :—

(1) $(HOCN \rightleftarrows HNCO) + H_2O = CO_2 + NH_3$.

(2) $HOCN + NH_3 = NH_4 . OCN$.

(3) $HN:CO + NH_3 = HN:C {\overset{\diagup NH_3}{\underset{\diagdown O}{|}}}$.

Secondary changes :—

(4) $NH_3 + CO_2 + H_2O = NH_4HCO_3$.

(5) Interaction of urea and HNCO = biuret.

(6) Production of cyamelide.

In an aqueous solution of cyanic acid at 0°, and at concentration approximately $N/4$, the primary changes are completed in from seventy-five to ninety minutes, and under such conditions the secondary changes, with the exception of No. (5) are completely suppressed up to the point at which the primary are just completed.

Reaction (5) is restricted chiefly to the early stage of the change (i.e. when the concentration of cyanic acid is relatively high), and, whilst small in amount, is of primary importance since it must be a sequence of reaction (3). (See Chapter IV.)

The results obtained when 2·30 grams of cyanic acid in 250 c.c. of solution underwent hydrolysis at 0° are shown in the following table.

The values are for 25 c.c. of solution, which were taken for analysis at intervals of fifteen minutes.

TABLE II.

Time in Minutes.	Cyanic Acid Present (Free, and as NH₄OCN). Gram.	Urea Formed (Theoretical). Gram.		Urea Found. Gram.
—	0·230	—		—
15	0·195	0·024		0·018
30	0·165	0·045	Total urea	0·038
45	0·129	0·070	at this stage	0·063
60	0·109	0·084	= 0·313.	0·081
75	0·101	0·090		0·087
90	0·094	0·094		0·089
1230	0·061	0·118		not estimated

The values in the third column were calculated from the amounts of cyanic acid which had disappeared after each interval, on the basis $2\ HNCO \rightarrow CON_2H_4$, i.e. a combination of reactions (1) and (3).

It will be seen, under the conditions stated, that the hydrolysis of cyanic acid is comparatively slow, about ninety minutes, at the outside, being required for the completion of the primary reactions. After this any urea formed could only arise from the slow transformation of ammonium cyanate, as a result of its hydrolytic dissociation, thus :—

$$NH_4OCN = NH_3 + (HOCN \rightleftarrows HNCO).$$

This is strikingly shown by the last result, where, in the interval between ninety and 1230 minutes, only 0·033 gram of cyanic acid (as ammonium cyanate) had been removed, and when this is considered in connection with the fact that in seventy-five minutes from the commencement of the change 0·313 gram of urea was formed, there can be no doubt that the latter can only have been produced as the direct result of reaction (3). Now, after seventy-five minutes, when the disturbing effects of reaction (4) were just noticeable, half of the solution (125 c.c.) had been used ; that is 1·15 grams of cyanic acid, capable of yielding 0·8 gram of either urea or ammonium cyanate, had taken part in the completion of reactions (1), (2), and (3). Hence (0·8—0·313) 0·487 gram of ammonium cyanate was formed, which shows that cyanic acid, in aqueous solution at 0°, had reacted with ammonia as a mixture of HOCN = 60·9 per cent and of HNCO = 39·1 per cent, a result almost identical with that arrived at from the study of the polymerisation of the anhydrous acid at the same temperature.

Walker and Wood (1900), by combining cyanic acid and ammonia in ethereal solution at − 17°, obtained, according to their analyses, pure ammonium cyanate.   It is quite possible that at this temperature cyanic acid in solution in ether may be wholly present in the enol-form.

They also obtained the ammonium salt, apparently quite free from urea, by bringing the vapour of cyanic acid, largely diluted with dry hydrogen, slowly in contact with dry ammonia, similarly diluted with air at the ordinary temperature.

The fact remains that whereas ammonium cyanate in aqueous solution at 0° changes very slowly into urea,[1] the latter is rapidly and abundantly formed when cyanic acid is hydrolysed at 0°.   In the light of such evidence it would be difficult to maintain that urea is not the product of a direct action between ammonia and one form of cyanic acid.

Four isomerides are theoretically possible from the union of the four atoms C, H, N, and O; neither fulminic acid $C : NOH$, nor

formonitrile oxide $\begin{matrix} CH : N \\ \diagdown \diagup \\ O \end{matrix}$ has been isolated, though derivatives of

each are known.   Since cyanic acid evidently represents the two remaining forms, it is a typical example of a tautomeric substance.

Whilst alkyl derivatives of the type $R . N : C : O$ are well known (Wurtz, 1854), so far compounds of the type $R . O . C . N$. have only been isolated in the polymeric form $(R . OCN)_3$.   It is not surprising, therefore, that cyanic acid should be highly unstable.   Its isolation is probably made possible in virtue of its power of existing as a mixture whereby a very feeble, or critical, condition of electrostatic equilibrium is attained.   Thus in the keto-form, the acid may be looked upon as ammonia in which the weak electronegative group —CO— has replaced two atoms of hydrogen.   Carbamyl chloride $CONH_2Cl$, which is formed from the union of cyanic acid and HCl, may be considered as a salt $(CO : NH . HCl.)$ produced from " carbonyl ammonia."   On the other hand, when cyanic acid is in solution in ether (i.e. di-ethyl oxide) the possibility of the formation of an " oxonium " compound from the enol-form, must not be overlooked, which might be sufficient to cause the acid to react wholly in this form when present in such a solvent, particularly at a low temperature.

Michael and Hibbert (1909) have studied the behaviour of tertiary amines towards cyanic acid in the state of vapour, and also in ethereal

[1] Hydrolysis to ammonium carbonate is indeed the greater change.

solution.   They conclude that the acid is really carbonimide, CO : NH.
The salts formed are represented thus :—

$$OC : NH$$

$$\searrow \downarrow$$
$$NR_3$$

It does not appear to the writer that the arguments used in support of
their conclusions are convincing.   The reader is referred to the original
paper for details of the views put forward.

Palazzo and Carapelle (1906) found that when an ethereal solution
of cyanic acid at $-12°$ was poured into an ethereal solution of
diazomethane at $-5°$, and the mixture treated with dry ammonia,
methylurea was the main product.   They concluded from this that
free cyanic acid is not tautomeric, and has the formula $O : C : NH$.

Whilst this result is in agreement with the existence of the acid in
the latter form at a low temperature, it does not prove the non-
existence of the enol-form of the acid under such condition.

The behaviour of cyanic acid in different solvents is a subject which
awaits further investigation.

CHAPTER IV.

THE DECOMPOSITION OF UREA BY HEAT.

THE action of heat was the first analytical test used to study the constitution of urea.

Fourcroy and Vauquelin (1799) carried out a distillation of impure urea; they recorded the evolution of a white vapour which condensed and crystallised in the neck of the retort, and the conversion of the remainder into a dry infusible mass, which finally was completely sublimed when the temperature was raised to low redness. The first sublimate was considered to be merely ammonium carbonate, whilst the final product was believed to be uric acid. The error, in the latter case, as Wöhler remarked many years later, was pardonable considering the period.

Fourcroy and Vauquelin also examined the action of heat on urea nitrate, and here they made an interesting and acute observation which is best recorded in their own words: "Il se transforma en nitrate d'ammoniaque pendant qu'il se dégagea un gaz piquant, qui avait une grande analogie avec ce que notre confrère Berthollet a nommé acide prussique oxigéné."

This was a distinct recognition of the generation of cyanic acid from urea, thirty years before Wöhler's synthesis of the compound from this source.

In 1830 Wöhler obtained cyanuric acid in considerable amount by the action of heat on pure urea, and later in the same year, in conjunction with Liebig, it was clearly pointed out that ammonium carbonate is not a product of the decomposition of urea by heat, as Wöhler had previously believed.

They showed that the sublimate which was formed during the preliminary heating contained ammonium cyanate. Particular attention was drawn to this fact by their observation that "the carbonic acid formed when the vapours were brought in contact with hydrochloric acid was the result of the decomposition of cyanic acid which accompanied ammonia in the vapour."

Thus, very early in the history of urea, its reversion to ammonium cyanate was recognised by these distinguished chemists.

23

Fifteen years later Liebig and Wöhler (1845) announced the formation of "melanurenic acid," as a product of the prolonged decomposition of urea by heat. This "new body" was shown by Laurent and Gerhardt (1847) to be identical with the substance ammelide, $C_3H_4N_4O_2$, which Liebig had obtained several years previously (1834) by the action of sulphuric acid on melam. Curiously enough, Laurent and Gerhardt, in giving directions for the preparation of ammelide from urea, appear to have overlooked Liebig and Wöhler's observation referred to above, since they speak of heating urea until the vapours of ammonia and carbonate of ammonia cease to be emitted.

In 1848 Wiedemann isolated biuret, $C_2H_5N_3O_2$, from the product left after heating urea at 150°-170°. He proposed this name for the new body, since he believed, from its composition, that it was produced from the union of two molecules of urea, with loss of ammonia.

In later years with the advent of the "carbamide" formula the production of biuret appeared to be easily explained as follows :—

$$H_2N . CO . \boxed{NH_2 + H}HN . CO . NH_2$$
$$= H_2N . CO . NH . CO . NH_2 + NH_3.$$

In fact, the formation of biuret, on this assumption, is supposed to lend support to the "carbamide" structure of urea, and an extension of this reaction, between biuret and unchanged urea, with loss of two molecules of ammonia, has been suggested as an explanation for the formation of cyanuric acid by the action of heat on urea.

The origin of the erroneous views which have prevailed as regards the mechanism of the changes involved during the decomposition of urea by heat must be attributed to the failure to recognise that the first effect of heat on urea is to bring about its dissociation into the two compounds from which it is formed, namely, ammonia and cyanic acid. All the consecutive changes can be easily explained on the basis of this fact.

When the structural formula of urea suggested by the writer is considered, it is seen that the decomposition by heat is, in the first instance, a simple and straightforward change, thus :—

$$HN : C \diagup \begin{matrix} NH_3 \\ | \\ O \end{matrix} \qquad = \qquad \begin{matrix} NH_3 \\ + \\ HNCO \rightleftharpoons HO . CN \end{matrix}$$

in which no secondary products are formed, so far as the volatile substances are concerned.

The instability and reactivity of cyanic acid are responsible for the products subsequently formed.

By polymerisation of the acid in the keto-form, cyanuric acid is produced, and it is obviously quite unnecessary to look outside this cause for its origin.

The temperature being relatively very high, no cyamelid can be formed, the absence of which was pointed out by Hantzsch (1905), though no explanation was offered.

The reason is not far to seek. Cyanic acid in the enol-form can only be present in the vapour as it cools. Here it is in contact all the time with an excess of ammonia, and hence ammonium cyanate is present in the sublimate. The more effectively the vapour is cooled the larger the proportion of ammonium cyanate formed.

Biuret arises from the interaction of cyanic acid and unchanged urea, and since, as the writer has shown, the change is reversible, above the melting-point (192°) of biuret, this is represented thus :—

$$HN:C\begin{matrix}NH_2\\OH\end{matrix} + HN:CO \underset{\text{above 190°}}{\overset{135°\text{-}190°}{\rightleftarrows}} \quad \begin{matrix}HN:C.OH\\|\\NH\\|\\HN:C.OH\end{matrix} \rightarrow \begin{matrix}O:C.NH_2\\|\\NH\\|\\O:C.NH_2\end{matrix}$$

(Urea in reactive form.)   Biuret (enol-form).   (Keto-form.)

As regards the experimental evidence to support this equation, it is only necessary to point out, so far as the change from left to right is concerned, that Finckh, in 1861, obtained biuret by passing the vapour of cyanic acid into urea heated to its melting-point (132°). Moreover, in recent years several substituted biurets have been prepared by Bruce (1904) from the cyanates of the so-called iso-ureas of the type $HN:C(NH_2).O.R.$

The formation of biuret during the hydrolysis of cyanic acid, referred to in the preceding chapter, shows that the reaction can take place in aqueous solution even at a low temperature.

A simple demonstration of the formation of biuret in this way may be shown by adding a small quantity of pure potassium cyanate to a gram or two of urea dissolved in a few cubic centimetres of 20 per cent hydrochloric acid solution. On addition, after a short interval, of copper sulphate and excess of alkali, the solution will be found to give quite a strong biuret reaction, i.e. a deep purple-red colour. The quantitative results given under Table III. (see further) supply proof of the change from right to left.

Since biuret is dissociated above 190° into the products from which it was formed, it represents but a transitory effort towards the attainment of stability under the stress of the disturbing effects of heat. The result is largely attained even in the early stages by the formation of stable cyanuric acid, and when the heating is pushed further, whilst the latter accumulates, it is supplemented by the formation of the equally stable ammelide, which takes origin thus :—

$$HN{<}^{CO\,.\,NH_2}_{CO\,.\,NH_2} + HN:CO = HN{<}^{CO\,.\,NH}_{CO\,.\,NH}{>}C:NH + H_2O.$$

Biuret.   Ammelide.[1]

If biuret was formed, according to the view which has so long prevailed, namely, by the condensation of two molecules of urea with loss of ammonia, there is no reason why it should not be possible to convert urea quantitatively into biuret by heating, say, at $150°$-$170°$, i.e. a temperature at which the former is rapidly decomposed and at which the latter suffers no change.

The following quantitative results of the decomposition of urea and of biuret respectively by heat, obtained by the writer (1913), show that the different products mentioned are produced from the outset of the decomposition :—

TABLE I.

ACTION OF HEAT ON UREA.

	Expt. I. Heated very Slowly; Heat removed as soon as Opalescence Set In. Time, 12 Minutes. Per Cent.	Expt. II. Heated at a Moderate Rate until Appearance of Opalescence. Time, 7-8 Minutes. Per Cent.
Loss (NH_3 + HNCO) . . .	8·40	12·20
NH_4OCN (in sublimate) . . .	0·58	0·21
Biuret	18·26	24·50
Cyanuric acid	3·35	5·93
Ammelide	0·83	3·94
	31·42	46·78
Unchanged urea (by difference) . .	68·58	53·22

	Expt. III. Heated rather Rapidly until Appearance of Opalescence. Time, 5 Minutes. Per Cent.	Expt. IV. Heated very Rapidly; Heat Continued, after Appearance of Opalescence, until Gas Evolution had Practically Ceased Time, 6-7 Minutes. Per Cent.
Loss	15·00	19·00
NH_4OCN	0·06	0·42
Biuret	16·66	10·25
Cyanuric acid	9·16	15·34
Ammelide	3·30	8·46
	44·18	53·47
Unchanged urea (by difference) . .	55·82	46·53

[1] This is the tautomeric form of $HN{<}^{CO-NH}_{CO-N}{>}C\,.\,NH_2$, which is also used to express the constitution of ammelide, since the substance possesses feeble basic, in addition to pronounced acidic, properties.

In experiments I. and II. the temperature was not raised beyond 180°; in III. and IV. the temperature was about 195°.

The proportions of biuret and cyanuric acid respectively, calculated on the amount of urea actually decomposed in each experiment, are given below :—

TABLE II.

	Expt. I.	Expt. II.	Expt. III.	Expt. IV.
Biuret . .	58·1	52·4	37·7	19·1 per cent.
Cyanuric acid	10·6	12·7	20·7	28·6 ,, ,,

It will be seen that rapid heating, since it must naturally promote polymerisation of cyanic acid, introduces a factor which militates against the formation of biuret, a result which is in agreement with the explanation of its origin.

The decomposition of biuret by heat has been described, in the literature, by the simple statement that it gives off ammonia and yields cyanuric acid. That this is very short of the true result is plainly evident.

TABLE III.

DECOMPOSITION OF BIURET BY HEAT.

	Expt. I. Heated at 195°-198° until Pasty Mass Formed. Time, 5 Minutes. Per Cent.	Expt. II. Heated until Gas Evolution Ceased (195°-200°). Time, 7 Minutes. Per Cent.	Expt. III. Heated Rapidly (195°-205°) until Residue Solid. Time, 10 Minutes. Per Cent.
Volatile (NH_3 + HNCO) . . .	8·25	13·75	23·12
Sublimate	4·95	6·37	3·75
Cyanuric acid	37·24	37·08	57·96
Ammelide	3·57	5·87	5·37
Biuret (unchanged) . . .	12·34	10·40	0·77
	66·35	73·47	90·97
Urea, generated	33·65	26·53	9·03

The sublimate in the above experiments consisted chiefly of urea, and might therefore be added to the amounts of urea recorded as generated. The values are percentages of the weight of biuret taken in each experiment.

In accordance with the theory of its formation, it is obvious that the yield of ammelide cannot be other than small, because the temperature which is otherwise favourable to its formation lies about the point at which biuret is rapidly decomposed and at which cyanic acid undergoes very rapid polymerisation.

This fact disposes of an alternative explanation of the possible origin of ammelide, namely, as a result of the direct interaction of ammonia and cyanuric acid, thus :—

$$HN\begin{matrix} CO.NH \\ CO.NH \end{matrix}\!\!\Big\rangle CO + NH_3 = HN\begin{matrix} CO.NH \\ CO.NH \end{matrix}\!\!\Big\rangle C:NH + H_2O.$$

(Cyanuric acid.)   (Ammelide.)

Since ammonia is continuously evolved during the decomposition of biuret, an increase in the yield of ammelide should keep pace with an increase in the production of cyanuric acid.

That this is not so, is seen on comparing the results of experiments II. and III. in the above table, III.

Thus the mechanism of the series of changes which accompany the progressive action of heat on urea may be illustrated by the following scheme, in which it is seen that the phenomenon of dissociation and the instability and reactivity of nascent cyanic acid are the active agents in the process :—

$$(a) \quad HN : C \Big\langle \begin{matrix} NH_2 \\ O \end{matrix} \quad = \quad \begin{matrix} NH_3 \\ \downarrow \\ HN : CO \rightleftarrows HOCN \end{matrix} \quad = \quad NH_4 . O . CN$$

Urea.

(Present in sublimate.)

By polymerisation $= (HNCO)_3$
(Cyanuric acid.)

$$(b) \quad HN : C \Big\langle \begin{matrix} NH_2 \\ OH \end{matrix} \quad \begin{matrix} HN : C . OH \\ | \\ NH \\ | \\ HN : C . OH \end{matrix} \quad + \quad \Big\{ \begin{matrix} HN : CO = NH \Big\langle \begin{matrix} CO . NH \\ CO . NH \end{matrix} \Big\rangle C : NH \\ \uparrow \end{matrix}$$

$$+ \quad \rightleftarrows$$

$$HOCN$$

Biuret.

Ammelide.
$+ H_2O$

Whilst the cyclic formula (a) is used to represent the constitution of urea in the first stage of the decomposition, it is not unlikely that the direct dissociation of urea into ammonia and cyanic acid by heat is also accompanied by a change in constitution represented by the hydroxylic formula (b); this alteration in structure would be determined by the presence of a negative agent, such as cyanic or cyanuric acid in the fused product.

So far as the writer's experience is concerned, no products other than those shown in the above scheme are formed as a result of the direct decomposition of urea by heat, and it is clear that no hypothetical intermediate compounds need be assumed in order to explain their formation.

All investigators who have studied the action of heat on urea, in recent years, have considered the decomposition from the point of view of the "carbamide" formula. This has led to some rather singular results.

It is true that the formation of ammelide is of no practical importance. No doubt for this reason it has been looked upon as a secondary product which was not worthy of any further consideration. Its theoretical significance is evident, since it represents the final "fixing" of cyanic acid in a stable molecule, and its formation cannot be suppressed during the decomposition of urea.

Hantzsch and F. Hofmann (1905) examined the action of heat on urea, and claimed to have obtained a compound which they named tricyano-carbamide $C_3N_3(NH.CO.HN_2)_3$, in spite of the fact that all the properties of the substance were in agreement with those possessed by ammelide.

Béhal (1914) described a substance obtained in small quantity when urea was heated above 200° in the presence of chlorine to which he has given the name "Caluret." From the results of analyses, which it is admitted were not concordant,[1] the formula $C_4H_8N_6O_3$ was assigned to the product, which, it is also admitted, showed properties which were undistinguishable from those of ammelide.

A structural formula was proposed for "caluret" on the assumption that it originates from a condensation of urea and guanidine, with elimination of ammonia, guanidine being supposed to result from an interaction of urea and ammonia during the decomposition. In verification of this view "caluret" was prepared by heating guanidine carbonate with an excess of urea to 235°. Now this is one of the methods which was recommended by Smolka and Friedreich (1889) for the preparation of ammelide.

The writer has not been able to obtain any evidence of the existence of either "tricyanocarbamide" or "caluret."

Béhal explains the origin of cyanuric acid from urea by assuming the formation of a hypothetical triuret $(H_2N.CO.NH.CO.NH.CO.NH_2)$ as a result of a reaction between biuret and urea, with elimination of ammonia. By a further loss of ammonia from triuret, cyanuric acid is assumed to be finally produced.

The undue attention which has all along been given to the evolution of ammonia, whilst the simultaneous evolution of cyanic acid (as NH_4OCN) has been almost completely overlooked, is largely responsible for this particular line of reasoning which has been adopted in endeavouring to explain the action of heat on urea.

It may be said that since the discovery of biuret the careful observations of Liebig and Wöhler have been allowed to pass almost into oblivion. To prevent their revival nothing better than the "carbamide" formula could have been devised. Its effect is well illustrated by the results of an investigation on the compressibility of the vapour of "carbamide" by Isambert (1883). The vapour of urea

---

[1] Estimations of nitrogen varied from 44·2 to 49 per cent, and 49·41 per cent (instead of 43·75) is erroneously given as the theoretical value for nitrogen in ammelide.

was found to behave under changes of pressure almost exactly like a mixture of ammonia and carbon dioxide (in the proportions of 2 vols. to 1 vol.), whilst the condensation of the vapour was accompanied by a development of heat equal to 39·8 calories, a value identical with that found for the heat of formation of urea. The remarkable conclusion arrived at was that " solid carbamide may be regarded as formed by a simple addition of carbonic acid and ammonia gas," and "the volatilisation of this body (urea) is therefore a phenomenon of dissociation."

Whilst the latter remark is quite true, it is evident that, taken in conjunction with the former, Isambert has completely ignored the existence of the vapour of cyanic acid as a product of the dissociation of urea. In these experiments urea was vaporised at 61°-62°, under a much reduced pressure. Since the molecular weights of cyanic acid and of carbon dioxide are as 43 to 44, a mixture of the vapour of the former and ammonia would be likely to behave as Isambert found.

At all events carbon dioxide is not present in the vapour given off from urea until the formation of ammelide has set in. The trace of water generated as a by-product when ammelide is formed tends to hydrolyse some of the cyanic acid present in the vapour. This fact has been clearly demonstrated by the writer.

Proof of the direct dissociation of urea into ammonia and cyanic acid has been supplied by Escales and Köpke (1911), who showed that when urea was sublimed in a vacuum at 160°, the sublimate was ammonium cyanate. Their remark that, if Wöhler had sought to purify his synthetical urea by sublimation in this way, his famous discovery might never have been made, is one with which the writer is by no means prepared to agree.

Wöhler was a much too shrewd and careful observer to overlook the properties of a substance so different from ammonium cyanate. Had not his own observations on the subject discussed in the present chapter been overlooked by many others, much unnecessary work might have been spared.

CHAPTER V.

THE DECOMPOSITION OF UREA WHEN HEATED IN SOLUTION WITH ACIDS AND WITH ALKALIS RESPECTIVELY. THE HYDROLYSIS OF CYANATES.

FOURCROY and Vauquelin (1799) found that when heated with "potash," "l'urée s'est changée en ammoniaque et en acides carbonique et acéteux,[1] avec l'acide sulfurique aidé de la chaleur il y a conversion lente en ammoniaque et les mêmes acides." The reference to a slow conversion in the latter case is interesting when we come to consider the change later on. It is evident they noticed a difference in the velocity of the reactions in the two cases.

It was not until the composition of urea had been definitely established by Prout that quantitative results of any value were likely to ensue from a study of its decomposition in the presence of acids, or alkalis. Having confirmed the accuracy of Prout's analyses, Dumas (1830) showed that when urea was heated with strong sulphuric acid, all of the nitrogen was readily obtained in the form of ammonia, whilst the whole of the carbon was evolved as carbon dioxide. On the other hand, Dumas was not successful in obtaining theoretical yields of the decomposition products, when urea was heated with very strong solution of potassium hydroxide. Fusion with the alkali was resorted to, and whilst even this failed to yield all of the nitrogen as ammonia, the residue was apparently potassium carbonate, which on *acidulation* gave the theoretical proportion of carbonic acid.

Dumas showed that since the formula of urea when subtracted from that of "sous-carbonate d'ammoniaque" leaves only a difference of water ($2H_2O$ according to modern notation), urea must simply combine with water when heated with acids or alkalis.

In 1849 Bunsen proposed the first method for the estimation of urea, based on its supposed direct hydrolysis to ammonium carbonate, according to the equation :—

$$CON_2H_4 + 2H_2O = (NH_4)_2CO_3.$$

[1] This was possibly cyanic acid which was mistaken for acetic acid, or may have been due to the impure material used.

31

An ammoniacal solution of barium chloride (the equivalent of barium hydroxide) was used by Bunsen to promote hydrolysis, the weight of barium carbonate produced, in accordance with the change,

$$CON_2H_4 + Ba(OH)_2 = BaCO_3 + 2NH_3$$

giving a measure of the amount of urea present. In this method, which was specially devised for the estimation of urea in urine, it was recommended to use not more than about 2 c.cs. of the fluid (roughly equal to 0·05 gram. urea) for analysis. In order to realise the above reaction it was necessary to heat in a sealed tube either at 180°-220° for not less than eight hours, or at 220°-240° for at least five hours. Remarkably severe conditions, it must be admitted, for the complete hydrolysis of such a small quantity of an " amide."

Nevertheless, with the general acceptance of the " carbamide " formula in later years, the hydrolysis of urea, as a simple change on the above lines, became an accepted fact. Indeed it seemed so obviously in agreement with the requirements of the formula, that it has been constantly put forward in the literature as evidence in support of it.

There were dissentients, as we have seen, but they were in a small minority.

The apparently obvious nature of the change explains why it remained so long without investigation.

In 1902 Fawsitt studied the velocity of the decomposition of urea in aqueous solution alone, and in the presence of acids and alkalis respectively. The results were all the more interesting since they were very different from what was to be expected. The experiments were made in sealed tubes at 99·2°.

1. It was found that the rate of change was in agreement with the equation for a simple unimolecular reaction.

2. In the presence of hydrochloric acid, for example, the rate of change was diminished when the concentration of acid was relatively high. This is shown in the following results :—

		$K \times 10^{-5}$.
1. N HCl + N Urea.	. . . . .	60
2. N/2 ,, + N/2 ,, .	. . . . .	80
3. N/4 ,, + N/4 ,, .	. . . . .	92
4. N/8 ,, + N/8 ,, .	. . . . .	103
5. N/10 ,, + N/10 ,, .	. . . . .	102
6. N/16 ,, + N/16 ,, .	. . . . .	102

When the concentration of urea was the same at the outset of the experiments, whilst that of the acid was diminished, the results were as follows :—

		$K \times 10^{-5}$
7. N . HCl + N/8 Urea	. . . . .	50
8. N/2, HCl ,, ,,	. . . . .	72
9. N/16, ,, ,, ,,	. . . . .	102
10. N/32, ,, ,, ,,	. . . . .	100
11. N/64, ,, ,, ,,	. . . . .	99

It will be seen from the values for experiments 4, 5, 6, 9, 10, and 11 that a concentration of acid lower than N/8 had practically no further effect on the rate of change.

3. In the presence of sodium hydroxide it was found that unless the concentration of alkali was very high (and that of urea relatively so) the velocity of the change was lower than in the presence of hydrochloric acid. Thus for N/8 NaOH + N/8 Urea, K = 78 × 10⁻⁵, as compared with K = 103 × 10⁻⁵ for hydrochloric acid.

4. The presence of free ammonia had a considerable retarding effect on the velocity of the decomposition, thus—

		$K \times 10^{-5}$
N. Urea solution	. . . .	6·4
N. Urea + N · NH₄OH	. . .	3·6

Fawsitt did not venture to doubt the validity of the " carbamide " formula, and in order to explain the results which had been obtained, it was concluded that :—

(a) An isomeric transformation of urea was the first step in the change, ammonium cyanate being the substance actually hydrolysed, thus—

$$\text{I. } CON_2H_4 \rightleftarrows NH_4 . OCN.$$
$$\text{II. } NH_4 . OCN + 2H_2O = (NH_4)_2CO_3.$$

(b) Since the velocity of hydrolysis is lowered by an increase in the concentration of acid, it is only urea which is " free " in solution that is concerned in change I.

Whilst this is a perfectly correct inference, the reason is not obvious when " carbamide " is supposed to have the same constitution in solution whether " free " or when present as a salt, such as $CO(NH_2)_2$. HCl.

(c) As regards the effect produced by sodium hydroxide, it was naturally assumed that ammonium cyanate is decomposed more rapidly in presence of acids than in presence of alkali hydroxides.

Whilst this again appears to be a reasonable explanation, it must be remembered that there would be a greater concentration of " free " urea in an alkaline than in an acid solution. Since this should promote the change in the former case we must look to some other cause to explain the "apparently" abnormal result.

The effect of ammonia on the change is of special interest, since it now becomes an established fact that the transformation of either isomeride into the other is retarded by the presence of this compound in the free state. Such a result cannot be made to harmonise with an ionic theory of the isomeric change.

Walker and his co-workers claim to have shown that potassium cyanate, through the agency of the CNO′ ion, it has been assumed, accelerates the conversion of ammonium cyanate into urea, but retards the reverse change. Convincing experimental proof of the latter effect is still lacking.

Now, an isomeric transformation of urea, as a preliminary to its decomposition in solution, as suggested by Fawsitt (1902) is an unnecessary assumption, when it is remembered that dissociation into ammonia and cyanic acid is the first change which accompanies the action of heat on urea.

All phenomena connected with its decomposition in solution, either alone, or in the presence of acids, or alkalis, are then easily explained.

According to this simple theory, the decomposition of urea in the presence of acids, for example, was explained by the writer (1918) as follows :—

Phase I. $HN : C \underset{O}{\overset{NH_3}{<}} + HCl = NH_4Cl + (HNCO \rightleftarrows HOCN).$

Phase II. $(HNCO \rightleftarrows HO . CN) + H_2O + HCl = NH_4Cl + CO_2.$

Since cyanic acid is very rapidly hydrolysed, the velocity of the whole reaction will be regulated by the rate of dissociation of urea (at 100°), when both products of dissociation are removed practically as fast as they are generated.

The basic property of urea is much more pronounced than that commonly associated with acid amides, a fact which in itself may be used as an argument against such a structure,[1] and when hydrochloric acid is added to an aqueous solution of urea, an equilibrium is established between the base and its hydrochloride. Thus, in a normal solution, Walker and Wood (1903) found that 45 per cent of urea

---

[1] In this respect urea bears a much greater resemblance to the amino-acids, a type of constitution which is implied by the cyclic formula.

hydrochloride was undissociated, a condition which, according to the writer's views, is represented by the following equation :—

$$HN : C \begin{cases} NH_3 \\ | \\ O \end{cases} + HCl \quad \overset{(a)}{\underset{(b)}{\rightleftarrows}} \quad HN : C \begin{cases} NH_2, HCl \\ \\ OH \end{cases}$$

55 per cent.　　　　　　　　　　　　　45 per cent.

Now, since it is only " free " urea which gives rise to the first phase of the decomposition, the velocity of the change might be expected to diminish with an increase in the concentration of hydrochloric acid. This, however, would be only slightly perceptible at all concentrations much below normal, since by far the greater part of the urea would be in the free state at the outset, and hence only a small amount of change in direction (b) would be involved throughout the whole progress of the reaction.

If, on the other hand, most of the urea was " fixed " at the outset as urea hydrochloride, the velocity of the change would be determined by the diminished rate of dissociation of free urea at low concentration, and this would be maintained fairly constant up to a certain point,[1] since the change in direction (b) would only keep pace with the rate of disappearance of free urea.

The following results, obtained by heating solutions of urea with hydrochloric acid to the boiling-point under reflux, suffice to illustrate the points just mentioned :—

TABLE I.

DECOMPOSITION OF UREA IN THE PRESENCE OF HYDROCHLORIC ACID.

(I.) Urea, N/5 ; HCl, N/2·5. Molecular ratio, 1 : 2.

Time.		Urea Decomposed.	Time.		Urea Undecomposed.
1 hour	=	21·25 per cent.	5 hours	=	63·75 per cent.
2 hours	=	33·50 ,, ,,	6 ,,	=	68·90 ,, ,,
3 ,,	=	44·50 ,, ,,	7 ,,	=	78·50 ,, ,,
4 ,,	=	59·25 ,, ,,	8 ,,	=	79·25 ,, ,,

(II.) Urea, N/5 ; HCl, N/5.　　　　　(III.) Urea, N/2·5 ; HCl, N/2·5.

Equal mols.

Time.		Urea Decomposed.	Time.		Urea Undecomposed.
1 hour	=	22·0 per cent.	1 hour	=	25·0 per cent.
2 hours	=	34·5 ,, ,,	2 hours	=	44·75 ,, ,,
3 ,,	=	47·00 ,, ,,	145 minutes	=	50·0 ,, ,,
222 minutes	=	50·0 ,, ,,			

A comparison of the results under (I.) and (II.) (urea $= N/5$) shows the effect of an increase in the concentration of hydrochloric acid in lowering the velocity of the change ; the difference was most marked during the third hour, that is, when the concentration of hydrochloric acid, in the case of (II.) was very low as neutralisation was approached, since the maximum amount of urea that could be decomposed, up to

[1] The neutralisation of free acid by ammonia would naturally exert a disturbing effect on the above equilibrium, which would be more marked at the higher concentration.

the point of neutralisation in the presence of one molecular proportion of hydrochloric acid, is only half of the total present, on account of the simultaneous progress of the two phases of the reaction. The long period required to decompose urea when two molecular proportions of hydrochloric acid were present was due to the slow dissociation of urea as its concentration diminished, and the results show that the velocity of the change was determined solely by the concentration of "free" urea. The results under (III.) furnish additional proof of this; thus it will be noticed that the maximum amount of urea ($N/2\cdot5$) was decomposed in 145 minutes, as compared with 222 minutes, which were required to effect the same amount of change when the concentration of urea at the outset was at $N/5$ (II.).

Fawsitt found that it required 2600 minutes to decompose all urea in a solution which contained at the outset urea ($N/8$) and hydrochloric acid ($N/2$), that is, four molecules of acid to one of urea.

In the decomposition of urea in the presence of acids, since the function of the latter is simply to remove the dissociation products, ammonia and cyanic acid, as soon as they are generated, it is easy to understand why the decomposition of all the urea is such a tedious process. The velocity of Phase I. is directly proportional to the concentration of "free" urea, and this is inversely proportional to the strength of the acid present, all other conditions being equal. Hence, after a certain time a similar condition is attained, no matter what acid may be present, since practically all the residual urea will be "free" when the concentration of acid has fallen very low as a result of its gradual neutralisation.

It can be shown that before such a condition is attained the velocity of the decomposition of urea is greater the weaker the acid present.

A comparison of the effects of acetic, nitric, and hydrochloric acids respectively on the rate of change are given below:—

The ratio of urea to acid was 1 : 2 molecular proportions.

The concentration at the outset was urea = $N/2$, acid = N.

The experiments were performed at 100° and under reflux.

TABLE II.

Time.				Acetic Acid. Per Cent.	Nitric Acid. Per Cent.	Hydrochloric Acid. Per Cent.
1 hour	.	.	.	19·5	15·7	13·3
2 hours	.	.	.	31·8	25·8	23·2
3 ,,	.	.	.	(a) 41·0	35·0	32·2
4 ,,	.	.	.	(b) 53·4	46·4	40·8
5 ,,	.	.	.	(c) 64·2	57·0	48·4
				(Urea decomposed.)	(Urea decomposed.)	(Urea decomposed.)

The above results were calculated from titrations of the residual acidity at the end of each experiment, with the exception of the values (*b*) and (*c*) for acetic acid, which were obtained from determinations of the residual urea, the only trustworthy method in these two cases. As the concentration of ammonium acetate produced during the reaction increased, there was loss of ammonia by its hydrolytic dissociation, whereby residual acidity gave too low a result. Whilst by the titration method (*b*) was approximately 47, and (*c*) 51, there was but little difference in the case of (*a*) when checked by the estimation of residual urea.

When the concentration of a very weak acid, such as acetic, falls considerably as the reaction proceeds, it is not able to fix ammonia to complete the reaction

$$(HNCO \rightleftarrows HO . CN) + H_2O + HX' = NH_4X' + CO_2,$$

with the result that more or less urea is regenerated, thus—

$$2HNCO + H_2O = CON_2H_4 + CO_2.$$

That this is the case is readily proved by adding potassium cyanate to an excess of a 2 per cent solution of acetic acid, when after a few minutes urea can be detected in the solution.

For this reason it takes a longer time to decompose all the urea in the presence of a weak acid than in the presence of a strong one, although the velocity of the change (Phase I.) is greater, up to a certain point, in the former case.

It is seen from the results in the above table, that nitric acid behaves towards urea as a weaker acid than hydrochloric. Price (1919) found a similar result, and Fawsitt found sulphuric to be also weaker than hydrochloric acid at $N/2$. The relative values are—

	$K \times 10^{-5}$		
	HNO_3	H_2SO_4	HCl
$N/2$-Urea + $N/2$-acid	107	96	77

Fawsitt and Price have considered the decomposition of urea from the point of view of the ionic theory, which, in the opinion of the writer, is not applicable to this particular reaction. Price found that such salts as ammonium nitrate, potassium nitrate, ammonium chloride, and potassium chloride respectively had a distinct accelerating effect on the decomposition of urea in the presence of nitric acid.

$$\text{Mean value of } k \times 10^{-5}.$$

$N/2$ Urea $+ N/2$ HNO$_3$	102
$N/2$ „ $+ N/2$ „ $+ N/2$ NH$_4$NO$_3$ . .	122
$N/2$ „ $+ N/2$ „ $+ N/2$ KNO$_3$ . .	118
$N/2$ „ $+ N/2$ „ $+ N/2$ NH$_4$Cl . .	118
$N/2$ „ $+ N/2$ „ $+ N/2$ KCl . . .	116

The writer (1920) has found a similar acceleration effect as shown by the following results, expressed in percentages of urea decomposed for comparison with Table II.

The concentrations of urea and of acid were as before. The salts were $N/4$ at the outset.

TABLE III.

Time.	Acetic Acid + NH$_4$NO$_3$.	Nitric Acid + NH$_4$NO$_3$.	Hydrochloric Acid + NH$_4$Cl.
	Per Cent.	Per Cent.	Per Cent.
1 hour	22·0	19·9	14·0
2 hours	35·1	31·78	29·1
3 „	45·4	37·40	41·2
	(Urea decomposed.)	(Urea decomposed).	(Urea decomposed.)

The concentration of ammonium salts increased as the reaction progressed, and in the case of the nitrate there was appreciable loss of ammonia towards the end of three hours; hence comparable results could not be obtained beyond this period when the heating at 100° was carried out under normal pressure.

As Price has correctly pointed out, the addition of the ammonium salt, or of any salt containing an ion common with the acid used, should produce a retarding effect on the velocity of decomposition, if the change was an ionic one.

As the result of a misunderstanding as regards the use of the term "dissociation," Price concluded that the writer's dissociation theory of the decomposition of urea was not applicable in the presence of nitric acid.

This is an example of the tendency to overlook the legitimate use of the term in question. The separation of urea into ammonia and cyanic acid, and not into NH$_4^{\cdot}$ and OCN$'$ ions, was clearly indicated as the first step in the writer's theory of the change.

"Free" urea is not ionised, and hence the presence of "ions" can neither retard nor promote its decomposition, which is entirely a function of the temperature and pressure.

The effect of temperature is very well shown by the following

results obtained by Price, and by Burrows and Fawsitt (1914), in the
presence of nitric and hydrochloric acids respectively :—

Temperature.	N/2 - Urea + N/2 - Nitric Acid. $k \times 10^{-5}$.	Temperature.	N/10 Urea + N/10 Hydrochloric Acid. $k \times 10^{-5}$.
100°	102·0	98·2 °	83·6
89	23·0	71·25	2·77
80	9·3	61·05	0·713
70	2·4		

Such a great fall in the velocity of decomposition compared with
a relatively small fall in temperature is explained by the fact that the
dissociation of urea in solution only starts at a fairly rapid rate at
about 90°.   At 60° it is almost nil.

It is scarcely necessary to point out that if urea was an "acid
amide," such behaviour would be remarkably abnormal.   Berthelot
and André (1887), in the belief that urea was " carbamide," claimed to
have shown that it was decomposed (hydrolysed) in the cold in the
presence of acid.

About a gram of urea (1·0293) was dissolved in 100 c.c. of water
to which 10 c.c. of strong hydrochloric acid were added.   After
twenty-four hours the solution was made up to a litre ; it was neutralised
by addition of a small excess of magnesium oxide, and distilled for
one and a half hours.   The ammonia evolved was equal to nearly
11 per cent of the total nitrogen of the urea.

A control experiment with urea alone gave, after distillation with
the addition of magnesium oxide, ammonia equal to 4 per cent of the
total nitrogen present.   It was assumed that urea was not decomposed
in the presence of magnesia, and whilst the latter result was believed
to give the amount of urea actually hydrolysed by water alone in the
cold, the former was taken to represent the increased effect brought
about by the presence of free acid.

There can be no doubt that the accelerating effect of a relatively
large amount of magnesium chloride on the decomposition of urea
during distillation was responsible for the result obtained in this
experiment.

The Stability of Urea in Solution, and in the Presence of Acid, or of Alkali in the Cold.

Walker and Hambly (1895) showed that after a solution of urea
has been heated for a few minutes, at 98°-100°, and subsequently
cooled, the presence of the cyanate radicle could be readily proved on
addition of silver nitrate.

Fawsitt (1902) found that 450 hours were required to decompose and hydrolyse 98·9 per cent of the urea originally present in a semi-normal solution at 99°, in a sealed tube. This can be easily understood in the light of the dissociation theory.

If the dissociation products could persist at a constant temperature, an equilibrium, represented thus,

$$HN:C\begin{matrix} NH_3 \\ | \\ O \end{matrix} \rightleftarrows HN:CO \rightleftarrows HO.CN \rightleftarrows NH_4.OCN,$$

would obtain, and the decomposition of urea and of ammonium cyanate would be completely arrested. The velocity of the change is determined by the very slow hydrolysis of cyanic acid under highly unfavourable conditions, since ammonia could not escape, whilst dissociation of urea is checked in consequence.

The progress of the change may be mentally compared to the working of a syphon in which the flow of liquid through the downward tube is seriously checked by a very narrow outlet.

Since urea is not dissociated in solution at the ordinary temperature, an equilibrium between it and ammonium cyanate can only arise on the application of heat. Judging from certain statements in the literature of the subject, the views on this point do not appear quite clear, since it is sometimes stated that the equilibrium is independent of the temperature. This idea is the result of an erroneous conception regarding the mechanism of the decomposition.

A solution of pure urea ($N/2$) in distilled water, sterilised by saturation with toluene, or chloroform, was found unchanged after nine months. It remained neutral and gave a negative result when tested from time to time with silver nitrate and with barium hydroxide respectively. A similar solution of urea in non-sterilised water gave a marked opalescence with the respective reagents after fourteen days. At the end of six months, the solution contained ammonium carbonate, but no ammonium cyanate, since, after precipitation with barium hydroxide, the carefully neutralised filtrate gave no precipitate on the addition of silver nitrate. This latter result is of interest, since the decomposition of urea in this case was unquestionably brought about, through the agency of urease, by micro-organisms which had developed in the solution.

As is well known, moulds soon develop in a solution of urea at the ordinary temperature, and these are responsible for the decomposition. The remarkable "hydrolysis" of urea by urease is fully dealt with in Chapter XI.

A solution of· urea (N/5) in normal hydrochloric acid was titrated at intervals of four days over a period of six weeks. No change in the titre was observed.

A solution of urea (N/2) in pure sodium hydroxide (N/2) solution, after remaining at the laboratory temperature for five months, showed no change.

It is, therefore, clearly evident that urea in neutral, in acid, or in alkaline solution, does not undergo a reversion to ammonium cyanate, until the temperature at which it commences to dissociate is reached.

The Decomposition of Urea in the Presence of Alcohol.

Burrows and Fawsitt (1914) found that the addition of alcohol to a solution of urea (N/10) + hydrochloric acid (N/10) produced a marked decrease in the velocity of decomposition, in proportion to the amount of alcohol added :—

Temperature.	Water. $k \times 10^{-5}$.	10 Per Cent Alcohol. $k \times 10^{-5}$.	20 Per Cent Alcohol. $k \times 10^{-5}$.	40 Per Cent Alcohol. $k \times 10^{-5}$.
98·2°	83·6	78·3	73·9	62·4
71·25°	2·77	2·51	2·47	2·24

This result, they state, "was not exactly what we anticipated," since "alcohol increases the velocity of transformation of ammonium cyanate into urea, and the decomposition of urea is closely related to its formation."

Now the addition of alcohol should undoubtedly produce an increase in the velocity of the decomposition of urea if this is solely dependent on its dissociation and all other conditions are the same. A consideration of the conditions implied by the equilibrium scheme just given will show why this result is not effected. Since alcohol promotes the dissociation of ammonium cyanate, it must also inhibit to a corresponding degree any tendency to its formation at all temperatures above its dissociation point, and hence its presence brings about a limitation on one side which counterbalances its promotive effect on the other. The ulterior effect of alcohol will therefore depend on its power of facilitating or retarding the removal of one or other of the dissociation products, and since a check on the rate of hydrolysis of cyanic acid will be the effect, as suggested by Burrows and Fawsitt from a somewhat different point of view, the velocity of the decomposition of urea will be retarded in consequence. The increased pressure produced by alcohol, particularly at high concentration, and at the higher temperature $(98\cdot2°)$, would also check dissociation of urea.

In the conversion of ammonium cyanate into urea, on the other hand, the promotive effect of alcohol is in no way interfered with, since both dissociation products are removed with great rapidity by the formation of urea at a temperature much below its dissociation point, and hence there is little or no opportunity for hydrolysis of cyanic acid.

Decomposition of Urea in Aqueous Solution in the Presence of Sodium Hydroxide.

Since the acidic property of urea is very feeble, when sodium hydroxide is added to its aqueous solution, an equilibrium represented as follows,

$$HN:C{<}^{NH_3}_{O} + NaOH \rightleftarrows HN:C{<}^{NH_2}_{ONa} + H_2O,$$

would only obtain to a small extent when the concentration of both was very high. In solutions below normal, for example, it is certain that nearly, if not, all the urea would be in the free state. Therefore, according to the dissociation theory, the velocity of decomposition of urea in the presence of sodium hydroxide should be greater than in the presence of hydrochloric acid at all concentrations.

This was found, by the writer (1918), to be the case, which is contrary to the general result arrived at by Fawsitt. The two phases of this reaction, which are easily distinguished experimentally, may be represented as follows:—

$$\text{Phase I. } HN:C{<}^{NH_3}_{O} + NaOH = NH_3 + NaOCN + H_2O.$$

Phase II. (a) $NaOCN + 2H_2O = NH_3 + NaHCO_3.$

In the first phase, cyanic acid is temporarily fixed as alkali cyanate ; hydrolysis of the latter quickly follows, and the two phases continue to proceed simultaneously with velocities which vary as the conditions change during the progress of the reaction.

During the earlier stages, sodium cyanate accumulates in considerable quantity in solution, since the velocity of its formation in the first phase is much greater than the speed of its disappearance (by hydrolysis) in the second phase. As the concentration of urea diminishes, the velocity of its dissociation is exceeded by that of the hydrolysis of the alkali cyanate, and hence in the later stages the second phase becomes the predominant change.

The different results obtained after heating urea in solution with sodium hydroxide, under such conditions that ammonia was removed as it was evolved, whilst the concentration was maintained as nearly constant as was possible, are given in the following tables.

The proportion of change under phase I. corresponds with the amount of alkali cyanate found in the cold solution at the end of an experiment, while phase II. represents the amount of alkali cyanate which had been hydrolysed during the progress of the reaction, calculated from the amount of ammonia evolved, after the necessary correction, on the basis of equation (*a*), phase II.

TABLE IV.

Urea, N/5 ; sodium hydroxide, N/5. Molecular ratio, 1 : 1.

Time.		Phase I.	Phase II.	Urea Decomposed.
1 hour	.	17·7 per cent.	4·40 per cent.	22·10 per cent.
2 hours	.	30·8 ,, ,,	9·0 ,, ,,	39·80 ,, ,,
3 ,,	.	36·0 ,, ,,	18·25 ,, ,,	54·25 ,, ,,

Urea, N/2·5 ; sodium hydroxide, N/2·5. Molecular ratio, 1 : 1.

Time.		Phase I.	Phase II.	Urea Decomposed.
1 hour	.	21·25 per cent.	4·15 per cent.	25·40 per cent.
2 hours	.	32·00 ,, ,,	10·00 ,, ,,	42·00 ,, ,,
3 ,,	.	38·90 ,, ,,	18·80 ,, ,,	57·70 ,, ,,
4·5 ,,	.	36·05 ,, ,,	48·72 ,, ,,	84·77 ,, ,,

Urea, N/5 ; sodium hydroxide, N/2·5. Molecular ratio, 1 : 2.

Time.		Phase I.	Phase II.	Urea Decomposed.
1 hour	.	19·05 per cent.	4·52 per cent.	23·57 per cent.
2 hours	.	27·50 ,, ,,	13·12 ,, ,,	40·62 ,, ,,
3 ,,	.	35·35 ,, ,,	19·82 ,, ,,	55·17 ,, ,,
4 ,,	.	36·10 ,, ,,	28·95 ,, ,,	65·05 ,, ,,

Urea, N/5 ; sodium hydroxide, N. Molecular ratio, 1 : 5.

Time.		Phase I.	Phase II.	Urea Decomposed.
1 hour	.	20·0 per cent.	6·75 per cent.	26·75 per cent.
2 hours	.	28·9 ,, ,,	16·55 ,, ,,	45·45 ,, ,,
3 ,,	.	34·2 ,, ,,	27·65 ,, ,,	61·85 ,, ,,

When the above results are compared with those obtained in the presence of hydrochloric acid (Table I.) at similar concentrations, it will be seen that the proportions of urea decomposed were greater in the presence of sodium hydroxide.

The results are therefore in perfect agreement with the dissociation theory of the mechanism of the change. The reason they appear as a contraversion of the conclusions arrived at by Fawsitt is explained by the difference in the experimental methods adopted.

All Fawsitt's experiments were made in sealed tubes, and herein lies the cause of the discrepancy, which supplies further evidence in support of the writer's theory. It is obvious that accumulation of ammonia in solution under pressure would seriously check the dissociation of urea, and so retard the change to an extent which would have no parallel in the case of the decomposition in the presence of an acid, where both dissociation products were removed as fast as they were generated. Thus, when urea and sodium hydroxide, in equal molecular proportions and at concentration $N/5$, were heated for three hours at $100°$ in a sealed tube, only 33 per cent of urea was decomposed, as against $54·25$ per cent (exp. 3, Table IV.) when the experiment was performed in an open vessel, all other conditions being equal.

It will be noticed that the amount of urea decomposed in the former case is also considerably less than that decomposed in the presence of hydrochloric acid $(N/5)$ in an open vessel where the value was 47 per cent.

When the relative effects of acids and alkalis on the velocity of the decomposition of urea are considered, there can be no doubt that in Fawsitt's experiments, on account of the use of sealed tubes, a departure from comparable conditions was quickly brought about.

The dissociation of "free" urea at $100°$ is much more sensitive to external conditions than might be supposed. It was found that variations in the length and diameter of the reflux tube, and in the shape and volume of the flask were sufficient to introduce distinct disturbing effects in the velocity of the decomposition of urea in the presence of acids in an open vessel.

Curiously enough, Fawsitt made no attempt to estimate the amount of the cyanate radicle present in solution at any time during the progress of the decomposition of urea in the presence of sodium hydroxide.

The reactions

$$(1) \quad CON_2H_4 \rightleftharpoons NH_4^{·} + OCN'$$

$$(2) \quad NH_4.OCN + H_2O + NaOH = 2NH_3 + NaHCO_3$$

were assumed to express the decomposition. The amount of change at the end of each experiment was determined apparently by the estimation of the ammonia generated.

As a matter of fact reaction (2) can never have been completed in any of Fawsitt's experiments, since more or less sodium cyanate must have been still present in the solution even after several hours' heating. No error, however, was introduced thereby because the tubes were opened under an excess of normal acid, with the result that the amount neutralised by the residual sodium cyanate was equivalent to that required for $2 NH_3$, thus:

$$NaOCN + H_2O + 2HCl = NaCl + NH_4Cl + CO_2.$$

Had the amount of free ammonia actually present in the tubes been determined, a much lower value would have been recorded for urea decomposed (i.e. so far as hydrolysis was concerned) than what had really taken place.

Decomposition of Urea in Aqueous Solution in the Presence of Barium Hydroxide.

In view of the severe conditions required for the estimation of urea by Bunsen's method (1849), it is remarkable that the progress of the decomposition was never studied until the writer investigated the reaction in 1918.

In this case the changes are represented thus :—

$$\text{Phase I.} \quad 2HN:C\overset{NH_3}{\underset{O}{\Big\langle}} + Ba(OH)_2 = Ba(OCN)_2 + 2NH_3 + 2H_2O.$$

$$\text{Phase II.} \quad \begin{cases} (b) \; Ba(OCN)_2 + 3H_2O = BaCO_3 + 2NH_3 + CO_2, \text{ and} \\ (c) \; Ba(OCN)_2 + 2H_2O = BaCO_3 + CON_2H_4. \end{cases}$$

The following results were obtained when urea and barium hydroxide in equal molecular proportions were heated at 100° in aqueous solution, and whilst ammonia was removed as it was evolved :—

TABLE V.

Urea, N/8 ; barium hydroxide, N/8.

Time.	Phase I.	Phase II.	Urea Decomposed.	BaCO₃ Precipitated.	NH₃ Evolved.
	Per Cent.	Per Cent.	Per Cent.	Per Cent.	Per Cent.
1 hour . .	16·0	3·0	19·0	6·0	11·0
2 hours . .	23·9	8·55	32·45	12·5	20·5
3 ,, . .	28·7	15·15	43·85	18·5	29·5
4 ,, . .	29·9	17·55	47·45	22·5	32·5

(Columns "BaCO₃ Precipitated." and "NH₃ Evolved." are headed "Calculated on the Usual Equation.")

The numbers in the two last columns are given to prove the fallacy underlying the usual interpretation of the change. Thus, after one hour, whilst the amount of barium carbonate formed indicated the decomposition of only 6 per cent of the urea originally present, the ammonia evolved was equal to the decomposition of 11 per cent; in reality, the amount of urea which had been decomposed was equal to 19 per cent, that is, 8 per cent of the nitrogen of urea was present in solution as barium cyanate.

In these experiments, phase II. commenced (judged from the sudden appearance of opalescence) about seven minutes after phase I. had been in progress. Since one molecular proportion of barium hydroxide can theoretically complete the decomposition of two molecular proportions of urea, the results of the two phases should be compared with the third series under Table IV. When the true mechanism of the change is brought to light, it can be readily understood why such severe conditions have been found necessary in order to estimate urea by means of this reaction.

It will now be recognised that the decomposition, or the so-called "hydrolysis" of urea in an acid solution, is nothing more than the "hydrolysis" of free cyanic acid, whilst in a plain aqueous solution, or in the presence of fixed alkali, the hydrolysis of ammonium cyanate, or of a metallic cyanate, is in question. In the latter conditions a peculiar consequence arises, namely, a tendency to the regeneration of urea during its decomposition.

Mechanism of the Formation of Urea During the Hydrolysis of Metallic Cyanates.

It was shown by O. and I. Masson (1910) that the hydrolysis of potassium cyanate at 80° was completed, in accordance with the equation

$$(d) \quad 4KOCN + 6H_2O = 2K_2CO_3 + (NH_4)_2CO_3 + CON_2H_4,$$

whilst in the case of barium cyanate the whole of the nitrogen appeared in the form of urea, as represented by equation (c) shown above.

Cumming (1903) had previously shown that lead cyanate was quantitatively transformed into lead carbonate and urea when boiled with water, thus—

$$Pb(OCN)_2 + 2H_2O = PbCO_3 + CON_2H_4.$$

Assuming ionisation of the cyanate as the first step, O. and I. Masson have accounted for the formation of urea in reaction (d) thus—

$$(A) \quad CNO' + 2H_2O \rightarrow NH_4^{\cdot} + CO_3''.$$

$$(B) \quad CNO' + NH_4^{\cdot} = CON_2H_4.$$

Now equation (B), which is similar to that originally proposed by Walker, fails to throw any light on the mechanism of the change, since no account even is taken of the probable constitution of the cyanic ion, which, in the writer's opinion, should be O . C : N', or N : C : O', if it exists at all.

Metallic salts derived from weak acids are well known to suffer hydrolytic dissociation, whilst they are but feebly ionised. The properties of cyanic acid are distinctly those of a weak acid.[1] The ease with which its ammonium salt is dissociated, whereby urea is formed, is evidence of the fact.

When this is considered, the formation of urea from metallic cyanates is explained in a simple manner, on the basis of hydrolytic dissociation as the first step in the change, thus—

$$KOCN + H_2O \rightleftharpoons KOH + (HOCN \rightleftharpoons HN:CO)$$

$$HOCN + H_2O = NH_3 + CO_2 = KHCO_3$$

$$HN:CO + NH_3 = HN:C\begin{matrix} NH_3 \\ | \\ O \end{matrix}, \text{ and } HOCN + NH_3 = NH_4 . OCN.$$

The following results show how slowly potassium cyanate is hydrolysed in aqueous solution at the ordinary temperature :—

Potassium Cyanate, $N/2$. Mean $t° = 16°$.

Time.	KOCN Hydrolysed.	Time.	KOCN Hydrolysed.
7 days	11·4 per cent.	42 days	81·8 per cent.
13 ,,	22·4 ,, ,,	49 ,,	87·8 ,, ,,
21 ,,	43·2 ,, ,,	56 ,,	91·6 ,, ,,
28 ,,	56·8 ,, ,,	63 ,,	94·5 ,, ,,
35 ,,	69·7 ,, ,,	70 ,,	98·7 ,, ,,

The amount of urea found in solution at the end of ten weeks was equal to 62·7 per cent of the theoretical for O. and I. Masson's equation (d). The conditions were less favourable for the formation of the urea than when hydrolysis was effected at 80°, at which temperature there would be no ammonium cyanate formed.

When potassium cyanate was hydrolysed at 100° under reflux, urea was formed to the extent of 18·44 per cent of the theoretical, for equation (d). No urea was found when potassium cyanate (N/5) was hydrolysed at 100° in presence of sodium hydroxide (N/2·5). It may therefore be safely concluded that no urea would be regenerated during the progress of its decomposition in the presence of sodium hydroxide in an open vessel ; on the other hand, a condition favourable to its regeneration, to some extent, would be brought about in a sealed tube, more particularly in the later stages of the reaction. This fact must also be taken into account in considering the results obtained by

[1] It has been suggested, because the alkali cyanates show a neutral reaction, that cyanic acid must be a strong acid. Against this suggestion may be placed the fact that alkali nitrites have also a neutral reaction, yet nitrous acid is an extremely weak acid, $K = 6 + 10^{-4}$. Further, cyanic acid is readily displaced from its salts by acetic acid.

Fawsitt for the velocity of the decomposition of urea in the presence of alkalis.

Ever since the introduction of the "carbamide" formula the production of ammonium carbonate from urea has always been held forth as a typical example of the normal hydrolysis of an amide. It is common to find it cited in the literature as a change analogous to the conversion of acetamide into ammonium acetate. The experimental evidence which has been discussed in the present chapter proves that the mode of decomposition of urea in the presence of acids and of alkalis respectively is in itself sufficient to throw discredit on the "carbamide" formula.

CHAPTER VI.

THE INTERACTION OF UREA AND NITROUS ACID.

WÖHLER (1830) appears to have been the first to draw attention to the necessity for using pure nitric acid in the preparation of urea nitrate. The nitrous acid which is present in the impure material, he remarked, decomposes urea with evolution of much gas. No attempt was made to study this decomposition until Claus investigated the reaction in 1871.

At this period the several syntheses of urea had been made known, and the "carbamide" formula was in general use. Claus found that when nitrogen trioxide, or nitrous anhydride, was led into a solution of urea, decomposition, apparently in accordance with the equation

$$(1) \quad CON_2H_4 + N_2O_3 + CO_2 + 2N_2 + 2H_2O$$

was only completed by heating the solution.

When the solution of urea was cold, ammonium carbonate seemed to be formed, and the incomplete decomposition, so far as the evolution of gas was concerned was represented by the equation

$$(2) \quad 2\,CON_2H_4 + N_2O_3 = (NH_4)_2CO_3 + 2N_2 + CO_2.$$

Since the ratio of carbon dioxide to nitrogen evolved is shown to be the same in both equations, it was assumed that urea was in part directly hydrolysed during the progress of the decomposition.

Emmerling (1886) studied the decomposition of urea by nitrous acid in the presence of nitric and acetic acid respectively, both in cold and in hot solutions. The volume of nitrogen evolved was found never to be equal to the theoretical required for either equation.

So strong has been the general belief in the "carbamide" formula that neither the results of Claus, nor of Emmerling, have been allowed to interfere with the universal view taken of this decomposition.

The text-books have been unanimous in stating that urea is decomposed in a normal manner by nitrous acid like all other amides. The simple equation

$$(3) \quad CON_2H_4 + 2HNO_2 = CO_2 + 2N_2 + 3H_2O$$

being given as the correct expression for the change.

4

Theoretically, this reaction should be available for the estimation of urea, on the basis of the volume of nitrogen evolved, and indeed this is commonly suggested in the literature.

It is never used for this purpose, and it never has been, since experiment has proved it to be quite valueless.

On the other hand, it constitutes a well-known method for the estimation of nitrous acid, with a very fair degree of accuracy, on the supposition that the above equation is true.

It was no doubt for this reason, and on account of the employment of other methods for the estimation of urea, that this reaction was not considered deserving of any further investigation.

A careful quantitative study of the behaviour of urea towards nitrous acid was made by the writer in 1917. The results have supplied convincing evidence in support of the cyclic formula of urea.

The following facts were clearly established :—

1. Urea and pure nitrous acid in aqueous solution do not interact.

2. The presence of a strong acid (hydrochloric, or nitric) quickly promotes a brisk interaction, even in dilute solutions, and the reaction is then completed in a relatively short time.

3. The presence of a weak acid, such as acetic acid, does not promote an interaction, unless the concentration is abnormally high, and even then the velocity of the reaction is extremely slow.

4. The volume of nitrogen evolved is not a direct measure of the amount of urea decomposed, calculated on the basis of equation (3) ; the quantity decomposed is much greater than that indicated by the evolved nitrogen.

5. Only when urea is present in considerable excess is the volume of nitrogen evolved an approximately true estimate of the amount of nitrous acid decomposed.

6. The volume ratio of carbon dioxide to nitrogen (1 : 2) required by the equation is never obtained ; the proportion of carbon dioxide is always much higher ; moreover, the composition of the gas is liable to much variation with small changes in concentration.

It is obvious that, so far as the usual explanation of this reaction is concerned, all these facts stand out as anomalies for which the ordinary equation offers no explanation.

Now, anomalies in such a reaction can have no reality ; their apparent existence is the natural consequence of an erroneous conception of the change, and when the true constitution of urea is considered they appear as normal phenomena which reveal the true mechanism of the interaction.

The experimental evidence has shown that the progress of the interaction of urea and nitrous acid takes place in the following manner.

The decomposition, by nitrous acid, of aliphatic compounds containing an amino-group is dependent upon the readiness with which this group is oxidised, thus—

$$R \cdot NH_2 + O:N \cdot OH = R \cdot OH + N_2 + H_2O.$$

Hence, since *pure* nitrous acid in aqueous solution does not react with urea, the amino-group cannot be present. (See note at end of chapter.)

The condition necessary for attack is brought about by the production of a salt of urea on the addition of a sufficiently strong acid, thus—

$$HN:C{\overset{\displaystyle NH_3}{\underset{\displaystyle O}{\big|}}} + HX = HN:C{\overset{\displaystyle NH_2,\ HX}{\underset{\displaystyle OH}{}}}$$

The first stage of the reaction then takes place, in accordance with the equation [1]

$$(a)\ HN:C{\overset{\displaystyle NH_2,\ HX}{\underset{\displaystyle OH}{}}} + HNO_2 = N_2 + HNCO + 2H_2O + HX.$$

The cyanic acid is decomposed in two ways as fast as it is generated. It is hydrolysed thus—

$$(b)\ HN:CO + H_2O + HX' = NH_4X' + CO_2$$

and directly attacked by nitrous acid, according to the equation

$$(c)\ HN:CO + HNO_2 = CO_2 + N_2 + H_2O.$$

Both of these decompositions proceed simultaneously with the primary reaction (a), but the relative proportions in which they take place can be varied at will, within certain limits, by adopting suitable conditions which will be presently referred to.

That cyanic acid is actually formed during the progress of the reaction has been demonstrated by its isolation in the form of its silver salt. In an experiment, recorded by the writer, a yield of silver

---

[1] No doubt this decomposition originates through the medium of diazotisation thus :—

$$HN:C{\overset{\displaystyle N=N \cdot OH}{\underset{\displaystyle OH}{}}} \rightarrow N_2 + HN:C{\overset{\displaystyle OH}{\underset{\displaystyle OH}{}}} \rightarrow HNCO + H_2O.$$

4 *

cyanate was obtained equal to 42 per cent of the theoretical, calculated on the equation

$$(d) \quad HN:C\begin{smallmatrix}NH_2, HNO_3 \\ \\ OH\end{smallmatrix} + HNO_2 + AgNO_3$$

$$= N_2 + AgOCN + 2HNO_3 + 2H_2O.$$

Considering the favourable conditions for hydrolysis of cyanic acid, such a result was even more successful than could reasonably have been expected.

It will be seen now that when urea (in the form of a salt) and nitrous acid interact, a certain proportion of nitrogen from the urea is always fixed as an ammonium salt, and herein lies the fallacy of the reaction, so far as the estimation of urea is concerned.

The variations observed in the ratios of carbon dioxide to nitrogen are thus easily explained, since the volume of nitrogen evolved is lowered in proportion to the amount of cyanic acid hydrolysed. The latter change can be only partly suppressed, even under the most favourable conditions (that is, high concentration and nitrous acid in excess), with the result that the ratio of carbon dioxide to nitrogen evolved is never that which has been erroneously assumed.

Now, according to the above explanation, the interaction of urea and nitrous acid is theoretically clearly divisible into two stages, during the first of which one molecule of urea is completely decomposed by one molecule of nitrous acid, instead of by two molecules, as has been commonly, but falsely, supposed.

This has been easily proved experimentally, by adopting the exact conditions which the theory rigorously demands, namely, (1) the presence of urea in excess at the outset, (2) a low concentration of nitrous acid, (3) the presence of mineral acid in excess of that required to neutralise ammonia generated from the hydrolysis of cyanic acid, and so to maintain the proper configuration of the urea molecule. Under these conditions the decomposition of cyanic acid by nitrous acid can be almost completely suppressed in favour of its decomposition by hydrolysis.

The following results, which were obtained by adding the theoretical proportion of nitrous acid (as $NaNO_2$ of known purity) slowly, and at intervals, to an acid solution of urea contained in a Lungé nitrometer, illustrate the degree of success which was attained in proving the true nature of the reaction :—

TABLE I.

	I. $CON_2H_4 + HNO_2$.	II. $CON_2H_4 + HNO_2$.	III. $CON_2H_4 + HNO_2$.
Molecular ratios . .	1 : 1	1·5 : 1	2 : 1
Nitrogen evolved, calculated on the theoretical	92·5 per cent.	95·73 per cent.	99·34 per cent.
HNCO hydrolysed .	87·0 ,, ,,	96·0 ,, ,,	99·5 ,, ,,
HNCO decomposed by HNO_2 . . .	13·0 ,, ,,	4·0 ,, ,,	0·5 ,, ,,
Proportion of urea actually decomposed by one molecule of HNO_2 .	79·5 ,, ,,	91·73 ,, ,,	98·84 ,, ,,
Composition of gas evolved . . .	$CO_2 = 43·1$ per cent. $N_2 = 53·6$,, ,, $NO = 3·2$,, ,,	$CO_2 = 43·2$ per cent. $N_2 = 54·5$,, ,, $NO = 2·2$,, ,,	$CO_2 = 44·2$ per cent. $N_2 = 54·3$,, ,, $NO = 1·3$,, ,,
Ratio CO_2 to N . .	1 : 1·24	1 : 1·26	1 : 1·22

It will be seen from the above results, that the amount of urea decomposed by one molecular proportion of nitrous acid, according to the equation

$$HN:C \Big\langle {}^{NH_2, \ HX}_{OH} \ + \ HNO_2 \ = \ N_2 \ + \ HNCO \ + \ 2H_2O \ + \ HX$$

was less than that indicated by the volume of nitrogen evolved. The difference was most marked when the exact proportions (equal molecules) of urea and nitrous acid required by the equation were used, since the conditions were less favourable for a quantitative realisation of the second change, namely,

$$HNCO \ + \ H_2O \ + \ HX \ = \ NH_4X \ + \ CO_2,$$

than when a considerable excess of urea was present. In the latter case, the desired object was almost fully attained (III.), and the true nature of the primary stage of the reaction thereby established.

As regards the composition of the evolved gases, the ratio of carbon dioxide to nitrogen was in each case approximately 1 : 1·20; this, of course, was not the true value, since a very sensible amount of carbon dioxide was held in solution in the residual liquid; when corrected, in the case of result III., for example, the true ratio was $CO_2 = 1$, $N = 1·02$, or 1 : 1 as required by the combination of the two equations, (a) and (b).

Now, in the above experiments, a very low concentration of nitrous acid was ensured throughout the progress of the reaction.

When the molecular proportion of nitrous acid was added all at once, the concentration at the outset being $HNO_2 = N/6$, the results, as was to be expected, were very different, as shown below :—

TABLE II.

	I. $CON_2H_4 + HNO_2$.	II. $CON_2H_4 + HNO_2$	III. $CON_2H_4 + HNO_2$
Molecular ratios . .	1 : 1	1·5 : 1	2 : 1
Nitrogen evolved . .	91·46 per cent.	94·40 per cent.	96·48 per cent.
HNCO hydrolysed .	71·5 ,, ,,	74·5 ,, ,,	76·0 ,, ,,
HNCO decomposed by HNO₂ . . .	28·5 ,, ,,	25·5 ,, ,,	24·0 ,, ,,
Urea actually decomposed by HNO₂ . .	62·96 ,, ,,	68·90 ,, ,,	72·48 ,, ,,
Composition of gas evolved . . .	CO_2=36·5 per cent. N_2 =59·2 ,, ,, NO = 4·2 ,, ,,	CO_2=37·8 per cent. N_2 =59·08 ,, ,, NO = 3·06 ,, ,,	CO_2=43·6 per cent. N_2 =54·1 ,, ,, NO = 2·2 ,, ,,

Whilst the volume of nitrogen evolved was only slightly below that previously observed, the amount of urea decomposed was, in each case, much less than before. This was the natural result of the much greater facility offered for the decomposition of cyanic acid by nitrous acid at the higher concentration. The latter was also responsible for the slight increase in the proportions of nitric oxide.

It is remarkable that no attempt had been previously made to ascertain the amount of urea decomposed by a definite quantity of nitrous acid. In view of the equation,

$$CON_2H_4 + 2HNO_2 = CO_2 + 2N_2 + 3H_2O,$$

so generally accepted in order to make the reaction fit in with the "carbamide" formula, it is interesting to note the results which were obtained when two molecular proportions of nitrous acid, at different concentrations, were added to an acid solution of urea.

TABLE III.
$CON_2H_4 + 2HNO_2$.

	Nitrogen Evolved. Per Cent.	Composition of Evolved Gases. Per Cent.
I. HNO₂ N/3 Urea N/6 (2 c.c. N-HCl)	72·02	CO_2=35·0, N_2=55·4, NO=9·5
II. HNO₂ N/6 Urea N/12 (2 c.c. N-HCl)	71·99	CO_2=32·1, N_2=58·2, NO=9·6
III. HNO₂ N/8 Urea N/16 (2 c.c. N-HCl)	69·19	CO_2=32·6, N_2=57·3, NO=10·0
IV. HNO₂ N/10 Urea N/20 (3 c.c. N-HCl)	72·07	CO_2=31·1, N_2=58·1, NO=10·4

Mean ratio $CO_2 : N_2 = 1 : 1·75$.

In each case it was readily proved that all the urea had been decomposed, whilst an excess of nitrous acid remained, yet in round numbers only about 70 per cent of the theoretical proportion of nitrogen was evolved. The remainder of the nitrogen was, of course, present as ammonium chloride in the residual solution. It will be noticed also that, even without allowing for carbon dioxide held in solution, the ratio of carbon dioxide to nitrogen was still well below that of 1 : 2 as required.

A still greater divergence from the "theoretical" results was obtained when the reaction was carried out in two separate stages, as shown in the following table :—

Concentration $CON_2H_4 = N/6$, $HNO_2 = N/6$, at outset. Decomposition of Urea by two molecules of nitrous acid, added in separate molecular proportions.

	First Stage. Per Cent.	Second Stage. Per Cent.
Urea decomposed	=62·96	37·04
HNCO hydrolysed	=71·50	57·60
HNCO decomposed by HNO_2 . .	=28·50	42·40
Composition of evolved gas . . . $\begin{cases} CO_2 = 36·5 \\ N_2 = 59·2 \\ NO = 4·2 \end{cases}$		40·5 50·1 9·3
Ratio $CO_2 : N_2$	1 : 1·62	1 : 1·23

Since nitrous acid was in considerable excess in the second stage, the proportion of cyanic acid attacked by it to cyanic acid hydrolysed was much greater than in the first stage.

It is obvious, according to the text-book explanation of the change, that the procedure explained above should give similar results for each stage. That this is not so, proves conclusively, together with the other results, that the behaviour of nitrous acid towards urea had never been seriously studied with the object of obtaining evidence of the "carbamide" formula.

Whilst the study of this reaction has supplied further proof of the cyclic formula, it has also brought to light yet another of the many fallacies which abound throughout the chemistry of urea.

The origin of these is not far to seek.

Instead of a careful study of the properties and reactions of urea being made the groundwork for solving the problem of its constitution, an almost infallible belief in the truth of the carbamide formula has all along been the predominant factor in determining what these properties and reactions should be.

Secondary changes, seemingly unimportant by-products, apparent abnormalities in certain reactions, and so forth, have been pushed aside as of little consequence so long as the end result could be made to fit in with the "carbamide" structure.

Further evidence of this will be found when we come to consider the mechanism of the several syntheses of urea.

It will be noticed that in all the reactions between urea and nitrous acid, a variable amount of nitric oxide is evolved along with the carbon dioxide and nitrogen. This arises from the decomposition of a corresponding proportion of nitrous acid, thus—

$$3HNO_2 = HNO_3 + 2NO + H_2O,$$

and even when the concentration of the acid is as low as $N/20$, and urea in excess, the evolution of nitric oxide is not completely suppressed.

Under such conditions as are commonly adopted, in the estimation of nitrous acid by the aid of urea, the proportions of nitric oxide may easily amount to between 6 and 8 per cent of the evolved gases, according to the particular concentration of the solution used. This fact appears to have been generally overlooked.

It is obvious when the ratios $HNO_2 : N$ and $3HNO_2 : 2NO$ are compared that the presence of nitric oxide must lead to a result in excess of the true value ; for example in the case of result III., Table I., if the nitric oxide found was included as nitrogen, the yield of the latter would appear as 101·8 per cent. of the theoretical.

Rây, Dey, and Ghosh (1917) have shown that at 0° the most concentrated solution of nitrous acid stable for only a short time was approximately $N/5\cdot5$, whilst at the ordinary temperature a solution of the acid at $N/30$ showed signs of decomposition after about an hour. It is this decomposition of nitrous acid which is responsible for the fact that a solution of, say, $HNO_2 = N/6$ can slowly attack urea : the generation of nitric acid gradually brings about the required condition.

In order to prove that urea is not attacked by pure nitrous acid alone, it is necessary that the concentration of the latter should not be greater than $N/30$. Under such condition, the solution being protected from the light which promotes decomposition of nitrous acid, no interaction was found to take place even after three days; yet on the addition of two drops of hydrochloric acid solution a brisk reaction was quickly promoted, and even at this low concentration of nitrous acid was almost completed at the end of half an hour.

The Interaction of Cyanic Acid and Nitrous Acid.

It has been proved beyond question that urea is completely decomposed (according to equation (a)) by one molecular proportion of nitrous acid when the conditions demanded by theory are realised.

The reason this is not accomplished under such conditions as are commonly employed is solely due to the disturbing effect of the reaction—

$$HN : C : O + HNO_2 = N_2 + CO_2 + H_2O.$$

Proof of this decomposition is necessary in order to place the explanation of the whole mechanism of the change on a sound experimental basis. The following details supply the information desired :—

0·081 gram of pure potassium cyanate and 0·071 [1] gram of sodium nitrite were dissolved in 2 c.c. of water and introduced into the nitrometer ; 3 c.c. of N-hydrochloric acid were added, that is, 1 c.c. of acid in excess, to counteract the neutralising effects of hydrolysis.

Concentration at outset, HNO_2 and $HNCO = N/5$.

The evolution of gas was very rapid, and the reaction was practically completed within five minutes.

Gas evolved after one hour = 34·3 c.c. at 16° and 757·8 mm. ; CO_2 = 19·1 c.c. ; NO = 3·6 c.c. ; N_2 = 11·6 c.c.

Volume of nitrogen at N.T.P. = 10·72 c.c. = 47·8 per cent of the theoretical. Therefore 52·2 per cent of cyanic acid had been hydrolysed, with production of ammonia which neutralised 5·22 c.c. of N/10 HCl.

The residual solution required for neutralisation 8·5 c.c. of N/10-sodium hydroxide, instead of 4·78 c.c. as required by the gasometric analysis. The apparent discrepancy was easily explained when the above results were considered. The volume of nitric oxide evolved (3·33 c.c. at N.T.P.) represents a decomposition of 22·3 per cent of nitrous acid, with the generation of nitric acid equivalent to 0·74 c.c. of N/10-sodium hydroxide, whilst the proportion of cyanic acid hydrolysed showed that free nitrous acid remained equivalent to 3 c.c. of N/10-sodium hydroxide. Hence 4·78 + 0·74 + 3·0 = 8·52 c.c. of N/10-sodium hydroxide were required, which is in complete agreement with the value actually found. The presence of unchanged nitrous acid in the residual liquid was easily proved.

Therefore the reaction between cyanic acid and nitrous acid takes place theoretically between equal molecular proportions, but at a concentration of N/5 the velocity of hydrolysis of cyanic acid is slightly higher than that of its decomposition by the acid.

[1] This was the equivalent of 0·069 (a milligram molecule) of pure NaOCN.

Note on the Behaviour of Nitrous Acid towards Compounds containing an Amino-group.

It was noticed by Bonner and Bishop (1913) and later by Rây, Dey, and Ghosh (1917) that a dilute solution of nitrous acid and urea sometimes failed to react.   The latter observers found that the addition of sulphuric acid was necessary to promote and complete a reaction. In both cases, it was remarked that there was no apparent reason for this result.   The explanation is now obvious.   The writer maintains that nitrous acid is a thoroughly reliable reagent for the detection of the amino-group, provided the compound under examination does not contain another group readily attacked by the same agent.   Thiourea furnishes an interesting case in point.

According to the views of the writer, the compound can exist in solution as

$$HN : C \Big\langle \begin{matrix} NH_2 \\ SH \end{matrix} \quad ;$$

it is rapidly decomposed by pure nitrous acid with production of HSCN, nitrogen, and water.   Since the sulphur remains in its original state of combination, the attack is by way of the amino-group.   On the other hand, when nitrous acid is added to a salt of thiourea $HN : C(SH) . NH_2 . HX'$ the amino-group is to a certain extent "protected" by its union with HX',[1] and in this case the more vulnerable SH group is oxidised first, i.e. hydrogen is removed from two molecules of the thiourea salt with production of the salt $HX' . H_2N . C(NH) . S . S . C(NH) . NH_2 . HX'$.   The further addition of nitrous acid then attacks the amino-group with evolution of nitrogen.

[1] See constitution of salts of ammonia as suggested by the writer, Chapter XIII.

CHAPTER VII.

THE MECHANISM OF THE SYNTHESES OF UREA FROM DERIVATIVES OF CARBONIC ACID.

THE natural outcome of the suggestion put forward by Dumas in 1830, as regards the probable relation of urea to ammonium carbonate, led to attempts to synthesise urea from immediate derivatives of carbonic acid.

The syntheses in question are most conveniently dealt with in their historical order.

I. The Interaction of Carbonyl Chloride and Ammonia.

The history of this reaction is of more than ordinary interest, since it has been the subject of several investigations.

It is obvious that if urea was the diamide of carbonic acid its formation by this reaction should be a simple and straightforward change, as follows :—

$$CO{<}^{Cl}_{Cl} + 4NH_3 = CO{<}^{NH_2}_{NH_2} + 2NH_4Cl$$

Regnault (1838) concluded that the reaction did take place in this way, but that the carbamide formed was not urea. He failed to obtain precipitation of urea nitrate after the addition of nitric acid to an aqueous solution of the product, and hence concluded that urea could not be present. The absence of ammonium carbonate was shown by the failure of barium nitrate to give a precipitate when added to the solution. On the other hand, when nitric acid was added to the solid product of the reaction, there was a gradual evolution of carbon dioxide. This was considered to be due to the hydrolysis of the "carbamide" present, which must be different from urea since the latter was not hydrolysed under such simple treatment.

Natanson (1856) repeated Regnault's experiment, and isolated urea by extraction of the product with alcohol, thus clearly proving its synthesis by this reaction. No attention was given to the formation of any secondary products.

Bouchardat (1869) confirmed Natanson's result, and showed that cyanuric acid and ammelide wcre formed as well as urea. It was assumed on the strength of rather weak evidence that[1] guanidine was also a product of the reaction.

In 1879 Fenton made a study of the change. He confirmed the formation of the secondary products found by Bouchardat, and whilst it was proved that the urea formed was identical in every respect with the natural substance, it was suggested that it was possibly the result of a secondary change on account of the relatively poor yield obtained.

Hantzsch and Stuer (1905) added to our knowledge of this reaction by showing that when ammonia was passed into a solution of carbonyl chloride in light petroleum at $0°$, cyamelide was formed in small quantity in addition to cyanuric acid, ammelide, and urea.

Until a quantitative study of this reaction was made by the writer (1918), no attention had been given to the so-called secondary products so far as their bearing on the mechanism of the change is concerned. The formation of urea was considered, beyond doubt, to take place in accordance with the reaction originally put forward by Regnault. This synthesis was held forth as conclusive evidence of the "carbamide" formula, since the change was believed to be analogous, for example, to the formation of acetamide from the interaction of acetyl chloride and ammonia, thus—

$$CH_3CO \cdot Cl + 2NH_3 = CH_3 \cdot CO \cdot NH_2 + NH_4Cl.$$

Now, there are no secondary products in the above change. Urea is a relatively stable substance. Why, then, should such products occur in the supposed analogous change? Their origin is not far to seek.

It is evident that the formation of cyanuric acid and cyamelide must arise from the polymerisation of cyanic acid as follows:—

$$\text{I. } CO {\Large\langle} {}^{Cl}_{Cl} + 2NH_3 = CO {\Large\langle} {}^{NH_2}_{Cl} + NH_4Cl.$$

Chloroformamide.[2]

$$\text{II. } CO {\Large\langle} {}^{NH_2}_{Cl} = HCl + \begin{array}{l} HO \cdot CN \to \\ \quad \updownarrow \\ HN : CO \end{array} \begin{array}{l} \text{Cyamelide} \\ \text{by} \\ \text{polymerisation} \\ \to \text{Cyanuric Acid.} \end{array}$$

---

[1] It was rather unfortunate, that Bouchardat should have selected the title "Une nouvelle synthèse de la guanidine" in giving an account of his research, as this compound is not formed in the reaction.

[2] This compound, which is also known as "carbamyl chloride," has been referred to in Chapter III. It is easily dissociated by gentle heat into cyanic acid and hydrochloric acid. At ordinary temperature it gradually changes into cyamelide and cyanuric acid, with evolution of HCl.

The origin of urea in this synthesis is self-evident, from the above scheme, since cyanic acid (HNCO) is produced in the presence of ammonia. In other words, it is nothing more than Wöhler's synthesis in a modified form.

If this view of the mechanism of the change is correct, it follows, since ammelide is one of the by-products, that biuret must also be produced in this reaction. Its formation had been overlooked by previous investigators, since there was no reason to suspect its presence, on account of the erroneous view which had been taken of the change.

The following results which were obtained after passing a current of dry ammonia into a 3 per cent solution of carbonyl chloride in benzene show that biuret, as a matter of fact, is one of the chief by-products of the reaction:—

	Expt. I.	Expt. II.	Expt. III.
Temperature	20°-25°	40°-50°	65°-70°
Products formed—	Per Cent.	Per Cent.	Per Cent.
Urea	31·7	37·3	41·2
Biuret	14·4	10·1	7·8
Ammelide	7·65	8·6	10·6
Cyanuric acid	3·45	6·4	5·98
Cyamelide	0·69	trace	none

The results are expressed in proportion to the respective theoretical yields, calculated on the following bases: thus $COCl_2$ = one mol. each of urea, cyanuric acid, and cyamelide, since the two latter are formed from the polymerisation of cyanic acid; $2COCl_2$ = one mol. of biuret; and $3COCl_2$ = one mol. of ammelide, thus—

$$HN{\Large\langle}\begin{array}{l}CO.NH_2\\CO.NH_2\end{array} + OC:NH \rightarrow HN{\Large\langle}\begin{array}{l}CO.NH\\CO.NH\end{array}{\Large\rangle}C:NH + H_2O.$$

It will be noticed that in Expts. I. and II. biuret constitutes the chief product after urea, and whilst the yield falls with rise of temperature, that of ammelide increases, since, in agreement with theory, the formation of the latter from its precursor biuret is promoted at the higher temperature. The conditions being unfavourable for the existence of free cyanic acid, the proportion of cyanuric acid generated was consequently small.

At a low temperature a small quantity of ammonium cyanate was formed, whilst more or less chloroformamide was easily detected in the benzene solution. This was undoubtedly the substance which gave rise to the evolution of carbon dioxide in Regnault's experiment, and which led him to the pardonable conclusion, considering the period, that "carbamide" was formed.

We have in this synthesis of urea a good example of the necessity of giving to the so-called secondary products the full consideration which they deserve, since they clearly indicate in this case the true mechanism of the change.

It is also interesting to note that in this reaction we have the production at low temperature of the same substances as are produced by the decomposition of urea at a high temperature. Since it has been shown that in the latter case the different products are the result of the generation of cyanic acid and ammonia, their formation in the former case must be ascribed to the same cause.

The interaction of carbonyl chloride and ammonia, therefore, does not supply evidence in support of the " carbamide " formula.

II. The Formation of Urea from Ethyl Carbonate.

Natanson (1856) obtained urea after heating ethyl carbonate with excess of ammonia in a sealed tube at 180° for two hours. This synthesis, which has also been considered to afford evidence of the " carbamide " structure is commonly represented by the simple equation

$$(a)\ \ CO:(OC_2H_5)_2 + 2NH_3 = CO(NH_2)_2 + 2C_2H_5OH.$$

The change in this case has been assumed to be analogous to the formation of acetamide from ethyl acetate and ammonia, or of oxamide from ethyl oxalate and ammonia. As a matter of fact, it is nothing of the kind. When the true mechanism of the reaction is brought to light it is seen to be another modification of Wöhler's synthesis.

Cahours (1845) showed that when ethyl carbonate was allowed to remain in contact with an excess of ammonia in the cold, or at 100°, the reaction did not go beyond the formation of ethyl carbamate, or urethane, $H_2N.CO.O.C_2H_5$, which in point of fact is a by-product of reaction (a) even under the conditions adopted by Natanson.

Now we have here an apparently abnormal phenomenon which has been disregarded in order that reaction (a) should fit in with the requirements of the "carbamide" formula.

It is obvious that, if urea was "carbamide," there appears no reason why it should not be formed from ethyl carbonate, or from ethyl carbamate, with the same ease as undoubted diamides are formed from esters and ammonia. That such is not the case is in itself sufficient to throw grave doubt on such a formula.

A study of the properties of urethane has enabled the writer (1918) to give the correct explanation of this synthesis of urea.

The vapour density of urethane (b.p. 182°) at 202·8° (b.p. of *m*-cresol) was found to be 43·22, whilst theory requires 44·5; on the other hand, when the ester was boiled under reflux, it was gradually dissociated in accordance with the equation

$$EtO . CO . NH_2 \rightarrow HCNO + EtOH ;$$
(polymerised)

thus, after two hours, 16 per cent of the theoretical yield of cyanuric acid was obtained.

The decomposition of the ester by alkali in aqueous solution was found to proceed on the same lines: the change is not a direct hydrolysis, as commonly stated in the literature, and is represented thus—

(1) $EtO . CO . NH_2 + NaOH \rightarrow H_2O + EtO . C(ONa):NH \rightarrow$
$$NaOCN + EtOH.$$

(2) $NaOCN + 2H_2O = NaHCO_3 + NH_3.$

The following results were obtained when urethane and sodium hydroxide (both in $N/5$ solution) were heated at 100°:—

Time in Minutes.	Urethane Decomposed. Per Cent.	Sodium Cyanate Formed. Per Cent.	Sodium Carbonate Formed. Per Cent.
5	50·9	32·9	18·0
15	62·5	37·25	25·25
30	63·95	29·70	34·25
60	66·80	28·80	38·0
90	71·0	17·0	54·0

At 15°, after three days, 18 per cent of urethane was decomposed, with the formation of 5·5 per cent of sodium cyanate and 12·5 per cent of sodium carbonate. The change was therefore independent of dissociation of the ester (compare decomposition of urea by alkali).

When urethane was heated in a current of hydrogen chloride, it was decomposed thus—

$$EtO . CO . NH_2 + 2HCl = CO_2 + EtCl + NH_4Cl.$$

This decomposition of urethane in two different directions may be represented thus—

in presence of alkali
$$EtO . CO . NH_2 \underset{\text{in presence of acid}}{\overset{\longrightarrow}{\longleftarrow}} EtO . C(OH):NH.$$
(basic form)   (acidic form)

Since urea is formed from the hydrolysis of cyanic acid, as explained in Chapter III., a change which may be represented for the moment by the simple equation

$$2HO.CN + H_2O = CON_2H_4 + CO_2$$

it follows that, in order to obtain urea from urethane it is necessary to reach the temperature at which the latter substance undergoes dissociation in solution.

In proof of this it was shown by the writer that when urethane was heated *alone* in aqueous solution in a sealed tube for two hours at 130°, 6 per cent of the theoretical yield of urea was formed; and after 6 hours the yield of urea was nearly 17 per cent. The presence of ammonia would obviously promote the change. It is evident, therefore, that the origin of urea in this synthesis is properly represented thus—

$$(1)\ CO\!\!<^{NH_2}_{O\,.\,C_2H_5} = {HN:CO \atop C_2H_5OH}\ ,\ (2)\ HN:CO + NH_3 = HN:C\!\!<^{NH_3}_{O}$$

It explains why urea is not formed by the action of ammonia in excess on urethane in the cold, no matter how long the two compounds may be left in contact.

Cahours (1873) showed that when urea is heated with alcohols carbamic esters are formed. The changes in question are commonly represented as a reversible reaction by the equation

$$CO\!\!<^{NH_2}_{O\,.\,C_2H_5} + NH_3 \underset{(a)}{\overset{(b)}{\rightleftarrows}} C_2H_5OH + CON_2H_4.$$

Now, urea dissociates into ammonia and cyanic acid with greater facility than urethane dissociates into cyanic acid and alcohol; hence it is natural to expect that the velocity of the reaction will be greater in direction (*a*) than in direction (*b*). When a 5 N-alcoholic solution of urea was heated for two hours at 150°, 41·6 per cent of the theoretical yield of urethane was formed, as compared with 33·3 per cent yield of urea from the interaction of urethane and ammonia in alcohol under similar conditions.

When urea is considered as "carbamide" it must be admitted that such a result appears abnormal, since it is well known that the formation of an amide from the interaction of an ester and ammonia takes place with ease, as compared with the reverse change, i.e. the formation of an ester from an amide and an alcohol. In fact, the reaction can be completed readily in direction (*b*), which of course is not possible in the above synthesis of urea. After urethane had been heated with an excess of strong solution of ammonia (D = 0·880) for twenty hours at 100°, a yield of urea was obtained equal to only 10·4 per cent. of the theoretical.

III. The Formation of Urea from Ammonium Carbamate, and from Ammonium Carbonate.

The prediction made by Dumas (1830) that urea might possibly be obtained from ammonium carbonate by a reaction similar to that by which oxamide is formed from ammonium oxalate has been referred to in the opening chapter.

Nearly forty years afterwards the prediction was realised by Basarov (1868), who obtained a small yield of urea from ammonium carbamate, after it had been heated in a sealed tube at 130°-140° for four hours.

The change has been supposed to be explained by the simple equation

$$CO\big\langle {}^{NH_2}_{O \,.\, NH_4} = CO\big\langle {}^{NH_2}_{NH_2} + H_2O.$$
(Ammonium Carbamate.)

Since it represented apparently the converse of the supposed direct hydrolysis of urea to ammonium carbonate, this synthesis has been accepted in the literature as evidence *par excellence* in favour of the "carbamide" formula.

Ammonium carbamate is readily hydrolysed to ammonium carbonate, and hence the relation between urea and the latter appeared to be clearly established from both sides.

In order to satisfy this view, it has been assumed without any proof, that in the above reaction water is eliminated from the group $.O.NH_4$, the production of urea being thus analogous to the formation of acetamide from ammonium acetate, or of oxamide from ammonium oxalate, in agreement with Dumas' prediction.

Bourgeois (1897), as the result of a series of experiments, obtained a yield of urea ranging from 3·2 to 9·5 per cent, calculated on the weight of the salt used, after heating ammonium carbonate in a sealed vessel for many hours at 130,° whilst from ammonium carbamate the yield of urea was from 2·6 to 3·7 per cent.

When ammonium carbamate (or carbonate) is heated under normal pressure it dissociates completely thus—

$$CO\big\langle {}^{NH_2}_{O \cdot NH_4} \rightarrow NH_3 + C\dot{O}\big\langle {}^{NH_2}_{OH} \rightarrow NH_3 + CO_2.$$

It is improbable that under pressure the salt would be so "stabilised" as to give rise to urea in the manner so generally assumed, i.e. simple loss of H_2O from the $.O.NH_4$ group.

5

Mixter (1882) obtained urea by passing carbon dioxide and ammonia through a tube heated to low redness. There can be no doubt that cyanic acid was generated in this case, thus—

$$CO_2 + NH_3 = HN{:}CO + H_2O,$$

as Mixter has suggested. It was shown by the writer (1920) that when ammonium carbamate was vaporised through a glass tube heated to incipient redness, ammonium cyanate and urea were found in small quantity in the cooled product. Whilst this is a confirmation of Mixter's experiment, it gives at once a clue to the origin of urea in Basarov's synthesis, which is the result of three distinct changes, as follows :—

$$(1)\ CO\begin{smallmatrix}NH_2\\O.NH_4\end{smallmatrix} \rightarrow NH_3 + CO\begin{smallmatrix}NH_2\\OH\end{smallmatrix} \rightleftarrows C\begin{smallmatrix}NH\\-OH\\OH\end{smallmatrix}$$

(Carbamic acid.)

$$(2)\ C\begin{smallmatrix}NH\\-OH\\OH\end{smallmatrix} \rightarrow (HN{:}CO \rightleftarrows HO.CN) + H_2O$$

$$(3)\ HN{:}CO + NH_3 = HN:C\begin{smallmatrix}NH_3\\|\\O\end{smallmatrix}$$

Apart from the fact that ammonium carbamate is readily dissociated, and the evidence of Mixter's experiment, there is apparently no means of obtaining direct proof of the above theory of the changes in the case of the simple ammonium salt. Hence we must rely largely on evidence by analogy, as supplied by the study of the decomposition of the homologues of ammonium carbamate. Such evidence, which is very convincing in this case, is greatly strengthened by what has already been proved in the two previous syntheses of urea from derivatives of carbonic acid.

Fichter and Becker (1911) showed that methylammonium methyl-carbamate, $NHMe.CO.O.NH_3Me$, and the ethylammonium analogue gave the respective symmetrical disubstituted carbamides, whilst no tetra-substituted carbamide could be obtained from diethylammonium diethylcarbamate. Since direct dehydration of the carbamates was assumed to represent the mechanism of the change, it follows that if the reaction

$$(a)\ CO\begin{smallmatrix}NHR\ [1]\\O.NH_3R\end{smallmatrix} \rightarrow CO\begin{smallmatrix}NHR\\NHR\end{smallmatrix} + H_2O$$

[1] $R = CH_3$, or C_2H_5, or any monovalent hydrocarbon radicle.

was the result of the direct elimination of water from the group
. ONH_3R, there seemed no reason why the change

$$(b)\ CO\big<^{NR_2}_{O\,.\,NH_2R_2} \rightarrow CO\big<^{NR_2}_{NR_2} + H_2O$$

should not take place with even greater facility than in the case of
reaction (a). Since the loss of water could take place in one way only,
and considering the stability of tetra-substituted carbamides, these
investigators were at a loss to explain the apparent abnormality.

Now, according to the three-phase change, or "dissociation
theory" here put forward, only carbamates which contain the system
. $CO\,.\,NHR$, capable of yielding $R\,.\,NCO$, can give rise to substituted
carbamides. Thus, in the decomposition of all such carbamates, change
(a), for example, is correctly represented by the following general
scheme :—

$$CO\big<^{NHR}_{O\,.\,NH_3R} \rightarrow \underbrace{\begin{array}{c}CO\big<^{NHR}_{OH} \xrightarrow{(Phase\ II.)} H_2O \\ + \qquad\qquad + \\ NH_2R \rightarrow + \leftarrow R\,.\,NCO\end{array}}_{(Phase\ III.)} RN:C\big<^{NHR}_{OH} \rightleftarrows CO\big<^{NHR}_{NHR}$$

(Phase I.)

It will be seen, therefore, that carbamates of type (b) cannot give
tetra-substituted carbamides, since the substituted carbamic acid produced in the first instance can only decompose thus—

$$CO\big<^{NR_2}_{OH} \rightarrow CO_2 + NHR_2.$$

On the other hand, a carbamic acid from a carbamate of type (a)
can be decomposed in two ways, viz. :—

$$CO\big<^{NHR}_{OH} \quad \begin{array}{l}\nearrow (1)\ CO_2 + NH_2R. \\ \searrow (2)\ H_2O + R\,.\,NCO.\end{array}$$

Whilst under normal pressure, change (1) alone prevails, and
urea is not formed under such conditions, change (2) must obtain
under considerable pressure.

The value of a theory is greatly enhanced if the predictions which
follow from it are proved to be true.

5 *

Carbamates of type

$$(c)\ CO\!\!<\!\!\begin{array}{l} NIIR \\ O\ .\ NH_2R_2 \end{array} \quad \text{and of type } (d)\ CO\!\!<\!\!\begin{array}{l} NR_2 \\ O\ .\ NH_3R \end{array}$$

were prepared by the writer, and heated in sealed tubes at 140°-150°. The former yielded tri-substituted carbamides, the latter did not.

Now, according to the direct dehydration theory, judging from analogy, the reverse result might have been expected, since type (c) contains the same group—$O\ .\ NH_2R_2$ as in type (b) which does not yield a urea, whilst type (d) contains the same group—$O\ .\ NH_3R$ as in type (a), which yields a di-substituted urea. In the case of type (c), as the result of Phases I. and II., $RNCO$ and NHR_2 are produced,

which react to give $CO\!\!<\!\!\begin{array}{l} NR_2 \\ NHR \end{array}$ as a result of Phase III.

In the case of type (d) the final result of dissociation can only be the production of CO_2, NHR_2, and NH_2R.

It is obvious that the theory of the direct dehydration of carbamates, which fails entirely to explain the facts just recorded, must be abandoned in favour of the dissociation theory. As a logical sequence thereof, Basarov's synthesis of urea can no longer be upheld as evidence of the " carbamide " structure.

Thus, the third synthesis of urea from a derivative of carbonic acid, proves, like the other two, to be nothing more than Wöhler's synthesis in another form.

A discussion of the mechanism of the production of urea from ammonium carbamate would be incomplete without reference to the views which have been suggested to explain the change on the assumption that dehydration is the chief factor to be considered.

Drechsel (1878) showed that metallic carbamates were decomposed by heat into cyanates and water, thus—

$$CO\!\!<\!\!\begin{array}{l} NH_2 \\ O.Na \end{array} = Na\ .\ O\ .\ CN + H_2O,$$

and on the basis of this fact, he suggested that urea was formed from ammonium carbamate, through ammonium cyanate, as follows:—

$$CO\!\!<\!\!\begin{array}{l} NH_2 \\ O\ .\ NH_4 \end{array} = H_2O + C\!\!<\!\!\begin{array}{l} N \\ O\ .\ NH_4 \end{array} \rightarrow CON_2H_4.$$

A few years later Drechsel (1880) made the interesting observation that urea was formed when a rapidly alternating electric current was passed through a solution of ammonium carbamate for ten hours. This result was attributed to the effects of successive oxidation and reduction whereby the elements of water were removed from the carbamate in accordance with the above equation.

Whilst this explanation of the change seemed a more reasonable one than that generally accepted, the implicit belief in the "carbamide" formula prevented it from receiving the attention it deserved. The theory that water is removed from ammonium carbamate in the manner indicated breaks down when an attempt is made to apply it to a substituted ammonium carbamate of type (a) $RHN . CO . O . NH_3R$, for example; on the other hand, it has the merit of showing that the formation of urea is finally similar to Wöhler's synthesis.

Fichter and Becker (1911) investigated the dehydration of ammonium carbamate to urea. The substance was heated in a steel bomb lined with tin. The yield of urea was found to rise rapidly from $115°$-$135°$, after which it slowly fell again. Close packing of the carbamate considerably improved the yield of urea at $135°$, and under these conditions 40 per cent of the carbamate was converted into urea in the course of four days.

It was concluded that the unvaporised ammonium carbamate only was dehydrated, the fall in the yield of urea above $135°$ being due to the larger proportion of carbamate vaporised. The change was represented as an equilibrium thus—

$$CO \begin{cases} NH_2 \\ O . NH_4 \end{cases} \rightleftarrows CO(NH_2) + H_2O.$$

60 per cent.   40 per cent.

The fact that urea would tend to decompose into ammonia and cyanic acid above $135°$ explains the diminution in the yield above that temperature, whilst according to the dissociation theory of the change, the above equilibrium would be more correctly represented thus—

$$CO \begin{cases} NH_2 \\ O . NH_4 \end{cases} \rightleftarrows H_2O + \begin{matrix} NH_3 \\ + \\ HNCO \end{matrix} \rightleftarrows HN : C \begin{cases} NH_3 \\ | \\ O \end{cases}$$

The reason that ammonium carbamate was found to be "stable" under pressure at $135°$ is due to dissociation being checked under such conditions. Since urea is much more stable in the presence of water than ammonium carbamate, if the direct dehydration of the latter was the only phase in the change, it would be reasonable to expect a greater amount of decomposition in the direction from left to right.

Fichter, Stutz, and Grieshaber (1912) and Fichter, Steiger, and Stanisch (1918) showed that when a concentrated solution of ammonium carbamate was electrolysed with a direct current, a small quantity of urea was formed *exclusively at the anode.*

A complex theory of the change, in which it was assumed that formamide and hydroxylamine were intermediate products, was at first put forward; this was abandoned in the later investigation in favour of the explanation that during oxidation at the anode (ammonium nitrate was formed) the heat set free was solely responsible for the production of urea, the formation of which was represented by the equation

$$H_2N . CO . O . NH_4 + H_2O \rightleftarrows (NH_4)_2CO_3 \rightleftarrows CO(NH_2)_2 + 2H_2O.$$

For reasons which are difficult to understand it was concluded that ammonium *carbonate* only was directly converted into urea, and this hypothesis is based on the assumption that the temperature elevation at the anode does not exceed 100°.

This admittedly "complex equilibrium scheme" would be certainly hard to accept, even assuming that urea is "carbamide." There seems no reason why urea should not be formed by merely boiling a concentrated solution of ammonium carbonate; yet no urea is produced under such conditions.

Now, Fichter and his co-workers have shown that small quantities of urea were formed by the oxidation of ammonium carbamate, by hydrogen peroxide, ozonised oxygen, and calcium permanganate respectively. Hofmeister (1897) and Halsey (1898), and other investigators later showed that urea is formed during the oxidation of a large number of organic substances in the presence of an excess of ammonia. The recent work of Fosse (1919-1921), which will be referred to later on, has shown that cyanic acid is produced as the intermediate substance from which urea is formed in such experiments.

Since urea was formed only at the anode in Fichter's experiments, there can be no doubt that the formation of cyanic acid by oxidation is the pre-final step in this synthesis. Indeed Fichter has himself supplied evidence in support of this conclusion. Urea was obtained by electrolysing a solution of ammonium acetate containing methyl alcohol. The latter, it is stated, gives carbon monoxide, and the change was represented thus—

$$CH_3OH \rightarrow CO \rightarrow H . CO . NH_2 \rightarrow H_2N . CO . NH_2.$$
$$\text{(Formamide.)}$$

Formamide, which was assumed to be produced (apparently by union of CO and NH_3), was oxidised to urea in the presence of ammonia.

The obvious explanation of the change is

$$CO + NH_3 + O = HN:CO + H_2O.$$

The fact that the formation of urea is promoted in all these reactions by the presence of free ammonia is easily understood, since the latter is necessary to "fix" the cyanic acid produced.   The formation of urea from ammonium carbamate furnishes a striking illustration of the difficulties which have been encountered in attempting to explain a simple phenomenon, solely as the result of the belief in the "carbamide" formula.

The formation of urea by heating ammonium thiocarbamate (Schmidt 1877), $H_2N . CO . S . NH_4$, is obviously similar in mechanism to the decomposition of the carbamate.   It is only necessary to point out that, if elimination of water took place as suggested by Drechsel in the case of the carbamate, ammonium thiocynate should be formed from the thiocarbamate, instead of urea.

CHAPTER VIII.

MISCELLANEOUS SYNTHESES, AND PREPARATIONS OF UREA.

SEVERAL syntheses of urea, from sources other than immediate derivatives of carbonic acid, have been recorded from time to time. The
mechanism of these different reactions, which have never been properly
explained, has now to be considered.

The Synthesis of Urea from Oxamide.

Williamson (1847) obtained urea in small quantity by heating a
mixture of oxamide and mercuric oxide. This fact had been accepted
as evidence of a close similarity in constitution between urea and the
diamide, the latter being supposed merely to lose a carbonyl group by
oxidation, thus—

$$\begin{array}{l} CO - NH_2 \\ | \\ CO - NH_2 \\ \text{(Oxamide.)} \end{array} + HgO = CO\!\!<\begin{array}{l} NH_2 \\ NH_2 \end{array} + CO_2 + Hg.$$

Werner and Carpenter (1918) showed that when mixtures of
oxamide and mercuric oxide in different proportions were heated to
the temperature (230°-240°), at which the oxide was completely reduced, no urea could be detected in the product. On heating oxamide
to a temperature just sufficient to effect complete volatilisation,
ammonium cyanate, urea, and biuret were found in the sublimate,
whilst ammonia, water, carbon monoxide, and hydrogen cyanide were
evolved.

These facts go to show that the mechanism of this synthesis is as
follows :—

(a)
$$\begin{array}{l} CO.NH_2 \\ | \\ CO.NH_2 \end{array} \rightarrow NH_3 + \begin{array}{l} CO \\ | \\ CO \end{array}\!\!>NH \rightarrow CO + \begin{array}{l} \rightarrow HOCN = NH_4OCN \\ \\ \rightarrow HN\!:\!CO + CON_2H_4 \end{array}$$

(b)
$$\begin{array}{l} HO.C\!:\!NH \\ | \\ HO.C\!:\!NH \end{array} \rightarrow H_2O + O\!\!<\begin{array}{l} C\!:\!NH \\ \\ C\!:\!NH \end{array} \rightarrow HN\!:\!CO + HCN$$

Since ammonia was first evolved (at about 110°) whether mercuric oxide was present or not, it is evident that the formation of urea from oxamide, in accordance with (a), is but another example of Wöhler's synthesis. The respective yields of ammonium cyanate and of urea were 2·9 and 4·18 per cent of the theoretical when oxamide was rapidly heated and the vapours quickly condensed by artificial cooling. When the amide was slowly heated without further precaution, the yields were 2·4 and 2·6 per cent respectively, whilst the formation of hydrogen cyanide was more evident than in the former case. The formation of biuret is obviously accounted for by the above explanation of the mechanism of the change.

Herroun's Synthesis of Urea.

Herroun (1881) showed that urea and ammonium cyanate were formed when air charged with ammonia and the vapour of benzene was passed over a red-hot coil of platinum wire. Ammonium carbonate, nitrite, and nitrate were also formed. The best yield of urea was obtained when the supply of air was controlled so as to avoid too vigorous oxidation, in which case the benzene vapour was entirely converted into carbon dioxide and water. An equally good result was obtained when acetylene was substituted for the vapour of benzene.

There can be no doubt that the origin of cyanic acid in this interesting experiment was partly due to a reaction similar to that in Mixter's experiment referred to in the previous chapter, and also to the change

$$\text{(A)}\quad CO + NH_3 + O = HN:CO + H_2O.$$

Since moderate oxidation gave the best results, this reaction was probably the predominant one. Its importance must not be overlooked, since it presages the economic fixation of nitrogen in the form of urea.

Millot's Synthesis of Urea.

When an approximately 15 per cent solution of ammonia was electrolysed using a positive electrode of purified gas carbon and a negative electrode of platinum, Millot (1885) showed that urea was formed. From a litre of ammonia solution 1 gram of pure urea was obtained after electrolysis during eight days. In the following year (1886) Millot made the further interesting observation, that biuret and ammelide were also formed during the electrolysis. Fettered to the "carbamide" formula, it was assumed that urea must originate from the action of "nascent carbonic acid" on ammonia with elimination of water,

$$CO_2 + 2NH_3 = CO(NH_2)_2 + H_2O,$$

whilst biuret and ammelide were products of its decomposition. It is evident from what has been shown regarding the mechanism of the formation of these two substances from urea, that their production in Millot's experiments supplies proof that cyanic acid is formed, no doubt according to equation (A) given above; urea is produced from it and ammonia.

Millot found that no cyanuric acid was formed. The reason is clear, since polymerisation could not take effect in the presence of a large excess of ammonia.

Synthesis of Urea from Carbon Monoxide and Ammonia.

Jouve (1899) showed that urea is formed when a solution of carbon monoxide in ammoniacal cuprous chloride is heated at 105° for six hours in a sealed vessel. Copper is separated, and the change was expressed thus—

$$CO + 2NH_3 = CO(NH_2)_2 + H_2, \text{ and } Cu_2Cl_2 + H_2 = Cu_2 + 2HCl.$$

Now, there can be no doubt that cyanic acid is produced in this synthesis on the lines of reaction (A), namely,

$$CO + NH_3 + Cu_2Cl_2 = HN:CO + Cu_2 + 2HCl,$$

or, if we consider an ammoniacal solution of cuprous chloride as containing very probably Cu_2O dissolved in ammonia, the change becomes similar to (A)—

$$CO + NH_3 + Cu_2O = HN:CO + Cu_2 + H_2O.[1]$$

A repetition of Jouve's experiment by the writer, hitherto unpublished, has shown that biuret is also formed in this reaction, thus proving the true mechanism of the synthesis.

A very interesting modification of this synthesis has been described by Jackson and Northall-Laurie (1905) which confirms the views just stated. When a mixture of dry carbon monoxide and ammonia was heated in the presence of platinum, subjected to the silent electrical discharge, to electric sparking, or treated with the high-frequency current, urea, in considerable amount, and ammonium cyanate were formed. Hydrogen, methane, nitrogen, and water were

---

[1] The writer has found that when an ammoniacal solution of cuprous oxide (containing a small quantity of NaOH) was saturated with CO, and allowed to remain in the cold for twenty-four hours, copper was deposited and the solution contained alkali cyanate.

produced as by-products. From about 8 litres of carbon monoxide over 10 grams of urea were obtained. The best results were secured when the mixed gases were passed over a heated spiral of platinum or heated platinised asbestos.

The primary reaction is obviously the formation of cyanic acid thus—

$$CO + NH_3 = CONH + H_2,$$

from which both urea and ammonium cyanate result in the presence of excess of ammonia.

The synthesis is one which certainly deserves further study for the reason referred to under Herroun's experiment.

It will be seen that the four syntheses just described go far to confirm the views which were discussed at the close of the previous chapter in connection with the electrolysis of ammonium carbamate.

The following miscellaneous syntheses of urea do not demand more than a passing reference.

Urea from Fulminic Acid.

After the removal of the copper by sulphuretted hydrogen from a solution of copper fulminate in ammonia, Gladstone (1849) obtained urea from the filtrate. Ammonium thiocyanate was also formed, and hence it was concluded that ammonium cyanate was formed as well, which then changed to urea.

It is now well known that fulminates generally when heated with aqueous solution of ammonia yield urea amongst other compounds. Whether the result is due to an isomeric change of fulminic acid, or to the hydrolysis of cyanogen produced from its decomposition, is at present unknown.

The formation of more or less urea when potassium cyanide is added to an ammoniacal solution of a copper salt, as shown by Liebig (1855), is readily explained, since this is the result of an oxidation, thus—

$$KCN + 2CuO = KOCN + Cu_2O.$$

The presence of the cyanic radicle can be readily demonstrated in the solution.

The production of urea from guanidine and from such derivatives of the latter, as biguanide, creatine, and arginine is not considered here, since the mechanism of the hydrolytic decompositions referred to in the literature has not yet been properly investigated.

The formation of carbon dioxide and ammonia has in some cases been taken as evidence that urea must be a product of the decomposition.

In the writer's opinion the constitution of "free" guanidine, as distinct from guanidine in the form of a salt, has yet to be established.

The Formation of Urea by the Oxidation of Nitrogenous and of Non-Nitrogenous Organic Compounds in the Presence of Ammonia.

There is no doubt that urea is an end-product of the oxidation of proteins during metabolism in the animal organism.

The first attempt to obtain evidence of this by experiment *in vitro* was made by Béchamp (1856). By the oxidation of egg-albumen, serum albumen, blood fibrin, and gluten respectively with potassium permanganate, Béchamp justly claimed to have obtained urea. Ritter (1871) confirmed [1] Béchamp's results, whilst Dreschel (1890) obtained urea by the combined electrolysis and hydrolysis of egg-albumen. Hugounencq (1901), after the complete oxidation of an ammoniacal solution of egg-albumen at 90° with ammonium persulphate, obtained urea equal in amount to 5 per cent of the albumen oxidised.

Hofmeister (1896) obtained urea by the oxidation of a great variety of organic compounds in ammoniacal solution with potassium permanganate. The following substances indicate the different types of compounds which were oxidised under the conditions stated: hydrocyanic acid, formamide, oxamic acid, acetone, methyl alcohol, glycocine, asparagine, leucine, gelatin, and egg-albumen.

From 10 grams of glycocine and of oxamic acid respectively 3 grams and 0·7 gram of urea nitrate were obtained, whilst in the case of egg-albumen the yield of urea nitrate was approximately equal to 5 per cent of the weight of the substance taken.

The production of urea was assumed to depend on the union of $- NH_2$, and $= CO$, and hence compounds free from nitrogen may, during oxidation, give rise to urea by the aid of ammonia. Hofmeister naturally considered the formation of urea solely from the point of view of the "carbamide" formula, and hence no attempt was made to show either the presence or absence of an alkali cyanate in the product after oxidation.

Urea was proved by preparation of the nitrate, and by its micro-

---

[1] It is unnecessary to refer to the work of those who refuted Béchamp's results, since the formation of urea by the oxidation of proteins is now an established fact.

The subject is fully discussed in Chapter XII.

scopical examination where only a small quantity was formed. This could scarcely be considered a very delicate test, and hence it is not surprising that Hofmeister was led to draw up a list of substances which he concluded did not yield urea when oxidised under the conditions examined. This included such substances as formaldehyde, dextrose, acetamide, acetic acid, propionic acid, glyceric acid, and succinic acid. Halsey (1898) arrived at the conclusion that, in all these cases where urea is formed during oxidation of a carbon compound in the presence of ammonia, formamide and oxamic acid are produced as intermediate compounds in the process.

Now, it is important to note that each of these compounds could easily give rise to cyanic acid by oxidation, thus—

$$\left(H . CO . NH_2 \rightleftarrows H . C{\overset{\displaystyle OH}{\underset{\displaystyle NH}{\diagdown}}} \right) + O = HOCN + H_2O$$

Formamide.

$$\left(HO . CO . CO . NH_2 \rightleftarrows HO . CO . C{\overset{\displaystyle OH}{\underset{\displaystyle NH}{\diagdown}}} \right) + O = HOCN + CO_2 + H_2O.$$

Oxamic acid.

Fosse (1912) showed that urea is formed in considerable amounts when dextrose, laevulose, sucrose, dextrin, inulin, starch, glycerol, and formaldehyde are oxidised by potassium permanganate in the presence of ammonium salts. In these experiments oxidation was effected at 50°-60°, and the urea formed was detected and separated by means of the insoluble condensation product which it forms with xanth-hydrol, and which was described by Fosse (1907).

The yield of urea from the oxidation of dextrose was equal to 7·33 per cent of the substance taken, and equal to 7·78 per cent of the weight of ammonia added in the reaction.

The reason Hofmeister failed to obtain urea by the oxidation of dextrose, or formaldehyde, among other substances, is explained by the following experiments.

Fosse (1919) showed that whereas substances such as casein and certain amino-acids gave only a small yield of urea after oxidation by potassium permanganate in the cold, when the solutions after oxidation were heated with aqueous ammonium chloride a much greater yield of urea was obtained. Similarly, when certain substances free from nitrogen were oxidised in the presence of ammonia, the yields of urea were almost negligible, but when the oxidised solutions were heated with the addition of ammonium chloride considerable yields of urea were obtained. This interesting fact is proved by the following results:—

	After Oxidation by KMnO₄. Urea Formed.	After Heating with NH₄Cl, after Oxidation. Urea Formed.	
Asparagine	trace	10·9 per cent.	Calculated on weight of substance taken.
Glycocine	0·57 per cent.	17·57 ,, ,,	
Glycerol	almost nil	12·57 ,, ,,	
Glucose	0·64 per cent.	13·50 ,, ,,	

The explanation is obvious. Cyanic acid is formed, but is " fixed " as potassium cyanate; urea in quantity is then generated after interaction with ammonium chloride, as a result of the isomeric transformation of ammonium cyanate.

It was shown later by Fosse (1919) that when very small quantities of glucose were oxidised in the presence of strong solution of ammonia, considerable proportions of cyanic acid and urea were formed. After transformation of the ammonium cyanate by heat, the yield of urea was found to exceed 70 per cent of the weight of the glucose taken. One molecule of glucose is capable of yielding more than two molecules of urea. In the case of formaldehyde, it was found that 100 parts could give as much as 140 parts of urea, after oxidation, etc., under similar conditions.

This fact has led Fosse to put forward the hypothesis that formaldehyde must be the precursor of urea in the artificial oxidation of carbohydrates in the presence of ammonia. He explains the formation of urea as follows:—

$$CH_2O + NH_3 + O = \begin{matrix} 2H_2O \\ + \\ HCN + O \end{matrix} = CO:NH + NH_3 \rightarrow CO(NH_2)_2.$$

The production of hydrogen cyanide, shown in the above scheme as the hypothetical intermediate substance which is oxidised to cyanic acid, is in the writer's opinion doubtful. Considering the mechanism of the different syntheses of urea which have been described so far, there seems no reason to depart from the simple equation

$$CO + NH_3 + O = HN:CO + H_2O$$

to explain the formation of cyanic acid and urea in all these oxidations of carbon compounds in the presence of ammonia.

Quite recently Fosse (1921) has shown that methyl, ethyl, and butyl alcohols, phenol, o-cresol, a- and β-naphthols, catechol and resorcinol, acetaldehyde, propaldehyde, and butaldehyde all give cyanic acid by oxidation with potassium permanganate in ammoniacal solution. To this list may be added, acetic acid, propionic, succinic acid, and acetamide, which have been found by the writer to yield cyanic acid and urea under similar conditions.

Since carbonic oxide is the pre-final product of the oxidation of all organic compounds, it is very probable that cyanic acid (and hence urea) will be found after oxidation of most carbon compounds in the presence of ammonia.[1]

The writer has proved that when a slow current of carbonic oxide is led through a strong ammoniacal solution of potassium permanganate heated to 60°-70°, urea can be separated, as the di-xanthyl derivative, from the product. The formation of either formaldehyde or hydrogen cyanide under such conditions seems out of the question. Neither could be detected at any time during the progress of the reaction.

Chloral hydrate has been found to give a good yield of urea when oxidised by potassium permanganate in the presence of ammonia. This is a compound which might be expected to give rise to "nascent" CO during oxidation in presence of alkali.

The interesting work of Fosse supplies not only further evidence of the uniform character of the numerous syntheses of urea, but it disposes, once and for all, of the erroneous idea that "carbamide" must originate from carbonic acid and ammonia during the oxidation of nitrogenous compounds.

The part played by carbonic acid and ammonia in the building up of urea, according to the change $CO_2 + NH_3 \rightarrow CO:NH + H_2O$, whereby cyanic acid is generated, is quite another matter.

[1] Fosse has shown recently that cyanic acid is formed by oxidation in ammoniacal solution of various alcohols, phenols, aldehydes, ketones, acids, amides, amines, nitriles, and isocyanides.

CHAPTER IX.

THE SYNTHESIS OF UREA FROM CYANAMIDE. THE CONSTITUTION OF CYANAMIDE AND ITS RELATION TO UREA.

WE have now to consider an interesting synthesis of urea, in which the compound is certainly not formed from the interaction of cyanic acid and ammonia.

In 1851 Cannizzaro and Clöez showed that when a small quantity of nitric acid was added to a solution of cyanamide in ether, crystals of nitrate of urea gradually separated.

Baumann (1873) obtained urea (originally as sulphate) by adding cyanamide to a 50 per cent. aqueous solution of sulphuric acid. He pointed out that very concentrated acid was necessary to obtain urea from cyanamide, and whilst more or less dicyanodiamidine ($C_2H_6N_4O$), or so-called guanyl-urea,[1] was always formed, the proportion of the latter increased with the dilution of the acid.

Drechsel (1880) prepared the compound $CN.NH_2, 2HCl$, by passing dry hydrogen chloride into a solution of cyanamide in anhydrous ether, and proved that when decomposed by water it did not afford urea, but only dicyanodiamidine.

No investigator,[2] so far as the writer is aware, has ever yet claimed to have obtained urea by heating cyanamide either with water alone, or with an aqueous alkaline solution.

In fact, "free" urea has never been directly obtained by the hydrolysis of cyanamide under any conditions.

Nevertheless the simple equation

$$CN.NH_2 + H_2O = H_2N.CO.NH_2$$

has been universally adopted to represent the production of urea from cyanamide, as if the reaction was one which proceeded on perfectly normal lines. The change, accepted in the above form, has always been put forward to support the "carbamide" formula, on the supposition that cyanamide is related to urea as a nitrile to an amide.

---

[1] The constitution of this compound has yet to be established; the free base has been but little investigated.

[2] Until quite recently, see page 89.

Now nitriles are readily hydrolysed to their related amides, when heated with either dilute acids, or alkalis, or even with water alone in most cases.   It is evident, therefore, that the very special conditions necessary to hydrolyse cyanamide to urea (as a salt) appear anomalous in the light of the above simple relationship.   The true mechanism of the change only becomes intelligible when due consideration is given to the constitution of cyanamide, and to the fact that the structure of the urea molecule in the free state is not the same as when present in the form of a salt.

The Polymerisation and Constitution of Cyanamide.

One of the most characteristic properties of cyanamide is its polymerisation, a phenomenon which must obviously be intimately connected with its constitution.

Bamberger (1890) represented the formation of dicyanodiamide thus—

$$H_2N \cdot CN + HHN \cdot CN = H_2N \cdot C(NH) \cdot NH \cdot CN.$$

Grube and Krüger (1913) studied the velocity of the polymerisation in the presence of bases, and concluded that the course of the change was according to the scheme

$$CN \cdot NH_2 + CN \cdot NH' = C_2N_2N_2H_3'.$$

(Cyanamidion.)   (Dicyanodiamidion.)

Ciamician (1918) proposed to represent the polymerisation as the result of a union between the two forms of cyanamide thus—

$$C:(NH)_2 + CN \cdot NH_2 = H_2N \cdot C(NH) \cdot NH \cdot CN.$$

Morrell and Burgen (1914) investigated the accelerating effects of acids and bases on the change, and arrived at the sound conclusion that an ionic theory of the polymerisation could not be made to harmonise with all the observed facts.

Cyanamide undergoes polymerisation when heated alone, in the absence of any solvent, and Drechsel (1878) showed that when heated in solution in dry ether (a non-ionising solvent) at 150°, dicyanodiamide was formed.   There is no reason to conclude that the mechanism of the polymerisation by heat is different from that under the conditions which have been commonly observed, and hence an ionic theory of the change fails to give an answer to the real question, namely: *Why does cyanamide polymerise, and how is the phenomenon brought about?*   The views of Bamberger and of Ciamician also fail in this respect.

Most interesting results were brought to light by Morrell and

Burgen, when they showed that in *neutral* aqueous solution cyanamide is remarkably resistant to polymerisation, a fact which was even more evident in the presence of alcohol. Indeed, their results went to show that under such conditions cyanamide probably does not suffer polymerisation at all, the small effect observed being initiated by alkali slowly extracted from the glass vessel.

Now the properties of cyanamide are characteristic of a tautomeric substance, and the constitution of the compound is properly expressed by the formulæ $C:(NH)_2$ and $CN.NH_2$.

In the writer's opinion both configurations of the molecule are present in a pure neutral solution, and the remarkable stability of cyanamide under such condition,[1] as shown by Morrell and Burgen, is very probably due to an electrostatic equilibrium between the two forms, which may be represented by the scheme

$$(a)\ NH:C:NH \quad \rightleftarrows \quad CN.NH_2\ (b).$$
Acidic form (−).　　　　　　Basic form (+).

When this view is taken, the mechanism of the polymerisation can be easily explained by the aid of a theory, similar to that put forward by the writer (1913), to explain the polymerisation of the related cyanic acid, which will be found to cover all the observed facts.

Thus the addition of either an acid or a base to a neutral solution of cyanamide will disturb the above equilibrium, and polymerisation will soon commence as the result of an effort to maintain the equilibrium; for example, if a sufficiently strong acid be added to the solution it will at once exert a neutralising effect on the electropositive form (b), and will cause form (a) to change into form (b) in order to meet the new condition; polymerisation will then take effect, as illustrated in the following scheme :—

$$(1)\ C\underset{NH}{\overset{NH}{<}} \rightarrow C\underset{NH}{\overset{N}{<}}\!\!\downarrow\!H \leftarrow C\underset{NH_2}{\overset{N}{<}}$$

(− .)　　　　　　(Phase 1.)　　　　(Phase 2.)

The union of two molecules in phase (2) will give rise to the formation of dicyanodiamide, thus—

$$HN_2.C\begin{smallmatrix}N\to\\\downarrow\ \leftarrow N\end{smallmatrix}C.NH_2 = H_2N.C\begin{smallmatrix}N\\N\end{smallmatrix}C.NH_2.$$

Hofmann's formula.[2]

[1] The writer has had in his possession an aqueous solution of pure cyanamide for more than four and a half years, at the end of which time it still contained a large proportion of the unchanged substance.

[2] The view put forward by Bamberger (1883) that dicyanodiamide should be represented as cyanguanidine $H_2N.C(NH).NH.CN$ is untenable in spite of the fact that it has been

On the other hand, if a base be added to the solution it will neutralise the electronegative form (a), and (b) will then change in the following order :—

$$(2) \quad C\overset{N}{\underset{NH_2}{\big\langle}} \quad \rightarrow \quad C\overset{N}{\underset{NH----}{\big\langle}}H \quad \rightarrow \quad C\overset{NH}{\underset{NH----}{\big\langle}}$$

$$(+.) \qquad\qquad (\text{Phase } 1.) \qquad\qquad (\text{Phase } 2.)$$

and the union of two molecules in phase (2) will give rise to the formation of dicyanodiamide, thus—

$$HN : C\overset{\leftarrow NH}{\underset{NH\rightarrow}{\big\langle}}C : NH \;=\; HN : C\overset{NH}{\underset{NH}{\big\langle}}C : NH$$

Baumann's formula.

Dicyanodiamide, like cyanamide, is also a tautomeric substance, but, unlike cyanamide, is not capable of yielding salts with either acids or bases, and is, as Caro and Grossmann (1909) have shown, a perfectly neutral substance ; it can therefore be only a transition product formed from the cyanamide in its efforts to attain equilibrium (neutrality) with the base or acid present. In the latter case equilibrium is quickly reached by the hydrolysis of the dicyanodiamide to the strong base, the so-called dicyanodiamidine. As a matter of fact, the latter change appears to proceed with at least as great a velocity as the polymerisation of the cyanamide, since dicyanodiamidine can be detected in the solution as soon as cyanamide commences to disappear. For this reason it has not been found possible to isolate any dicyanodiamide from the product of the action of an acid on a solution of cyanamide.

In the case of the action of bases, dicyanodiamide can be easily obtained, this being the method commonly employed for its preparation ; nevertheless, this does not represent final equilibrium under the conditions.

Dicyanodiamide is sensitive to hydrolysis by alkalis, a fairly strong acid, Hallwachs' amidodicyanic acid, being formed (ammonia and carbon dioxide being by-products), which ultimately neutralises the alkali. The velocity of the change is in this case much slower than the velocity of polymerisation of cyanamide in the presence of alkali.

Whilst cyanamide affords a neutral solution, its acid character in so far as the production of metallic derivatives is concerned, is well

so generally accepted. It is sufficient to state here that evidence of the formation of the true cyanguanidine has been obtained by the writer from a study of the action of cyanogen bromide on guanidine. It is a basic substance with properties quite different from those of dicyanodiamide. The results have not yet been published.

known, and is very much more pronounced than the basic power;
thus, according to Grube and Krüger (1913), the salt NaN : C : NH in
a molecular solution is dissociated only to the extent of about 3 per
cent.

It is evident, therefore, that a weak base should have a much
greater disturbing effect on the equilibrium between the two forms of
cynamide than a correspondingly weak acid, and hence cause a much
greater acceleration of the polymerisation.

In order to test this point, the behaviour of cyanamide in the
presence of acetic acid has been examined; the results are given
below, and for comparison a few values, calculated from Morrell
and Burgen's experiments in the presence of ammonia, have been
added.

The concentration of cyanamide was approximately 2 per cent.

(*a*) Cyanamide heated in a water-bath at 100° for two hours :—

	Per cent. of cyanamide polymerised.
In N/20-Acetic acid	6·3
,, N/10 ,, ,, ...	8·8
,, N/4 ,, ,, ...	16·3
,, N/2 ,, ,, ...	21·9

(*b*) Cyanamide, heated as above in N/2-acetic acid, was polymerised as follows :—

(1) 3 hours, 28·8.   (2) 4 hours, 33·8.   (3) 5 hours, 38·1 per cent.

(*c*) Cyanamide heated in the presence of normal acetic acid for
ten hours was polymerised to the extent of 63·5 per cent.

(*d*) Cyanamide heated as above in the presence of ammonia
(M. and B.) :—

In N/70-Ammonia.		In N/7-Ammonia.	
Time.	Cyanamide polymerised.	Time.	Cyanamide polymerised.
2·5 hours . .	28·0 per cent.	1 hour . . .	80·1 per cent.
4·5 ,, .	39·5 ,,	1·5 hours . . .	92·4 ,,
8·5 ,, .	52·0 ,,	3 ,, . . .	100·0 ,,

It will be noticed that in order to obtain well-marked results with
acetic acid it was necessary to start with a concentration of not less
than N/20, and an inspection of the values obtained shows at once the
enormously greater accelerating power of the weak base.

Thus the amount of polymerisation produced by N/2-acetic acid
is only equal to that produced by N/70-ammonia under approximately
the same conditions, whilst after five hours the effect of N/2-acetic
acid is less than half that produced by N/7-ammonia in one hour.
These results are quite in agreement with the equilibrium theory,
bearing in mind the properties of cyanamide.

The accelerating effect of even a trace of alkali on the polymerisation is so great, as was shown by the very careful experiments of Morrell and Burgen, that one might easily arrive at the erroneous conclusion that cyanamide was more stable in the presence of acetic acid than in aqueous solution.

For example, the following results were obtained (e) after heating a solution of cyanamide (3 per cent approximately) in ordinary distilled water at 100° in a soft glass tube, (f) after keeping the solution at the ordinary temperature :—

(e) Time in hours.				Cyanamide polymerised.	(f) Time.			Cyanamide polymerised.
2	.	.	.	27·5 per cent.	After 10 weeks	.	.	29·4 per cent.
4	.	.	.	33·2 ,,	,, 12 ,,	.	.	37·5 ,,
9	.	.	.	56·8 ,,	,, 11 months	.	.	81·8 ,,
16	.	.	.	86·5 ,,				

These results, which are higher than those recorded by Morrell and Burgen, are entirely due to basic matter extracted from the glass, and they serve merely to illustrate how the acceleration of the change may vary according to the quality of the glass vessel employed.

The polymerisation of cyanamide by heat alone, which is the chief factor in promoting the change, all other conditions being equal, can also be explained by the theory just described.

An increase in the vibratory motion within the molecule will naturally accompany a rise in temperature, and the stability of the cyanamide molecule will be thereby diminished, and the less stable form will tend to change into the more stable in accordance with one or other of the two schemes already given.

The direction of the change must depend on this relative stability of the two forms, and since the balance of evidence certainly favours the greater stability of the di-imino- or symmetrical form, the change will very probably take the course indicated in scheme (2).

The more complex polymerisation of cyanamide at high temperatures (above 200°) with the production of the very strong base melamine is also in agreement with this view.

The sudden depolymerisation of dicyanodiamide by heat will give rise for the moment to cyanamide in the di-imino-form, the tendency to co-exist in equilibrium with the amino-form will persist, and by the union of three molecules in phase (2),

$$H_2N \,.\, C \diagup^{N---}_{}$$

scheme (1), the very stable, six-membered ring melamine,

$$NH_2 . C \overset{N . C(NH_2)}{\underset{N : C(NH_2)}{\diagdown}} N,$$

will be formed.

It may be added, in further support of the scheme, that a small quantity of melamine has always been detected in the product from the polymerisation of cyanamide in the presence of acids, but could not be found when bases were used.

Independent evidence in favour of the writer's views (1915) regarding the constitution of cyanamide in solution has been obtained from a study of its decomposition by nitrous acid. When this reagent is added to an acidulated normal solution of cyanamide, an immediate brisk evolution of gas, composed almost entirely of nitrogen, ensues. The volume corresponds to half of the theoretical required by the equation

$$CN . NH_2 + HO . NO = N_2 + H_2O + HO . CN.$$

This is followed by a very slow and continuous evolution of gas largely composed of carbon dioxide, and therefore mainly due to the gradual hydrolysis of the cyanic acid generated in the first stage. An interval of one hour is required for the evolution of a volume of gas equal to that set free in the first few minutes. An examination of the residual liquid at this point shows that slightly over half of the cyanamide is still unchanged, whilst there is much nitrous acid present.

When the reaction is allowed to proceed for twenty minutes, nearly 60 per cent of the cyanamide is still unchanged, and when the reaction is allowed to continue for twenty hours, nearly 13 per cent of the cyanamide is still undecomposed.

In spite of the secondary change introduced by the continuous decomposition of cyanic acid, the results show that the course of the reaction is in perfect harmony with the equilibrium theory ; thus whilst all the cyanamide present at the outset in the amino-form is rapidly decomposed by nitrous acid in the usual manner, the more stable imino-form at the ordinary temperature changes very slowly into the amino-form, which is then attacked by nitrous acid as fast as it is generated. The results also indicate that in a normal solution of cyanamide the equilibrium mixture is approximately 60 per cent $C : (NH)_2$ and 40 per cent $CN . NH_2$.

The resistance of cyanamide to further attack by nitrous acid, after the first rapid action has been completed, suggests that the change

$C:(NH)_2 \rightarrow CN.NH_2$ must proceed at a very slow rate at the ordinary temperature, even in the presence of a dilute acid. It also explains why the velocity of polymerisation of cyanamide is slower in the presence of acids than in the presence of bases, according to the writer's theory of the change.

The Formation of Urea by the Hydrolysis of Cyanamide.

A comparison of the cyclic formula $HN:C\!\!\begin{smallmatrix} NH_3 \\ | \\ O \end{smallmatrix}$ with either of

the two formulæ of cyanamide shows that the relation of urea to the latter is not the simple one which has been hitherto supposed. The conditions under which urea can be formed show that cyanamide must assume the amino-form before hydrolysis, and since the ions $H^{\cdot}$ and OH' are undoubtedly the active agents which take part in the change, this may be represented by the following equation :—

$$C\!\!\begin{smallmatrix} NH_2 \\ \\ N \end{smallmatrix} + H^{\cdot} + OH' + HNO_3 = C\!\!\begin{smallmatrix} NH_2.HNO_3 \\ NH \\ OH \end{smallmatrix}$$

This reaction, which is analogus to the formation of "*iso*ureas" from cyanamide and alcohols in the presence of hydrogen chloride, thus—

$$C\!\!\begin{smallmatrix} NH_2 \\ \\ N \end{smallmatrix} + CH_3OH + HCl = C\!\!\begin{smallmatrix} NH_2.HCl \\ NH \\ O.CH_3 \end{smallmatrix}$$

shows that urea, when generated, has the "*iso*urea" structure, which is retained only in the salt, and in the presence of a small quantity of water. The mechanism of this synthesis of urea is clearly shown by the results of the following experiments made by the writer (1915).

Expt. I.—To 15 c.c. of a moist ethereal solution of cyanamide (0·638 gram CN_2H_2) 1·5 grams of nitric acid ($D^{15} = 1·425$) were added. This was slightly more than sufficient to form urea nitrate by the hydrolysis of all the cyanamide present. After two hours crystals commenced to separate, and the product was kept for twenty hours.

Weight of crystals deposited = 1·9 grams. Theory for urea nitrate = 1·87 grams. All the cyanamide had disappeared from the ethereal solution. The hydrolysis was therefore complete, although it should be mentioned that the crystals contained a small quantity of dicyanodiamidine nitrate.

Expt. II.—The last experiment was repeated, but only 1 gram of nitric acid was added.

Weight of crystals deposited after twenty hours = 1·57 grams.

The residual ethereal solution was shaken with 400 c.c. of distilled water, and then required 63 c.c. N/10-ammoniacal silver nitrate for the complete precipitation of the remaining cyanamide, which is thus found to be 20·7 per cent of the amount originally present.

Thus whilst all the nitric acid was removed as urea nitrate, the excess of cyanamide remained unchanged, although there was more water present than was necessary to effect its complete hydrolysis.

The remarkable stability of cyanamide and its indifference towards hydrolysis were shown by the following striking and conclusive result.

Expt. III.—0·42 gram of cyanamide was dissolved in 20 c.c. of moist ether, and 1 c.c. of fuming hydrochloric acid (D = 1·16) added ; the mixture was repeatedly shaken in a small stoppered separating funnel during an interval of six hours, and was then kept until the following morning. The small aqueous layer was removed, and after neutralisation with an excess of aqueous ammonia, the cyanamide was precipitated in the form of its silver salt.

Weight of Ag_2CN_2 obtained = 1·742 ; CN_2H_2 = 0·2856.

The ethereal solution required 46·1 c.c. N/10-ammoniacal silver nitrate ; CN_2H_2 = 0·0968. Hence 0·3824 gram, or 91·04 per cent of the cyanamide originally taken, was unchanged.

Thus, whilst in this experiment the amount of hydrochloric acid present was sufficient to form urea hydrochloride by the hydrolysis of the cyanamide, the amount of water present was too great to allow the undissociated urea salt to separate, and hence very little, if any, hydrolysis of cyanamide took place. A small quantity of dicyanodiamidine was found in the aqueous layer.

Now the hydrolysis of cyanamide to a salt of urea is a rapid change which proceeds at the ordinary temperature, in contrast to polymerisation, which is a very slow change unless aided by heat ; therefore, the formation of urea nitrate must be the outcome of a rapid effort to attain more stable equilibrium under the disturbing influence of the strong acid. This stability can only be attained provided the conditions are such that a salt of urea can be formed, because the *iso*-urea configuration of the urea molecule is too unstable to exist in the static condition, and hence urea can only be generated in quantity sufficient to form a salt with the particular amount of acid present. It follows, therefore, that if the salt cannot exist even though acid be present, a condition brought about, for example, by the presence of too much water, no urea can be formed, which, as the experiments have shown, is actually the case.

Apart even from the remote relationship between cyanamide and urea, as indicated by the cyclic structure of the latter, the fact that cyanamide has not been, and probably cannot be, directly hydrolysed to yield urea in the free state, is in perfect agreement with the above explanation of the mechanism of the change.

Thus whilst it is true that urea in its static condition is a more stable compound than cyanamide, it is equally true that the latter must be much more stable than urea when this is in its tautomeric or " isourea " configuration, and hence the more stable compound cannot be produced through the intermediary of a substance less stable than cyanamide itself.

It may be added that if cyanamide was related to urea, as nitrile to amide, and if urea had the " carbamide " structure both in the free state and as a salt, there appears no reason why cyanamide should not be hydrolysed in the normal manner, and be capable of directly furnishing urea whether a certain fixed quantity of acid were present or not.

It must be concluded therefore that the synthesis of urea from cyanamide, instead of lending support to the " carbamide " formula, actually supplies evidence which goes to disprove it.

In order to lay emphasis on the resistance of cyanamide to hydrolysis, the writer (1915) proved that no urea was formed after an aqueous solution of cyanamide had been heated in a sealed tube at 120°-130° for three hours. Similarly a 4·25 per cent solution of cyanamide in ether saturated with water suffered no change after heating at 100° for ten hours in a sealed tube of soft glass.

Since these results were published Schmidt (1917) claimed to have obtained urea and dicyanodiamide from a solution of cyanamide in moist ether after it had remained for fourteen days at the ordinary temperature. The amount of urea obtained (isolated as the di-xanthyl derivative) was 0·05 gram from 10 grams of cyanamide. When cyanamide was *repeatedly* evaporated to dryness with water 0·097 gram of urea was obtained from 10 grams. The method adopted for " proving " the formation of urea consisted in extracting the residue with ether to remove unchanged cyanamide, after which the residue was dissolved in glacial acetic acid, and a solution of xanthhydrol in the same solvent added.

In the writer's experience the removal of *all* the cyanamide from such a residue is a very tedious process. For example, 1 gram of cyanamide and 2·5 grams of dicyanodiamide were dissolved in 50 c.cs.

of warm water, after which the solution was evaporated to dryness at 90° in a porcelain capsule. The residue, after seven extractions with ether, using 25 c.cs. of the solvent on each occasion, was still found to contain quite an appreciable amount of cyanamide. The very small quantity of urea obtained by Schmidt was in all probability generated by the action of glacial acetic acid on cyanamide still present in the residue. Schmidt showed that when an ethereal solution of oxalic acid was added to a solution of cyanamide in moist ether, a precipitate of urea oxalate was rapidly formed. Since the hydrolysis of cyanamide to a *salt* of urea is a rapid change when the proper conditions are established, if there was any tendency for cyanamide to be directly hydrolysed to " free " urea, there seems no reason why this should be limited to the insignificant extent found by Schmidt.

Actually his first experiment represents a yield of urea equal to 0·35 per cent of the theoretical, on the fallacious equation

$$CN . NH_2 + H_2O = CON_2H_4.$$

Since these experiments of Schmidt's were made, the writer has had in his possession a 10 per cent solution of cyanamide in moist ether to which was added a few drops of 5 per cent acetic acid to counteract alkalinity of the glass vessel. At the end of two years the solution contained 9·8 per cent of unchanged cyanamide. In view of this result it would be difficult to accept the conclusions arrived at by Schmidt.

Can Cyanamide be Obtained from Urea?

If cyanamide cannot combine directly with water to form urea, the question naturally arises : Can the elements of water be removed from urea with production of cyanamide?[1]

The first attempt to realise the possible change was made by Fenton (1882), who failed to obtain any cyanamide after heating urea with phosphorus pentoxide, calcium chloride, and other dehydrating agents. By heating urea with metallic sodium, Fenton claimed to have obtained cyanamide, the production of which was represented by the equation

$$2CON_2H_4 + Na_2 = 2CN . NH_2 + 2NaOH + H_2.$$

[1] The well-known production of cyanamide by the de-sulphurisation of thiourea by metallic oxides, such as HgO, PbO, Ag_2O (Volhard, Mulder, 1874), is the result of a reaction in which the removal of hydrogen by oxidation is the first step, the formation of a metallic sulphide following as a natural consequence. The change is dependent on thiourea having the configuration $HN : C(NH_2) . SH$, the group —SH being the vulnerable part of the molecule in this case. Hence the " theoretical " removal of the elements of water from urea to give cyanamide cannot be viewed as analogous in its mechanism to the removal of H_2S from thiourea. Oxidation can play no part in the former case, whereas it is an essential factor in promoting the change in the latter case.

The reaction has been assumed to correspond to the removal of water from urea.

After a careful study of this experiment, the writer has been unable to confirm the formation of cyanamide from urea as indicated by the above equation.

When metallic sodium in small pieces is added to urea heated to its melting-point ($132°$) in a glass tube, a violent reaction takes place as each piece of the metal is introduced. Hydrogen and much ammonia are evolved. In spite of the heat generated, the product solidifies when somewhat less than half of the theoretical amount of sodium has been added.

The change which takes place under these conditions is expressed as follows :—

$$HN:C{\overset{NH_3}{\underset{O}{\big<}}} + Na = H + HN:C{\overset{NH_2}{\underset{O\,.\,Na}{\big<}}} \rightarrow NaOCN + NH_3.$$

The solidification of the product is due to the formation of sodium cyanate, and of the sodium derivative of urea. On addition of ammonio-silver nitrate in excess to a solution of the product in water, a copious pale yellow precipitate of di-argentic urea $CON_2H_2Ag_2$ is formed. The filtrate, when neutralised with dilute nitric acid, yields a white precipitate of silver cyanate.[1] Under these conditions no cyanamide is formed. If, on the other hand, a mixture of urea and sodium is heated in a porcelain crucible, and the product strongly heated after the first violent reaction has been completed, the presence of cyanamide in the residue can be easily proved.

It arises from the decomposition of the sodium cyanate previously formed, thus—

$$2NaOCN = Na_2CN_2 + CO_2.$$

Drechsel (1878) showed that cyanamide was formed in quantity when sodium cyanate was heated with sodamide, and since it is not unlikely that a small amount of the latter is formed during the decomposition, cyanamide may be produced from this source, thus—

$$NaOCN + NaNH_2 = Na_2CN_2 + H_2O.$$

Emich (1889) obtained cyanamide by heating a mixture of urea and calcium oxide to a high temperature. In this case calcium cyanate was first formed, and cyanamide produced by its decomposition, as was shown by Drechsel (1878).

[1] This, as is to be expected, contains some silver cyanide.

The writer has found that when an intimate mixture of urea and pure calcium oxide is heated to 140° until ammonia is no longer evolved, no cyanamide is formed, whilst a yield of calcium cyanate equal to 70 per cent of the theoretical is obtained.

It has been considered of theoretical interest to demonstrate the formation of cyanamide from urea, since such a result should lend support to the "carbamide" formula. It is clear that in this respect the experiments just described have completely failed.

Cyanamide cannot be Produced by the Direct Removal of the Elements of Water from "Free" Urea.

Now "isoureas," when heated under ordinary pressure, are decomposed into cyanamide and alcohols, thus—

$$HN:C\diagup\begin{matrix}NH_2\\O.R.\end{matrix} = R.OH + C:(NH)_2.$$

It follows, therefore, that any hope for success in effecting a similar decomposition in the case of urea must lie in attacking the latter when in the form $HN:C\diagup\begin{matrix}NH_2\\OH\end{matrix}$, and this, as has been shown, can only exist when urea is present as a salt,

$$HN:C\diagup\begin{matrix}NH_2HX'\\OH\end{matrix}$$

This condition was no doubt realised by Moureau (1894), who showed that cyanamide was formed when urea was brought in contact with thionyl chloride. Heat was gradually developed, whilst there was evolution of sulphur dioxide and hydrogen chloride.

Moureau's experiment was only qualitative, since the yield of cyanamide was only sufficient to demonstrate its formation. This is not surprising, as cyanamide, as the writer has found, is violently attacked by thionyl chloride. A quantitative experiment, following carefully the directions given by Moureau, gave a yield of cyanamide equal to 0·11 per cent of the theoretical. The equation

$$CON_2H_4 + SOCl_2 = CN_2H_2 + SO_2 + 2HCl$$

is therefore rather misleading so far as the production of cyanamide is concerned. In the writer's experience urea is very slowly attacked by thionyl chloride under the conditions described by Moureau.

A more interesting demonstration of the formation of cyanamide from urea is shown in the following manner. A current of hydrogen chloride is passed into a mixture of urea and phosphoric oxide; a viscous mass is soon formed, accompanied by a slight development of heat.   After about twenty minutes the product is dissolved in a saturated solution of sodium hydrogen carbonate containing an excess of the salt in suspension.   The solution is extracted with ether.   The latter when evaporated at a gentle heat over a small quantity of water leaves a solution which gives a bright yellow precipitate of silver cyanamide on addition of ammonio-silver nitrate solution.   A quantitative experiment with four grams of urea gave a yield of silver cyanamide equal to 2·4 per cent of the theoretical on the weight of the urea decomposed.

Urea and phosphoric oxide alone do not interact until a temperature is reached which precludes all chance of isolating cyanamide; moreover the change is then mainly confined to a removal of ammonia with formation of cyanuric acid (Weltzien, 1857).

The special conditions necessary for the production of cyanamide from urea are in perfect agreement with the writer's theory of the constitution of the latter in the free state, and in the form of a salt.   As cyanamide can be hydrolysed only to a salt of urea, so from a salt of urea only can it be regenerated.

The Preparation of Derivatives of Iso-Urea Directly from Urea.

Compounds of the type $HN : C . (OR) . NH_2$ are commonly known as iso-ureas.   The simplest member of the group methylisourea, $NH : C(OCH_3) . NH_2$, was originally prepared by Stieglitz and McKee (1900) from the union of cyanamide and methyl alcohol in the presence of hydrogen chloride.   Several derivatives of the types $HN : C(OR) . NH_2$, $RN : C(OR) . NH_2$, and $RN : C(OR) . NHR$ have since been obtained by analogous reactions, sodium ethoxide being used in some cases to bring about the changes since these isoureas are stable in the free state.

The writer has shown (1914) that methylisourea can be readily obtained directly from urea by heating the latter with methyl sulphate. The reaction is represented by the equation

$$HN : C \underset{OH}{\overset{NH_2}{<}} + (CH_3)_2SO_4 = HN : C \underset{O . CH_3}{\overset{NH_2CH_3HSO_4}{<}}$$

(Methylisourea methylhydrogensulphate.)

Whilst iso-urea is not capable of existing in the free state, the above result is of interest, since it supports the view that urea changes to the iso-form in all those reactions which take place with various reagents at a relatively low temperature. When urea combines with an acid the product is a salt of iso-urea.

In short, substituted iso-ureas and substituted carbamides are derivatives of one and the same body, for neither "carbamide" nor iso-urea can exist free (see next chapter).

Urea and Acetic Anhydride.

This reaction, studied by the writer (1916) from the point of view just mentioned, supplies further interesting evidence. When urea is heated with acetic anhydride at 138°, the boiling-point of the latter, the main change is the result of an interaction between the dissociation products of urea (NH_3 and $NH : CO$) and the anhydride, namely, acetamide, diacetamide, and carbon dioxide. The yield of acetylurea, $HN : C(OH) . NH . CO . CH_3$, was not more than 35 per cent of the theoretical. When the reaction was "catalysed" by the addition of a trace of sulphuric acid, i.e. to change urea to the reactive form of iso-urea, the yield of the acetyl-derivative was raised to nearly 80 per cent of theory. Acetylurea (m.p. 214°) separates unchanged from its solution in warm acetic anhydride, and if further heated with the reagent, it is gradually decomposed with evolution of carbon dioxide and formation of the products previously mentioned. When, on the other hand, a drop or two of sulphuric acid is added to a solution of acetylurea in acetic anhydride at 60°, a quantitative yield of di-acetyl-isourea is obtained.

This compound (m.p. 153·5°) has the constitution

$$HN : C \begin{cases} NH . CO . CH_3 \\ O . CO . CH_3 \end{cases},$$

since it is readily hydrolysed by sodium hydroxide in the cold, or by water alone at 100°. The acetyl group in union with oxygen being removed with formation of the more stable mono-acetyl derivative. The latter is only very slowly decomposed by water at 100°.

All attempts to isolate a "di-acetylcarbamide,"

$$CO < (NH . CO . CH_3)_2$$

have been unsuccessful. From theoretical considerations, which are discussed in the following chapters, it appears likely that such a compound is not capable of existing.

CHAPTER X.

THE SYSTEM : $C(NH_2)_2$, AND THE CONDITIONS WHICH ARE NECESSARY FOR THE EXISTENCE OF TRUE CARBAMIDES.

THE occurrence of a series of peculiarly delusive syntheses and decompositions, all of which seemed to lend support to the "carbamide" formula, has been an outstanding feature of the chemistry of urea. We have seen how this formula gradually gained credence in the minds of chemists, and how it ultimately came to be generally accepted.

It is no exaggeration to say that the great trust put in the "carbamide" formula was, in a large measure, responsible for the hasty conclusions which were frequently drawn from the study of the various reactions of urea.

Wöhler's synthesis gave an early indication of a close relationship between the two isomerides, yet it was not considered to convey any particular information which could be used to solve the constitution of urea. The belief that the latter must be an immediate derivative of carbonic acid was the cause why little or no importance was attached to the constitution of cyanic acid.

It is remarkable, in view of the available evidence, that theoretical considerations affecting the "carbamide" formula were not allowed to have any influence in connection with its acceptance. It now seems clearly proved that the molecular configuration represented by "carbamide" cannot exist. There must be a reason for this fact.

It has long since been accepted as an axiom in organic chemistry that the system : $C(OH)_2$ cannot form part of a stable molecule.

The writer (1918) maintains, as a rational inference from the facts, that a similar conclusion must be accepted as regards the system : $C(NH_2)_2$, a point which, curiously enough, has been quite overlooked. It is only necessary to point out that the only substances which have been investigated, and which have been assumed to contain two amino-groups [1] in union with a carbon atom are urea, thiourea, and guanidine.

---

[1] Di-amino-malonamide $C(NH_2)_2 (CONH_2)_2$, Conrad and Bruckner (1891), has not been investigated in such a way as to establish this formula, whilst the alternative formula $CN . N : C(NH_2)_2$ for dicyanodiamide, suggested by Pohl (1908), is not based on any substantial evidence.

Considering the stability of the two former substances [1] one might reasonably expect to find numerous derivatives containing the system : $C(NH_2)_2$ among carbon compounds.

It is well known that such compounds cannot be obtained where their information might have been expected. All attempts to isolate methylenediamine, $CH_2(NH_2)_2$, have hitherto failed.

Knudsen (1914) claims to have obtained certain salts of the diamine by the hydrolysis of diformomethylene diamide, $CH_2(NH \cdot COH)_2$, with strong acids in the cold. According to this investigator, methylenediamine dihydrochloride, $CH_2(NH_2)_2 \cdot 2HCl$, decomposes rapidly in aqueous solution with production of formaldehyde and ammonium chloride. Whilst the free base could not be isolated, a solution in alcohol was claimed to have been obtained,[2] without, however, any evidence to prove it.

It may be remarked that di-amino compounds, such as

$$CH_3CH.(NH_2)_2, \quad C_6H_5 \cdot CH.(NH_2)_2 \text{ and } CH(NH_2)_2COOH,$$

for example, have never been obtained.

Now, according to the modern electronic conception of valency, the carbon atom is so constituted that, in combining with other elements, or radicles, it is equally disposed to part with or receive four electrons. As the theory implies, the carbon atom is therefore indifferently electro-positive, or electro-negative.

It may be represented to function in five different ways, as pointed out by Fry (1921),[3] thus :—

$$
\begin{array}{ccccc}
\overset{-}{-\,C\,-} & \overset{-}{-\,C\,+} & \overset{-}{-\,C\,+} & \overset{-}{+\,C\,+} & \overset{+}{+\,C\,+} \\
\underset{-}{} & \underset{-}{} & \underset{+}{} & \underset{+}{} & \underset{+}{} \\
CH_4 & CH_3OH & CH_2O & H.CO.OH & CO_2 \\
(1) & (2) & (3) & (4) & (5)
\end{array}
$$

---

[1] As regards guanidine, in the writer's experience, its preparation in a pure state is a difficult and very tedious operation. Apart from its great power of absorbing CO_2 from the air, the compound is not stable; it loses ammonia easily when kept in a desiccator over sulphuric acid, dicyanodiamide being one of the products formed. Attempts to obtain guanidine by the union of ammonia with cyanamide, as commonly referred to in the literature, thus $CN \cdot NH_2 + NH_3 = C(NH) \cdot (NH_2)_2$, have been a complete failure. The writer has kept cyanamide in ethereal, and in alcoholic solution in contact with an excess of ammonia for six months without obtaining evidence of the formation of a trace of guanidine. A *salt* of guanidine, on the other hand, is readily formed on heating cyanamide with a *salt* of ammonia. From this fact, the change referred to in the literature has been assumed to take place. Polymerisation of cyanamide is the only result when an attempt is made to cause it to combine with ammonia by the aid of heat.

[2] Experiments carried out in the writer's laboratory have not given results in agreement with the conclusions arrived at by Knudsen. Until these have been fully confirmed by independent observation, the preparation of free methylenediamine in solution, as claimed by Knudsen must be accepted with reserve.

[3] H. S. Fry, " The Electronic Conception of Valence," chapters ii. and iii.

On considering these five typical compounds, in which the hydrogen atoms function positively, and the oxygen atoms are negatively bivalent, it will be noticed that methane (1) and carbon dioxide (5) are the most stable compounds of the series.

The electronic theory, so far as it has been developed, helps towards an understanding of certain facts which have not been adequately recognised in considering the constitution of simple carbon compounds, and particularly the constitution of urea.

The most stable compounds are obviously those in which the carbon atom is in union, either with four strongly electro-positive or with four strongly electro-negative elements, or radicles.   The position which carbon occupies in the periodic system of the elements tells us that it cannot give rise to stable molecules by its union with feeble electro-positive or electro-negative radicles or with a combination of both.   The evidence seems in favour of the view that the amino-group must function as a more feeble radicle on the electro-positive side than the hydroxyl group on the electro-negative side.   Tri-amino-methane $CH(NH_2)_3$, and tetra-amino-methane $C(NH_2)_4$, are so far hypothetical compounds, comparable in this respect to trihydroxymethane $CH(OH)_3$ and to ortho-carbonic acid $C(OH)_4$ respectively.

A consideration of the following series of " hypothetical " compounds brings out clearly the points under discussion :—

$$
\overset{-}{\underset{-}{\text{CH}_2}}\!\!\underset{\text{OH}}{\overset{\text{OH}}{\big<}} \qquad
\overset{-}{\underset{+}{\text{CH}_2}}\!\!\underset{\text{NH}_2}{\overset{\text{OH}}{\big<}} \qquad
\overset{+}{\underset{+}{\text{CH}_2}}\!\!\underset{\text{NH}_2}{\overset{\text{NH}_2}{\big<}}
$$

I.	II.	III.

$$
\overset{-}{\underset{-}{\text{CO}}}\!\!\underset{\text{OH}}{\overset{\text{OH}}{\big<}} \qquad
\overset{-}{\underset{+}{\text{CO}}}\!\!\underset{\text{NH}_2}{\overset{\text{OH}}{\big<}} \qquad
\overset{+}{\underset{+}{\text{CO}}}\!\!\underset{\text{NH}_2}{\overset{\text{NH}_2}{\big<}}
$$

IV.	V.	VI.

The compounds I. to V. have admittedly never been isolated.

The substitution of the feeble electro-positive NH_2 group for $\overset{-}{O}H$ in compounds II. and III. is evidently not capable of producing a condition of electrostatic equilibrium sufficient to enable a compound to be isolated even though the carbon atom is at the same time in union with two $\overset{+}{H}$ atoms.   So far as carbonic acid (IV.) and carbamic acid (V.) are concerned, the substitution of the bivalent electro-negative

7

oxygen atom for $\overset{+}{H_2}$ likewise fails to bring about a stable condition.[1] Is it probable that such a condition is brought about in the case of the compound VI.?

Whatever may be the electro-chemical function of the radicles in union with carbon, in determining the structure and stability of the molecule, there seems no reason why any one of the five compounds in the series should not be just as stable as "carbamide" (VI.). Indeed, if the suggestion regarding the relative electro-chemical "strengths"[2] of the hydroxyl and amino-groups is accepted, and bearing in mind the existence of such compounds as $COCl_2$ and CH_2I_2, carbonic acid (IV.) and dihydroxymethane (I.) ought to be more stable than "carbamide." As a matter of fact, we have evidence of the existence of the two former compounds in aqueous solutions of formaldehyde and of carbon dioxide respectively, whilst we have no evidence of the existence of "carbamide."

The experimental evidence as regards the constitution of urea is therefore fully supported by theory, since the stability of the compound

---

[1] This also applies to the replacement of $\overset{+}{H_2}$ by the atom of sulphur.

[2] It is well known that the most stable compounds result from the union of strongly electro-positive, and strongly electro-negative elements. Whilst the same is true as regards the union of radicles, we have no means apparently of determining their relative values in terms of their electro-chemical differences, either in sign or degree. The methyl group CH_3, for example, is a stronger electro-positive radicle than the ethyl group C_2H_5; the difference is no doubt due to the higher ratio of $+ H$ to C in the former, where it is 3 to 1, as compared with 2.5 H to 1 C atom in the latter. Is the difference in electro-chemical value equal to half the positive charge on a hydrogen atom? The stability of carbon compounds is unquestionably regulated by the electro-chemical "strengths" of the radicles, and as regards this question the electronic theory of valence does not appear to give much help. The representation of formic acid and carbonic acid, for example, by the following electronic formulæ

$$\overset{+\ \ -\ +\ -\ \ -\ +}{H\!-\!\!-\!\!-\!C\!-\!\!-\!\!-\!O\!-\!\!-\!\!-\!H}, \text{ and } \overset{+\ -\ \ -\ +\ +\ -\ \ -\ +}{H\!-\!\!-\!\!-\!O\!-\!\!-\!\!-\!C\!-\!\!-\!\!-\!O\!-\!\!-\!\!-\!H}$$
$$\underset{-O-}{+\,\|\,+} \qquad\qquad \underset{-O-}{+\,\|\,+}$$

does not explain the wide difference in the stability of the two compounds. That is, it gives no information as to why the system : $C{<}{\overset{H}{\underset{OH}{}}}$ should be stable and the system : $C{<}{\overset{OH}{\underset{OH}{}}}$ very unstable. Since the most stable compounds are those in which the carbon atom is acting with its full electro-positive, or electro-negative valence $\overset{+}{\underset{+}{-\!-\!C\!-\!-}}$, or $\overset{-}{\underset{-}{-\!-\!C\!-\!-}}$, any intermediate stage would presumably represent a less stable configuration. If so, formic acid should be the less stable of the two compounds. Towards oxidation this is true, but this does not explain the difference between the stability of the two systems.

is not reconcilable with the "carbamide" formula (VI.), which is really that of a hypothetical compound in keeping with the other members of the group given above.

Further interesting theoretical evidence is forthcoming when we consider the substitution of the imino-group, NH, for two atoms of hydrogen, thus—

$$
\overset{-}{HN} : C \overset{\overset{-}{OH}}{\underset{\overset{-}{OH}}{}}
\qquad
\overset{-}{HN} : C \overset{\overset{+}{NH_2}}{\underset{\overset{-}{OH}}{}}
\qquad
\overset{-}{HN} : C \overset{\overset{+}{NH_2}}{\underset{\overset{+}{NH_2}}{}}
$$

VII.   VIII.   IX.

The imino-group is a weak electro-negative radicle, and hence a stable compound is not possible, having the constitution represented by imino-carbonic acid (VII.). So far as formula VIII. is concerned, the substitution of $\overset{+}{NH_2}$ for $\overset{-}{OH}$ is likewise without effect in producing a stable molecule, since "iso-urea" has never been isolated. As regards formula (IX.), which is that generally used to express the constitution of guanidine, there is every reason to believe that this must also represent a hypothetical compound.

We have here a theoretical explanation of the fact that cyanamide does not combine directly either with water to form "free" urea, or with ammonia to form "free" guanidine. In the case of the sulphur derivatives of carbonic acid, we have equally strong evidence of the instability of the system $: C(NH_2)_2$. Whilst neither $CS(OH)_2$ nor $CO(SH)_2$ have been isolated, $CS(S\overset{-}{H})_2$ and

$$
CS \overset{\overset{+}{NH_2}}{\underset{\overset{-}{SH}}{}}
$$

are known, though they are both very unstable compounds. Is it likely that the formula

$$
CS \overset{NH_2}{\underset{NH_2}{}}
$$

represents the constitution of such a stable substance as thiourea, to which this formula has been so generally ascribed?

It is a well-known fact that thiourea cannot be obtained from derivatives of sulphocarbonic acid under conditions similar to those which yield urea from analogous derivatives of carbonic acid.

7 *

Thus, in the following cases, (1) the interaction of thiocarbonyl chloride ($CSCl_2$) and ammonia, (2) the action of heat on ammonium dithiocarbamate,

$$CS \begin{cases} NH_2 \\ S \cdot NH_4 \end{cases}$$

and (3) the decomposition of ethyl dithiocarbamate,

$$CS \begin{cases} NH_2 \\ S \ Et \end{cases}$$

by ammonia, ammonium thiocyanate is the product where thiourea might have been expected. Since the latter is more stable towards heat than urea, its non-formation in the three reactions just mentioned is unintelligible in the light of the "thiocarbamide" formula. The mechanism of the respective changes is of course similar to that in the case of the corresponding derivatives of carbonic acid, but the reactions are brought about at temperatures which are much below the point at which ammonium thiocyanate dissociates. Ammonium dithio-carbamate, for example, is decomposed at $100°$ very rapidly into ammonium thiocyanate and hydrogen sulphide, thus—

$$CS \begin{cases} NH_2 \\ S \cdot NH_4 \end{cases} \rightarrow NH_4SCN + H_2S.$$

There are only two methods for preparing thiourea, namely, by the isomeric transformation of ammonium thiocyanate when heated above its melting-point ($150°$), as shown by Reynolds (1869), and by the combination of cyanamide with hydrogen sulphide, Baumann (1873).

Since $$CS \begin{cases} NH_2 \\ SH \end{cases}$$

has been isolated (Mulder and Bettink, 1868), there is every reason to expect that the imino-derivative

$$HN : C \begin{cases} NH_2 \\ SH \end{cases}$$

should also be capable of existence in the free state.

The fact that "free" thiourea can be obtained from cyanamide is a strong point in favour of this. The ease with which thiourea and alkyl haloids interact to yield derivatives of the type

$HN : C(SR^1)NH_2HX$, the production of methyl isothiourea:

$$HN : C\begin{cases} NH_2 \\ S\,CH_3 \end{cases}$$

when thiourea is brought in contact with diazo-methane, as shown by the writer (1919), in contradistinction to urea, which is not attacked by this reagent, and, finally, the decomposition of thiourea by pure nitrous acid alone, with production of thiocyanic acid (HSCN), all go to confirm the view that in a neutral solution thiourea must be present in two molecular forms in equilibrium, thus—

$$(a)\ \ HN : C\begin{cases} NH_3 \\ | \\ S \end{cases} \rightleftarrows HN : C\begin{cases} NH_2 \\ SH \end{cases}\ \ (b),$$

form (b) being the less stable, and consequently the more reactive of the two.

To sum up, it must be accepted as a logical deduction from all the evidence that the system $: C(NH_2)_2$ cannot be present in a stable molecule any more than the system $: C(OH)_2$, with which it may be compared in this respect.

Whilst the system $\qquad : C\begin{cases} OR \\ OH \end{cases}$

is still unstable, the further substitution of an electro-positive radicle for hydrogen at once promotes stability. It is only necessary to mention the esters of carbonic acid, methylal, $CH_2(OCH_3)_2$, acetal $CH_3CH(OC_2H_5)_2$, and their homologues to show that the system $: C(OR)_2$ is very stable. It is only reasonable to expect that a similar result will obtain when the substitution of electro-positive (or electro-negative) radicles for hydrogen in the system $: C(NH_2)_2$ is brought about. Hence a true "carbamidic" structure at once becomes possible in the case of the homologues of urea, and this structure becomes more stable as the substitution increases. Thus tetra-substituted carbamides

$$CO\begin{cases} NR_2 \\ NR_2 \end{cases}$$

can be distilled without decomposition at relatively high temperatures.

Whilst it is not intended to deal with the chemistry of substituted ureas in the present work, it may be mentioned here, that in the case

[1] R = any electro-positive hydrocarbon radicle.

of the monosubstituted derivatives the evidence goes to prove that in solution these are present in two forms in equilibrium thus—

(A) $H_2N . CO . NHR \rightleftharpoons HO . C(: NH) . NHR$ (B)

the proportion of each form being dependent on the electro-chemical nature of the radicle (R), Werner (1919). In the case of methylurea form (B) predominates, whilst in the case of phenylurea the predominating form is (A).

We have seen that the system

$$: C \Big\langle {\overset{\textstyle NH_2}{} \atop \underset{\textstyle OH}{}}$$

must be very unstable. On the other hand, the substitution of hydrogen by an electro-positive radicle in the hydroxyl group produces greater stability than substitution in the amino-group; thus whilst esters of carbamic acid,

$$O : C \Big\langle {\overset{\textstyle NH_2}{} \atop \underset{\textstyle O . R}{}}$$

are stable, substituted carbamic acids,

$$O : C \Big\langle {\overset{\textstyle NHR}{} \atop \underset{\textstyle OH}{}}$$

have not been isolated.

With the imino-group (NH) in the place of oxygen we have the two types of "*iso*-ureas"—

(C) $R . O . C : (NH) . NH_2$ and, (D) $HO . C : (NH) . NHR.$

Whilst the former are known in the free state, the latter are probably only known in solution, or as salts (see next chapter).

CHAPTER XI.

1. The Decomposition of Urea by Urease.

THE "alkaline fermentation" which urine quickly undergoes when
exposed to the air is a phenomenon which attracted early attention.

At the end of the eighteenth century, Fourcroy and Vauquelin
(1798-99) proved that the carbonate of ammonia formed during the
"fermentation" was produced from the urea originally present in the
urine.

The change has been considered, up to the present time, to be a
simple process of direct hydrolysis, according to the equation

$$CON_2H_4 + 2H_2O = (NH_4)_2CO_3$$

which, as we have seen, was suggested by Dumas in 1830.

Pasteur (1861) showed that a living organism was responsible for
the change, and that sterilised urine, when kept from contact with air
did not undergo ammoniacal fermentation. This fact, so well recognised to-day, was not accepted for many years by the upholders of
"spontaneous generation."

The particular organism was isolated by van Tieghem (1864), and
was later given the name *Micrococcus ureæ*. Ten years later, Musculus
(1874) obtained an enzyme from putrid urine, which he showed was
capable of decomposing a pure solution of urea, and was therefore
probably produced by the organism. Lea (1885) cultivated the *Micrococcus* in quantity, and confirmed the results obtained by Musculus.
Miquel (1890) described over thirty different varieties of micro-
organisms which he found were capable of decomposing urea in
solution. He proposed the term *Urease* for the particular enzyme,
which was no doubt common to all the micro-organisms examined.

So long as the source of urease was limited to microscopic
organisms, none of which were cultivated on a large scale for any
useful purpose, a thorough study of this remarkable zymolysis of urea
was bound to be delayed.

In 1909 Takeuchi showed that an aqueous extract of the crushed soy or soja bean, the seed of a leguminous plant (*Glycine Hispida*) largely grown in Japan, possessed in a high degree the power of decomposing urea into carbon dioxide and ammonia.

Whilst this was the first interesting discovery of the occurrence of urease in the higher plants, its presence in various leguminous and in certain other seeds has been recorded in recent years. The sword bean (*Canavalia gladiata*), and particularly the jack bean (*C. ensiformis*), according to Mateer and Marshall (1916), contain the enzyme in much larger amounts than the soy bean, from which Takeuchi showed it could be easily prepared.

Since a plentiful supply of the enzyme became accessible, much attention has been devoted to the study of the decomposition of urea by urease during the last twelve years. Results of practical value, in connection with the estimation of urea, and of much theoretical interest have been obtained.

The scope of the present work demands that those investigations which deal with attempts to solve the mechanism of the zymolysis, and which have, therefore, a direct bearing on the constitution of urea, should receive first attention.

Armstrong and Horton (1912) showed that urease (from soy bean) is without action on methyl-, ethyl-, sym-dimethyl-, sym-diethyl-, and asym-dimethylurea, and is also without action on biuret. To this list the writer can add, from his own experiments (1918), n-propyl-, phenyl-, and piperidylurea, thiourea, urethane, ethyl allophanate, and salts of guanidine and of dicyanodiamidine. The specific effect of urease has been confirmed by other observers, and quite recently Wester (1921) has found that urease from *Canavalia* beans had no decomposing effect on a number of substituted ureas examined. It may therefore be taken as established, until proof[1] to the contrary is forthcoming, that urease, at the average optimum point (45°-50°) of enzymes at all events, attacks urea only. So far as the progress of the reaction is concerned, Armstrong and Horton found that the addition of ammonia had a retarding effect on the decomposition of urea, whilst the presence of carbon dioxide increased the activity of the enzyme.

It was suggested, in explanation of the results, that urea is present

[1] Yi (1920) has examined the enzymic decomposition of urea by the powdered seeds of *Robinia pseudacacia*. It is stated that *Robinia* urease decomposes asym-dimethyl- and diethyl-ureas. Considering the negative results which have been obtained in this respect by other observers with urease from soy bean and from other sources, it is difficult to accept Yi's conclusions until they have received independent corroboration. The presence of two or more ureases, differing in physical properties, in *Robinia* seeds is suggested.

in solution in the hydrated form of "carbamide," $C(OH)_2(NH_2)_2$, which could give rise to cyanic acid by loss of ammonia and a molecule of water, and if hydrolysed could yield ortho-carbonic acid and ammonia. The latter change was assumed to be the one determined by the presence of urease.   Assuming that the enzyme must unite with the feebly basic urea in order to decompose it, the retarding effect of ammonia was explained by its power of interfering with such union. Carbon dioxide, by fixing ammonia, would facilitate the effect of the enzyme by leaving it free to act as a hydrolyst.

In a later study, Armstrong, Benjamin and Horton (1913) examined the effect of the presence of various substances on the reactivity of urease towards urea.   Generally speaking, the stronger acids were found to retard the action, whilst feeble acidic substances, with the exception of boric acid, had an accelerating effect.

According to van Slyke and Cullen (1913), the rate at which ammonia is formed by a given concentration of urease is not influenced by varying the concentration of urea from below 0·2 to 10 per cent. If the concentration of the enzyme is varied, then the initial rate of decomposition of urea varies proportionately.   It was concluded that urease must combine with a definite maximum quantity of urea, since the rate of the reaction was not affected by the presence of an excess of urea beyond this particular amount.

Marshall (1914) arrived at similar results, from which it may be taken as definitely shown that *the velocity of* (the assumed) *hydrolysis of urea by urease is proportional to the concentration of the enzyme*, under definite and limiting conditions.   He also examined the inhibitory effect of alcohol on the change.

As the result of a more detailed study of the reaction, van Slyke and Cullen (1914) have proposed an equation, based on the law of mass action, to explain the progress of the change, which it is suggested may be applied to enzyme action in general, on the assumption that two successive reactions are concerned in the change.

Since we are immediately concerned with the mechanism of the enzyme effect, rather than the progress of the reaction, the reader is referred to the original memoir for the full details of the latter.

In the destruction of urea by urease the two separate phases of the enzyme's action are assumed to be (1) combination of enzyme and substrate (urea); (2) disruption of the combination, with liberation of the urea as ammonia and carbon dioxide.

Whilst it seems almost obvious that there must be a combination, or attraction of some kind, between the enzyme and urea, the real question as to how the latter is actually decomposed is left untouched.

A study of the effect of changes in the concentration of hydrogen-ions on the progress of the reaction was made by van Slyke and Zacharias (1914). It was found, working over a range (P_H = 5·9 to 8·7), that the velocity of the combination of enzyme and substrate varied in inverse ratio to the hydrogen-ion concentration, i.e. the more alkaline the solution the more rapid the combination. The decomposition by the enzyme of the urea combined with it (the second phase of the reaction) was most rapid in neutral solution, and was retarded by either alkalinity or acidity. Alcohol at 30 per cent concentration had a retarding effect on both phases of the change.

Onodera (1915) found that methyl, ethyl, and propyl alcohols at molar concentration accelerated the activity of urease, but at higher concentrations (3·3 molar and upwards) they had a retarding effect. The inhibitory effect of acids on the change was further confirmed.

Bayliss (1915), in pursuing the theory that enzyme activity is manifested at the surface of contact between the solid enzyme and the substrate solution, has considerably amplified Marshall's and Onodera's observations on the activity of urease in the presence of alcohol.

The following results were obtained, after three days at room temperature :—

Alcohol.	Percentage of hydrolysis.
80·0 per cent	7·8
83·3 ,,	6·1
85·8 ,,	4·3
89·3 ,,	1·8

Thus the decomposition of urea by urease was effected even in the presence of nearly 90 per cent alcohol, i.e. a liquid in which the enzyme was shown to be quite insoluble.

Bayliss points out, amongst other reasons, that a considerable activity of the enzyme is not to be expected in the presence of strong alcohol, as the low concentration of water retards hydrolysis.

Yamasaki (1918-1920) claims to have detected ammonium carbamate as an intermediate product in the decomposition of urea by urease, and, in opposition to the views of van Slyke and Cullen, concludes that the mechanism of the change does not consist in the decomposition of a compound formed at the outset, with great velocity as suggested, from the union of urease with urea.

Yamasaki assumes that the decomposing effect of the enzyme is a successive hydrolysis of urea ; the reactions

$$CON_2H_4 \rightarrow H_2N . CO . ONH_4 \rightarrow (NH_4)_2CO_3$$

taking place with about the same velocity. The change is a "simple catalytic action," carried on in the substrate without the formation of an intermediate compound with the enzyme. The retarding effects of electrolytes on the change is assumed to be due to their adsorption by the enzyme, whereby its activity is diminished.

Armstrong and Horton found that ammonium chloride had a slight accelerating effect.

Barendrecht (1919) has put forward a "radiation" theory to explain enzyme action, which cannot be discussed here. So far as the system *urea-urease* is concerned, it is held that when the urease radiation strikes a molecule of urea it is absorbed, and as a result the urea is apparently directly hydrolysed. No explanation as to how this latter change is brought about is offered, yet this is an all-important question to be solved before any theory can give a satisfactory explanation of the change. Certain results and conclusions of previous investigators are adversely criticised, whilst others are shown to be in accordance with his radiation theory.

Barendrecht claims to have observed a reversion of the hydrolysis in solutions where the urease is shown to be "decaying," and to have observed a synthesis of urea from ammonium carbonate in any urease solution in which the enzyme is "decaying" through the combined effect of alkalinity, time, and temperature.

Mattaar (1920) disputes the validity of Barendrecht's claim, and showed that a certain amount of urea added to a solution of ammonium carbonate was destroyed by urease.

When we consider that Barendrecht's claim is based on an entirely erroneous conception of the relationship between ammonium carbonate and urea, and of the mechanism of the latter's hydrolysis, it will be seen that its validity is more than doubtful.

After considering the results of the several investigations which have just been reviewed, it is evident that the important question, "What is the mechanism by which urease brings about the destruction of urea at such a comparatively low temperature?" has been left unanswered.

Whilst different views have been put forward to explain the mode of action of the enzyme, considered from a purely physico-chemical point of view, all the investigators have been unanimous in assuming a *direct* combination of urea with water in accordance with the old equation

$$CO(NH_2)_2 + 2H_2O = (NH_4)_2CO_3$$

as the explanation of the final action of the enzyme.

A discussion of the several theories which have been suggested to explain enzyme action is outside the present work, yet there is one hypothesis which cannot be ignored in connection with the subject under consideration.

A theory which is favourably entertained by many, namely, that an enzyme acts catalytically as an accelerator of a change which is already in progress, is, in the opinion of the writer, untenable so far as the decomposition of urea by urease is concerned.

It is maintained that urea in solution in the presence of either acids, or alkalis is *not hydrolysed at the ordinary temperature*, and any change in this direction, which must be preceded by dissociation of urea, is perceptible only at about 60°, and is even then extremely slow (see p. 39).

The action of urease is therefore remarkable in bringing about a rapid change at a low temperature.

It is interesting to note than van Slyke and Cullen have placed the optimum temperature of urease at 60°, which is distinctly above the average optimum point for enzyme actions generally.

The specificity of urease, so far as it has been established, is another interesting fact, since it appears to support the view that the urea molecule has a constitution peculiar to itself.

On the other hand, the mechanism of the decomposition of mono-substituted ureas in the presence of either acids or alkalis is similar to that of urea. The velocity of the reaction is much slower, thus Fawsitt (1904) found $K \times 10^5 = 48 \cdot 5$ for methylurea at $99 \cdot 2°$, as compared with 101 for urea, all other conditions being equal. This also indicates that a higher temperature is required to reach the point at which methylurea undergoes dissociation than in the case of the less stable urea.

Now we have seen (Chapter V.) that the so-called "hydrolysis" of urea by acids and by alkalis respectively is not the direct change, erroneously and yet so persistingly, expressed by the simple equation given above. Nor is it a change in which ammonium carbamate may be considered as an intermediate product.

We know that the first stage in the hydrolysis of urea, i.e. dissociation into ammonia and cyanic acid, is a function of the temperature. Acids or alkalis each exert two effects which act simultaneously in opposite directions on the progress of the change. They retard the first stage by lowering the concentration of "free" urea, and accelerate the second stage by removing the products of dissociation so fast, more particularly in the case of acids, that the net result is a great acceleration of the change as compared with the effect of heat on a plain solution of urea. Alcohol, on the other hand, promotes the first stage, but retards the second, i.e. the true hydrolysis stage. The retarding effect on the second stage is greater than the promoting effect on the first stage, and hence a retardation of the decomposition of urea is the result in the presence of alcohols. It is remarkable that no attention was paid to Fawsitt's work (1902) on the hydrolysis of urea, published seven years before the discovery of urease in the soy bean, by any of the experimenters whose investigations have been considered.

Is there any reason to suspect that the mechanism of the decomposition of urea by urease, so far as the purely chemical part of the change is concerned, is essentially different from that of its decomposition in the presence of acids and alkalis respectively?

One of the most notable features of enzyme action is the low temperature at which a change is effected with much velocity, as compared with the conditions required to effect a similar change by artificial means. For reasons which have been fully emphasized, this feature is more remarkable in the special case of urease than with other enzymes.[1]

Now there is no doubt that urease attacks "free" urea only, and we have seen that dissociation into ammonia and cyanic acid is the first step in all the decompositions of urea in this condition.

Can urease initiate this dissociation as the first step in the "hydrolysis" of urea?

A comprehensive study of the urea/urease system has been recently carried out by Fearon (1921)[2] on the basis of the cyclic formula of urea. The interesting results obtained have given a convincing answer in the affirmative to the above question. The following facts have been experimentally proved :—

1. Cyanic acid has been isolated, as the silver salt, during the zymolysis of urea by urease in aqueous solution.

2. The concentration of cyanic acid was found to rise to a maximum, after which it remained constant during the greater part of the reaction. It was therefore being continually produced as fast as it was removed by hydrolysis.

3. Biuret was formed during the decomposition. This, we have

[1] Whilst the disaccharides are hydrolysed at the ordinary temperature by their special enzymes, this change can be demonstrated by the aid of acids under like condition; again, the action of lipoclastic enzymes in hydrolysing fats is a change which can be effected by the aid of alkalis at room temperature. This is not so with urea; it is not hydrolysed by acids nor by alkalis at a low temperature.

[2] Unpublished : will appear in "Biochemical Journal," 1923.

seen, could only arise, in all probability, from an interaction of cyanic acid and unchanged urea.

4. Urease was found to attack urea in the presence of absolute alcohol, or at all events in a liquid containing not more than 0.82 per cent of water. Ethyl allophanate, urethane, and biuret were the products formed, thus proving the formation of cyanic acid.

5. Urease was found to be capable of combining with ammonia and of adsorbing urea.

The mechanism of the reaction is explained by Fearon thus: urease condenses urea by adsorption on its surface; this is followed by the dissociation of the urea into ammonia, which combines with the enzyme, and cyanic acid which is hydrolysed by the solvent, in the case of water.

It is suggested that dissociation of urea may be brought about by (1) pressure in the adsorption area, (2) temperature of adsorption, (3) effect of an electric surface field, since urease has been found to carry an electro-negative charge and to combine with ammonia.

Apart from any theory of the mode of action of the enzyme in the first step of the change, the outstanding result of Fearon's researches proves that *urease is not directly concerned in the " hydrolysis" of urea at all.* The function of the enzyme is to bring about dissociation of urea into ammonia and cyanic acid. The hydrolysis of the latter follows as a secondary change in the presence of water.

The theory that urease acts as a dissociating agent in attacking urea offers a new conception of enzyme action which it is not unlikely may be applied to other cases.

We have in this theory a rational explanation of the specific action of urease. It was pointed out that methyl and ethyl-ureas require a higher temperature than urea for their dissociation, and hence the velocity of their " hydrolysis " when heated in the presence of acids and alkalis respectively is much slower than in the case of urea. Now, no enzyme has been found to exert its activity above 80°, whilst many are inactive at about 70°; hence if the enzyme cannot bring about the dissociation of a substituted urea below 80°, say, the latter cannot be "hydrolysed." Fearon (1921) has shown that whilst methylurea is not attacked by soy bean urease up to the limit temperature, ethyl-urea is attacked slowly by the enzyme at 70°. This is an interesting fact in support of the new theory, since it appears to indicate that urease is capable of bringing about the dissociation of ethylurea—less stable than methylurea—just below the temperature limit of its activity.

Quite recently Fearon has found that pure normal butylurea is attacked by soy bean urease at $45°$-$50°$.   Now this is a point of further interest, since this urea, being less stable than ethylurea, is dissociated at a lower temperature, and hence is attacked by the enzyme at a temperature below that at which it can decompose the ethyl derivative.

The possibility of effecting a synthesis of urea by urease from ammonium carbonate, as a result of a direct dehydration of the latter, as claimed by Barendrecht (1919-20), appears more remote than ever in the light of the "dissociation" theory.

The decomposition of urea by urease is another example of a reaction in the chemistry of urea, the interpretation of which has been greatly helped by a recognition of the cyclic formula.

2. The Constitution of Salts of Urea.

In addition to the evidence obtained from the study of the "hydrolysis" of urea, and of its behaviour towards nitrous acid, we have ample proof that the configuration of the urea molecule in the free state must be different from that when present as a salt.   This is explained by the change—

$$HN : C \overset{\displaystyle NH_3}{\underset{\displaystyle O}{\big|}} + HX = HN : C \overset{\displaystyle NH_2 . HX}{\underset{\displaystyle OH}{}}$$

The latter formula is generally considered to be hypothetical rather than real, with the result that the usual practice has been to represent salts of "carbamide" as $CO(NH_2)_2 . HX'$, no difference being assumed to exist in the constitution of urea when in the free state and when present as a salt.

It has been suggested by A. Werner (1902), since "carbamide" might be expected to yield salts of the type $CO(NH_2)_2 . 2HX'$, none of which of course are known, that the salts owe their existence to the subsidiary valency of the oxygen atom of the CO group rather than to that of the two amino groups.   In other words, to explain an apparent irregularity it is proposed to view the salts of "carbamide" as oxonium salts of the type $(H_2N)_2 : CO . . HX'$.   It is scarcely necessary to lay stress on the fact that there is no evidence for such a conclusion.

On the basis of the "carbamide" formula, the real difficulty is to understand why urea should form such stable salts as it does.   No true acid amide is capable of forming a salt, with an acid, which is not completely dissociated by water.

The formation of salts of urea with only one molecule of an acid is in complete agreement with the change of the cyclic form to the type $HN : C(OH) \cdot NH_2$, and the formation of metallic derivatives supplies further evidence of this change.

3. Metallic Derivatives of Urea.

Haller (1886) has shown that when urea is heated in a sealed tube with potassium hydroxide in alcoholic solution, the products are ammonia, water, and potassium cyanate.

The potassium derivative of urea, $CO.N_2H_3K$, described by Franklin and Stafford (1902), is no doubt first formed. This compound, which is prepared by the addition of potassium ethoxide to urea in alcohol, was found by the writer to decompose at about 230°, with copious evolution of ammonia, and production of a porous mass of practically pure potassium cyanate.

This decomposition indicates that the compound is formed according to the equation

$$HN : C\!\!\!\begin{array}{c} \diagup NH_3 \\ | \\ \diagdown O \end{array} + C_2H_5O.K = HN : C\!\!\!\begin{array}{c} \diagup NH_2 \\ \diagdown O.K \end{array} + C_2H_5OH.$$

Franklin and Stafford have described a di-potassium derivative as a gelatinous precipitate. The writer is inclined to think that the formation of such a compound is doubtful. When urea and two molecular proportions of potassium ethoxide were mixed in alcoholic solution, the product after distillation to dryness out of contact with the air was found to decompose in a manner similar to that of the mono-potassium salt. A substance having either the constitution $KN : C(NH_2)O.K$, or $HN : C(NHK).O.K$, might be expected to yield a residue containing potassium cyanamide, or potassium cyanide, or both. Neither was present; the residue consisted of potassium cyanate and free alkali.

Mulder (1873) has described a di-argentic derivative of urea, $CON_2H_2Ag_2$. Whilst the constitution of this compound awaits investigation, the conditions under which it is formed are of theoretical interest. It is obtained in quantitative yield, as a pale yellow precipitate, on the addition of pure sodium hydroxide to an aqueous solution of urea and silver nitrate, according to the equation

$$CON_2H_4 + 2AgNO_3 + 2NaOH = CON_2H_2Ag_2 + 2NaNO_3 + 2H_2O.$$

The silver derivative[1] is sparingly soluble in dilute solution of

---

[1] This is no doubt the compound which Fenton (1882) assumed to be a derivative of cyanamide, in the experiment on the action of sodium on urea. A silver salt was obtained which contained a percentage of silver intermediate between that required for CN_2Ag_2 and CN_2HAg; the mean is $Ag = 78.43$ per cent. Di-argentic urea contains $Ag = 78.83$ per cent.

ammonia, yet it is not formed on the addition of ammonio-silver nitrate solution to a solution of urea.

The addition of sodium hydroxide at once promotes the formation of the silver compound. Ammonia is not capable of changing free urea into the form $HN : C(NH_2) . OH$, from which the silver derivative is produced. Its constitution is probably represented by the formula $HN : C(NHAg) . O . Ag$. The compound $CON_2H_4 . Ag_2O$ mentioned in the literature has no existence.

The mercury derivative originally obtained by Liebig (1853) and represented as $CON_2H_4 . 2HgO$ is correctly expressed by the formula $HN : C(NH . HgOH) . O . Hg . OH$. When heated at 110°-120° this compound loses a molecule of water to yield

$$HN : C \begin{cases} NH . Hg \\ O . Hg \end{cases} O.$$

The mercury derivatives described by Ruspaggiari (1897), which have been assumed to contain the group

$$CO \begin{cases} NH—Hg\cdots \\ NH—Hg— \end{cases}$$

are no doubt all derived from the configuration $HN : C(NH_2) \cdot OH$.

The fact that urea yields salts with acids which can be isolated from their aqueous solutions, and can also form derivatives with the more electro-positive metals, makes it comparable in its properties to an amino-acid, with this difference, that the order of stability of the two types of derivatives is reversed. In its reactive form urea is *imino-amino formic acid*.[1] Its basic character, due to only one amino-group, is more pronounced than in the amino-acids, since it is enhanced by the presence of the imino-group (NH), which in combination with carbon in the form $HN : C <$ is the least reactive part [2] of the urea molecule.

This is an interesting theoretical point to which we shall return presently.

The salts of urea should therefore conform to the normal types required for a mon-acid base. This has been verified by Du Toit

---

[1] It may also be viewed as imino-carbamic acid, or as hydroxyformamidine.

[2] Whether the system $HN : C <$ is to be represented according to the electronic theory as

$$HN \overset{-}{\underset{-}{=\!=}} \overset{+}{\underset{+}{}} C <, \text{ or } HN \overset{+}{\underset{+}{=\!=}} \overset{-}{\underset{-}{}} C <$$

is by no means clear. At all events the union between the imino-group and the carbon atom appears to represent that part of the urea molecule which has attained the most stable electrostatic equilibrium. Hence it is the least reactive.

(1913) in the case of the nitrate, hydrochloride, sulphate, and oxalate, though represented as "carbamide" salts.

Heintz (1869), in obtaining evidence to support his views that urea is a mon-acid base (see Chapter I., page 6), prepared the platinichloride derivative, which was found to have the normal composition,

$$(CON_2H_4)_2H_2PtCl_6 . 2H_2O.$$

Pickard and Kenyon (1907) have assigned the formula

$$(CON_2H_4)_4 . H_2PtCl_6$$

to the compound which they obtained, though no evidence was given to prove that the salt was anhydrous.

The writer has prepared urea platinibromide, which, being less soluble than the chloro-salt, was more easily obtained pure. It was found to have the composition $(CON_2H_4)_2 . H_2Pt Br_6 . 2H_2O$, analogous to Heintz's salt. No evidence of the formation of a compound containing more urea than required for the normal salt was obtained.

Mono-substituted Derivatives of Urea Considered on the Basis of the Cyclic Formula.

Whilst the salts of urea are undoubtedly derived from the so-called "iso-urea" structure $HN : C\begin{smallmatrix} \diagup NH_2 \\ \diagdown OH \end{smallmatrix}$, we have seen, for reasons which have been discussed in the previous chapter, that this molecular configuration cannot exist in the free state.

So far as urea itself is concerned, the cyclic formula and its change in the formation of salts is simple, and in agreement with all the facts. A difficulty appears to be presented when we come to consider a substituted derivative of urea, but it is in fact more apparent than real.

Only two mono-methyl derivatives of urea are known in the *free* state :—

I. Methyl "iso-urea," $HN : C\begin{smallmatrix} \diagup NH_2 \\ \diagdown O . CH_3 \end{smallmatrix}$ a strong base, and

II. Methylurea, or methyl carbamide, $H_2N - C\begin{smallmatrix} \diagup NHCH_3 \\ \diagdown O \end{smallmatrix}$ a much weaker base than I.

Two more derivatives are *apparently* possible in theory :—

III. $HN : C\begin{smallmatrix} \diagup NHCH_3 \\ \diagdown OH \end{smallmatrix}$ and IV. $CH_3N : C\begin{smallmatrix} \diagup NH_2 \\ \diagdown OH \end{smallmatrix}$

It will be seen that methylurea (II.) could give rise to isomeride (III.) by migration of a hydrogen atom from the group NH_2 to oxygen, and to isomeride (IV.) by migration of hydrogen from the group $NHCH_3$ to oxygen.

Now, the instability of the system : $C{\overset{\displaystyle NH_2}{\underset{\displaystyle OH}{\Big<}}}$ on a par with : $C(OH)_2$

and with : $C(NH_2)_2$, is quite independent of the nature of the divalent radicle in union with carbon. Hence isomeride (IV.) is too unstable to exist in the free state.

As regards (II.) and (III.) there must obviously be a difference

between the relative stabilities of the systems : $C{\overset{\displaystyle NHCH_3}{\underset{\displaystyle NH_2}{\Big<}}}{\overset{+}{}}_{+}$ and

$:C{\overset{\displaystyle \overset{+}{N}HCH_3}{\underset{\displaystyle OH}{\Big<}}}_{\;-}$. In the former we have two electro-positive radicles,

differing in degree, in union with a carbon atom, whilst in the latter the two radicles are of opposite electrical sign, and would therefore tend to exert an attraction for each other. Configuration (III.) should therefore be more stable than configuration (II.), which represents the structure commonly assigned to methylurea.

From the behaviour of methylurea towards nitrous acid the writer (1919) has obtained convincing evidence that in an acid solution an equilibrium between the two configurations must obtain in which, in round numbers, 90 per cent is present in form (III.) and 10 per cent in form (II.). This does not mean that methylurea in the static condition, or in a neutral solvent, is represented by such an equilibrium. It is maintained that neither configuration can represent a stable compound such as we know methylurea to be in the free state. Both must be derived from the stable cyclic form in a manner which may be represented by the following scheme :—

$${\overset{\displaystyle NHCH_3}{\underset{\displaystyle H_2N}{\Big>}}}C:O \;\leftarrow\; HN:C{\overset{\displaystyle \overset{\displaystyle H}{\frown}NH_2CH_3}{\underset{\displaystyle O}{\Big<}}}_{\;\nearrow\,H} \;\rightarrow\; HN:C{\overset{\displaystyle NHCH_3}{\underset{\displaystyle OH}{\Big<}}}$$

(II.)　　　　　(V.) Methylurea in free state.　　　　(III.)

the tendency for an atom of hydrogen to migrate to oxygen being much greater than to migrate to the imino-group.

There are two methods for preparing methylurea : (1) the isomeric transformation of methylammonium cyanate, and (2) the interaction of ammonia and methyl carbimide, or isocyanate $CH_3N : C : O$.

8 *

The first method is obviously similar in mechanism to Wöhler's synthesis, namely, dissociation of the methylammonium salt, and union of methylamine with cyanic acid in the keto-form. This must lead directly to the stable cyclic molecule (V.) thus—

$$HN : CO + HNHCH_3 \rightarrow HN : C \Big\langle {}^{NHCH_3}_{OH} \rightarrow HN : C \Big\langle {}^{NH_2CH_3}_{O} .$$

$$\qquad\qquad\qquad\qquad\qquad (III.) \qquad\qquad\qquad\qquad (V.)$$

Now, to return to the consideration of isomeride (IV.):

$$CH_3N : C \Big\langle {}^{NH_2}_{OH}$$

Whilst this cannot exist free, there can be no theoretical objection to the existence in the free state of salts of the type

$$CH_3N : C \Big\langle {}^{NH_2 . HX'}_{OH}$$

nor to the cyclic configuration

$$(VI.) \ CH_3 . N : C \Big\langle {}^{NH_3}_{O}$$

from which such salts might be obtained.

As regards the two cyclic isomerides (V.) and (VI.), since there is probably a greater attraction between oxygen and methylammonia than between oxygen and ammonia, it seems reasonable to conclude that (V.) is the more stable of the two isomerides.

All chemical reactions tend towards the attainment of a state of maximum stability under the particular conditions. This must mean a distribution of the electrical forces within the molecules so as to maintain a state of maximum electrostatic equilibrium. Hence, if in a given reaction, the formation of two isomerides such as (V.) and (VI.) for example, is possible, the more stable will be formed either exclusively, or in the larger amount if an equilibrium between the two forms happens to represent a more stable condition than one form alone.

The second method of preparing methylurea would apparently give rise to the cyclic form (VI.) thus—

$$CH_3N : CO + HNH_2 - \quad CH_3N : C \Big\langle {}^{NH_2}_{OH} \rightarrow CH_3N : C \Big\langle {}^{NH_3}_{O}$$

$$\qquad\qquad\qquad\qquad\qquad (IV.) \qquad\qquad\qquad (VI.)$$

Does this represent a change to the state of maximum stability? The intermediate compound (IV.) could also give rise to the cyclic isomeride

$$\text{(V.) } HN : C \underset{O}{\overset{NH_2CH_3}{\big<}}$$

in accordance with the scheme—

$$\underset{\underset{(IV.)}{H_2N - C - OH}}{\overset{\nearrow N . CH_3}{\big<}} \rightarrow \underset{\underset{(III.)}{}}{HN : C \underset{OH}{\overset{NH . CH_3}{\big<}}} \rightarrow \underset{\underset{(V.)}{}}{HN : C \underset{O}{\overset{NH_2CH_3}{\big<}}} .$$

Since configuration (IV.) cannot exist in the free state, whilst (III.) is undoubtedly unstable, and the same is true of the "carbamide"

formula (II.) $H_2N - C : O \overset{NHCH_3}{\big/}$, the end product of the reaction will consist of one or other of the isomerides (V.) and (VI.), or of an equilibrium mixture of the two, depending on their relative stabilities.

A possible objection to the cyclic formula of urea, on the ground that it predicts the existence of two mono-methyl derivatives in cyclic form, would therefore appear to have support. But if, as suggested, form (V.) is more stable than form (VI.), then the objection is explained, since it means that experimental conditions necessary for the isolation of the less stable form (VI.) have not yet been realised. It is more than likely that further research will lead to the discovery of evidence which will dispose of the objection in question. A careful study of mono-substituted ureas in the static condition has never been made particularly as regards their decomposition by heat.

When methylurea is decomposed by heat it yields ammonia, methylammonia, N-dimethylcyanuric acid $(CH_3)_2HC_3N_3O_3$ and cyanuric acid, $H_3C_3N_3O_3$. The production of these four substances suggests an equilibrium between the two cyclic forms (V.) and (VI.) in fused methylurea. The simple mechanism by which one form can change into the other has been indicated by the changes already shown. Whilst form (V.) would yield methylammonia and cyanic acid (polymerised), form (VI.) would give ammonia and methylisocyanate (CH_3NCO). A combination of the latter with cyanic acid, at the moment of its generation, would yield N-dimethylcyanuric acid.

A quantitative study of the decomposition by heat of mono-substituted ureas, and a careful examination of their salts are subjects which require investigation.

CHAPTER XII.

ABOUT twenty-five years after Rouelle had isolated impure urea from human urine, Fourcroy and Vaquelin (1777) showed that it was the chief nitrogenous constituent of the urine of many different animals. It was during their examination of urine from such sources that they made their observation of the precipitation of urea by nitric acid. It is now well known that in the case of all carnivorous and omnivorous mammals the excess nitrogen is excreted by the kidneys chiefly as urea, whilst in herbivorous mammals it is supplemented by hippuric acid, which is present to a very small extent in human urine.

In birds and reptiles nitrogen leaves the system almost entirely in the form of uric acid.

Though there is apparently no chemico-physiological explanation for this difference in nitrogen metabolism between birds and mammals, it must be remembered that urea and uric acid are both immediate derivatives of cyanic acid in the keto-form.

It was shown long ago by Dumas and Prévost (1823) that urea is present in the blood of animals; modern research has proved its presence in practically all the fluids and organs of the body.

Since all animals obtain their nitrogen primarily from a vegetable source, the question of nitrogen metabolism in the vegetable kingdom requires first consideration.

Urea in its Relation to Nitrogen Metabolism in Plants.

Up to comparatively recent years urea was considered to be a product peculiar to animal metabolism.

Bamberger and Landsiedl (1903) appear to have made the first observations of its occurrence in the lower plants. They found urea to the extent of 3·5 per cent. in the capitulum of ripe specimens of the fungus *Lycoperdon Bovista*. Gaze (1905) isolated urea from the same fungus, and found that the amount varied but little whether from mature or immature specimens. Goris and Mascré (1908) found urea to the extent of 2·75 per cent in young specimens, and 4·3 per cent in mature specimens of the fungus *Psolliota Campestris*, calculated on the dry weight of the plant. Proof that urea was formed by the fungus and was not directly derived from the soil was not given.

Fosse (1912-13) has shown that a considerable number of the higher plants produce urea when germinated under such conditions that urea is excluded from the system. In the leaves of spinach, endive, potatoes, carrot, turnip, gourd, melon, and in the leaves and young plants of barley, maize, wheat, clover, beans, and peas urea was readily detected, and in several cases estimated by aid of the delicate xanthydrol reaction. In pea plants one month old 0·064 per cent of urea, calculated on the dry material, was found.

Urea was also isolated by Fosse (1913) from cultivations of *Aspergillus Niger* and *Penicillium glaucum*, grown on a solution in which nitrogen was supplied in the form of ammonium nitrate.

Whilst urea was found in several other higher plants besides those mentioned, Fosse (1913) has considerably extended our knowledge as regards the occurrence of urea in low forms of animal life. Its presence was proved in different types of the following invertebrates, and in their excretion products : coelenterata, echinoderms (starfish), worms, crustaceans (crayfish, lobster, and shrimp), insects (silkworm), molluscs (snail, oyster, mussel).

In the case of silkworms, the absence of urea in the mulberry leaves with which they were fed was proved. Whether this is an indication that urea is not formed in perennial plants is a subject for future investigation.

Of particular interest is the simultaneous presence of urea and urease in the same plant, shown by Fosse (1914, 1916).

Urea was found in green pea plants, fourteen days old; the expressed juice (5 c.c.) of plants from the same lot was mixed with 5 c.c. of a 1 per cent solution of urea in the presence of chloroform. After fifteen and a half hours at 44°, 30 per cent of the added urea was destroyed, and 78 per cent was destroyed after thirty-nine and a half hours. No urea was destroyed by juice which had been previously boiled.

Similar experiments were made with soja plants thirty-five days old. Urea was found in the cold juice expressed from 150 grams of the fresh plants ; four grams of the crushed plants added to 10 c.cs. of 0·5 per cent solution of urea in the presence of chloroform destroyed all the urea after five hours at 44°. A control experiment proved that plants which had been previously heated in an autoclave at 100° had no action on a solution of urea.

Reference was made in the previous chapter to the presence of urease in seeds other than those derived from leguminous plants.

Fosse (1916) found that crushed seeds from the following were capable of "hydrolysing" urea in solution in the presence of chloroform : ergot of rye, french grass, carrot, hemp, orange, mandarin, apple, pear, plum, almond, and marrow. An extract of the young leaves of the chestnut, lime, and nettle was also active in this respect.

On considering the results of all this interesting work one ventures to make the sweeping assertion that urea is a constant product of the breaking down of vegetable protein during the germination of all seeds.

As Fosse has pointed out, "the plant can be the seat of the two inverse phenomena of formation and destruction of urea." This condition, in all probability, can only obtain in young plants, since the function of urease is to destroy urea produced from proteins as the result of hydrolysis and oxidation.

We can understand why certain leguminous seeds, so rich in protein, should also be rich in urease. Those seeds which, in the dormant state, do not happen to contain the enzyme ready formed, produce it, no doubt, in quantity during the process of germination.

Urease in its relation to vegetable protein is therefore comparable to zymase in its relation to starch. Whilst the latter enzyme is the active agent in the final breaking down of starch into the simple products alcohol and carbon dioxide, urease is the active agent in the corresponding resolution of protein into the simple products cyanic acid and carbon dioxide. The ultimate oxidation of alcohol to carbonic acid and water, from which the plant originally prepared the starch, and the hydrolysis of cyanic acid to carbonic acid and ammonia, from which the protein was originally prepared, these are changes with which the enzymes are not directly concerned.

Theory of Protein Formation in Plants.

When the plantule has derived all the energy it can from the breaking down of the reserve protein in the seed, one of the chief functions of the developed plant is to build up protein by the assimilation of nitrogen and carbonic acid. It seems very probable that the first step in this mysterious process is brought about either by the change

$$CO_2 + NH_3 = HN : CO + H_2O, \text{ or } CO + NH_3 + H_2O_2$$
$$= HN : CO + 2H_2O,$$

a condensation of cyanic acid with "nascent" carbohydrates giving rise to the next step in protein formation, just as the condensation of $H_2 : CO$ molecules alone can give rise to the complex carbohydrates.

In addition to the results described in Chapter VIII., Fosse (1916) has proved the formation of urea by the oxidation of a solution containing 1·5 gram of glucose and 0·01 gram of ammonia per litre; that is a solution containing about the same proportion of glucose as is normally present in the blood, and even less ammonia than would be contained in the fluid of a living cell.

Now in all cases where the formation of urea has been shown by the oxidation of protein matter, of an amino-acid, or of a carbohydrate in the presence of ammonia, Fosse (1919, 1921) has demonstrated that cyanic acid is the precursor of the urea. Whilst the writer is not prepared to accept the theory of the formation of cyanic acid which has been put forward by Fosse (1919), which involves the intermediate production of hydrocyanic acid, the main point is the recognition of cyanic acid in all these oxidation changes.

It is obvious, as Fosse has pointed out, that the urea molecule cannot participate in nitrogenous nutrition without suffering a preliminary decomposition, which is assumed to be the production of ammonia and carbonic acid by the action of urease. We know now from Fearon's work that the action of the enzyme is limited to the production of ammonia and cyanic acid. If the latter, as suggested by the writer, is directly concerned in the building up of proteins, then its hydrolysis in the plant cells is a superfluous change. Interesting evidence in support of this view was given by the experiments carried out many years ago by Ville (1862). He showed that urea acted as a powerful stimulant to vegetation on plants grown in an artificial soil of sand. Urea was more efficacious than carbonate of ammonia, and its favourable results were manifested with great rapidity.

With ethylurea the results were very different : the growth was checked, the plants drooped and were stunted, the effect being the same as if the sand had not received the addition of any nitrogenous material. The experiments were repeated a great number of times over a period of two years. The results did not vary.

Seeds were found to germinate in the ordinary manner in the presence of ethylurea, but as soon as the young plants put forth their first leaves, the extremities of these became white and shrivelled, and the effect gradually spread over the rest of the leaf. The changes during germination being independent of the presence of an outside source of nitrogen, growth proceeded for a short time on normal lines.

Lutz (1898, 1901) has shown that many flowering plants, algae, and fungi can assimilate nitrogen supplied in the form of methylamine, or ethylamine. This goes to show that in Ville's experiments the results were due to nitrogen starvation, and not to any poisonous effect of ethylurea, or of ethylamine possibly generated from it.

The absence of an enzyme capable of decomposing ethylurea *at the ordinary temperature* into ethylamine and cyanic acid explains Ville's results in the light of modern investigations. Whilst the superior effect of urea, as compared with a simple salt of ammonia, in promoting vegetation is to be ascribed to its power of immediately supplying cyanic acid, the subsequent production of the latter from the ammonia generated at the same time requires consideration.

The formation of cyanic acid by the oxidation of ammonia in the presence of carbohydrates is no doubt a slower reaction, *at ordinary temperature*, than the decomposition of urea by urease.

Formaldehyde being the first product of carbon assimilation, the above change may be assumed to proceed on the following lines :—

$$(1)\ H_2:CO + NH_3 \rightarrow H_2:C \begin{smallmatrix} OH \\ \\ NH_2 \end{smallmatrix} \rightarrow H_2:C:NH + H_2O$$

$$(2)\ H_2:C:NH + O_2 = O:C:NH + H_2O.$$

It is probable that reaction (2) is brought about by the "catalytic" effect of one or other of the different types of enzymes collectively classed as "oxidases," and which are so widely distributed in plant cells.

According to the theory presented here, it follows that so far as assimilation of nitrogen from ammonia is concerned, the phenomenon is inseparably connected with carbon assimilation.[1]

Takabayashi (1897) found that 0·05 per cent solutions of carbonate of ammonia had an injurious effect on certain plants, such as barley, wheat, and onions, but this was counteracted by supplying the plants with cane-sugar or with glycerol. Experiments with other ammonium salts confirmed their injurious effect in the absence of sufficient sugar in the plant.

Since the function of the plant is to build up protein from urea, or from any other source of nitrogen available, it seems highly probable that the "formation" of urea in developed plants is accidental

---

[1] Since life must have been preceded by the formation of protein matter, it is evident that oxygen, carbon dioxide, water, and ammonia (leaving aside the part played by phosphorous and sulphur) were the active agents simultaneously engaged in the generation of the necessary material.

rather than intentional. Its occurrence is, in the writer's opinion, strong evidence of the production of cyanic acid as a first step in protein building.

The Formation of Urea in Animal Metabolism.

Dumas and Cahours (1842) were the first to suggest that urea is a product of combustion of nitrogenous matter in the body. It is now a recognised fact that the complex proteins are broken down in the tissues into simpler nitrogenous compounds, which are ultimately converted into urea. In this way nearly all the nitrogen of the food which is in excess[1] of the requirements of the tissues is passed out of the body.

Where is urea formed in the body, and what is the mode of its formation? These are two questions which have been the subject of numerous investigations by physiologists and chemists since the middle of the last century. The first question is mainly of physiological interest. Considered from a purely chemical point of view, it matters little where urea is formed. Though the intermediate stages in the breaking down of proteins may vary in different parts of the body, the mechanism of the final generation of urea must be the same, wherever the seat of its formation. Hence only the mode of the formation of urea is considered here, since its constitution and the mechanism of its syntheses are subjects of paramount importance in supplying an answer to the second question.

Whilst a good deal of advance has been made in recent years towards elucidating the constitution of the complex protein molecules, our knowledge is still far from sufficient to enable us to follow the separate stages in the cleavage of the protein molecule up to the ultimate formation of urea. For this reason only views regarding the nature of the immediate precursors of urea have been put forward from time to time in keeping with the advancement of our knowledge.

These views may be briefly summarised as follows :—

Formation of urea from

(1) Ammonium carbonate, by dehydration (Schmiedeberg, 1879).

(2) Ammonium cyanate, by isomeric transformation (Salkowski, 1877, Hoppe-Seyler, 1881).

---

[1] In the germination stage, plant metabolism is very similar to animal metabolism, since the young embryonic plant is at first wholly, and later partly, dependent on the complex reserve food material of the seed. Whilst energy is derived from the breaking down of the protein, and urea finally formed, this is not rejected as in the case of the animal, but with the aid of energy from the sun is used to build up protein again.

(3) Ammonium carbamate, by dehydration (Drechsel, 1881).

(4) Monoamino-acids by oxidation in presence of ammonia (Hofmeister, 1902).

(5) Arginine by hydrolysis (Kossel and Dakin, 1904).

The chief difficulty in explaining urea formation in the body is attributed by physiologists to our ignorance of the constitution of the proteins. The constitution of urea has, as a matter of course, been considered beyond dispute, and the "carbamide" formula has been the basis for all argument. This has really been the chief cause of the difficulty in understanding the mechanism of the final stages in the excretion of excess nitrogen from the body. The light which recent researches have thrown on the structure of the urea molecule, and on the mode of its formation in plants, must obviously help greatly to illuminate our views on the vexed question of urea formation in animals.

It has been abundantly proved that in all syntheses, without exception, of *free* urea, the final change is direct union of ammonia with cyanic acid in the keto form $O:C:NH$. Is there any reason to suppose that *free* urea is produced otherwise in the living cell?

The oxidation of a great variety of nitrogenous, and of non-nitrogenous carbon compounds in the presence of ammonia has been shown by Fosse to give rise to cyanic acid, from which urea is formed.

Of the different precursors of urea which have been suggested, it is perhaps remarkable that ammonium cyanate is the only one which has been almost unanimously turned down by modern physiologists as the least acceptable, on the ground that cyanates do not occur, or, to be precise, have not been detected in the body.

The form in which we might expect cyanic acid in the body—say in the liver, the chief seat of urea formation in the animal system—is the sodium, potassium, or calcium salt, but certainly not the ammonium salt as it would change to urea. Cyanic acid must be formed in the liver, *otherwise urea would not be found there.*

The theory of the formation of cyanic acid by oxidation of carbon compounds in the presence of ammonia has been already discussed in Chapter VIII. in connection with urea formation in plants, but it is well to point out here that cyanates and cyanic acid are very resistant to further oxidation. In view of all the facts, it seems reasonable to conclude that cyanic acid is the final product of the oxidation of the cleavage products of the proteins in the body.

In the various amino-acids derived from the proteins we have the groups,

$$\cdots H_2C - NH_2, \; \equiv\!\!\equiv HC - NH_2, \; \equiv\!\!\equiv C - NH_2, \text{ and } \equiv\!\!\equiv HC - NH\cdots,$$

which could readily yield $O : C : NH$ as the final stage of their oxidation. This is all that is necessary in order to attain the object required, namely, the elimination of excess nitrogen from the body in a practically neutral form. For it must not be forgotten that cyanic acid is quantitatively hydrolysed to urea by water alone, at the temperature of the body, thus—

$$2HNCO + H_2O = CON_2H_4 + CO_2.$$

Why should Nature proceed to the formation of such end products as carbon dioxide and ammonia, with the subsequent production of either ammonium carbonate, or carbamate, followed by a process of dehydration, in order to form urea? Since we know now that the formation of urea from ammonium carbamate—Basarov's synthesis— is dependent on the production of cyanic acid, it is useless to discuss any further the idea that carbon dioxide and ammonia are precursors of the formation of urea in the body.

Hofmeister's suggestion that the oxidation of amino-acids in the presence of ammonia is responsible for the formation of urea was deprived of its value as an essential advance in our knowledge of the subject by the fact that the production of cyanic acid as the immediate precursor of urea was not contemplated. Assuming—and the evidence in its favour is overwhelming—that cyanic acid is the final product in the "biotic" oxidation of protein, we will pass on to a consideration of this theory in its relation to the results which have been obtained in investigations to solve the "urea-formation" problem.

Cyanic Acid as the Immediate Precursor of Urea in the Animal Organism.

It is a well-established fact that the administration of ammonium salts to animals is followed by an increase in the output of urea.

The following extract from a standard work on physiological chemistry[1] will enable the reader who is not familiar with the results which have been obtained on this matter to appreciate the views which are entertained regarding it :—

"Ammonium carbonate and all other ammonium salts which are capable of being converted into it in the tissues are changed into urea by the animal organism. This applies to the carnivora as well as to the herbivora.

[1] "Text Book on Physiological Chemistry," E. Abderhalden (1908).

"After the administration of sal-ammoniac, NH₄Cl, to rabbits, the increased elimination of urea corresponded exactly with the amount of nitrogen added in the form of sal-ammoniac. The results were not so definite with human beings and dogs. A part of the ammonia appeared in the urine, and, from the uncertain increase of urea, it remained undecided whether this was due to the ammonia diet, or an increased disintegration of albumin. The cause of the difference between the carnivora and the herbivora was soon discovered. It depends on the following: the food of the herbivora yields an alkaline ash, and during its combustion in the organism it forms potassium carbonate, which can react with ammonium chloride. Ammonia is liberated, and can be utilised for the production of urea. The food of the carnivora furnishes an acid ash. The hydrochloric acid is not separated from the ammonia in the tissues, and consequently the latter is not available for the production of urea. If, on the other hand, we feed some ammonium carbonate to a dog, we likewise observe an increase of urea. These experiments, therefore, indicate that the organism of mammals is capable of utilising ammonia for the production of urea. Observations have indicated the probability that ammonia normally—i.e. without being artificially administered—participates in the formation of urea.

"If the utilisation of ammonia in the formation of urea has been established, we must determine whether it is to be assumed that all, or at least the greater part, of the amino-groups present in the tissues are split off as ammonia, and thus take part in the production of urea."

It will be seen from the foregoing observations, that the formation of *free* ammonia is assumed to be an essential condition in order that urea may be produced from the oxidation of protein in the body.

Modern investigations appear to favour the view that ammonia is generated by hydrolytic "de-amination" of the cleavage products of the proteins, i.e. amino-acids. Now, according to the writer's theory of cyanic acid as the immediate precursor of urea in the body, the production of ammonia, *in addition to*, and *independently of*, cyanic acid is not necessary. Why, therefore, should Nature produce it? It is obvious that the artificial administration of ammonia must lead to considerable increase in the amount of urea excreted, without any increase in the amount of *urea formed* by the breaking down of protein. A comparison of the two equations

$$(1)\quad 2HN:CO + H_2O = CON_2H_4 + CO_2$$
$$(2)\quad HN:CO + NH_3 = CON_2H_4$$

shows that, theoretically, twice as much urea can be formed from the same amount of cyanic acid if ammonia is present so that equation (2) may be realised in the body in preference to equation (1).

It is a well-known fact that the administration of an excess of acid in the diet to animals tends to lower the amount of urea excreted, with a corresponding increase in the elimination of nitrogen as ammonia. In this case the result is readily explained by the equation

$$(3)\ HN : CO + H_2O + HX' = NH_4X + CO_2.$$

Thus it will be seen that by the production of cyanic acid as the end product of protein disintegration, Nature supplies the body with the means, metaphorically speaking, of actually "killing three birds with one stone."

Normal excretion of nitrogen as urea is represented by equation (1), excess of alkalinity (as ammonia) is disposed of by equation (2), whilst excess of acidity is dealt with according to equation (3).

In the healthy animal organism, therefore, the extent of protein oxidation—cyanic acid formation [1]—is the same whether the amount of urea excreted is increased, or diminished, by the administration of ammonia, or acids, respectively.

This distinction between the amount of urea *formed* and the amount *excreted* under abnormal conditions is not clearly indicated by any of the previous theories of the immediate precursors of urea.

The observations of Schmiedeberg (1877) that, after the administration of ethylamine carbonate to animals, ethylurea is found in the urine is interesting confirmation of the "cyanic acid precursor" theory. Any amino-compound, not easily broken down by oxidation, or hydrolysis, should appear in the urine in the form of the corresponding urea derivative. There is plenty of evidence on record that such is the case.

Are Carbamates Excreted in the Urine?

A few observers claim to have recognised the presence of carbamates in urine. Abel (1891) presumably obtained evidence of carbamates in considerable amounts in the urine of human beings and of dogs after the administration of milk of lime. Calcium carbamate apparently would be the salt present, but it is more than likely that this was mistaken for calcium cyanate, the possible presence of which was not contemplated.

---

[1] This really corresponds to what is generally termed urea formation in physiology on the basis of the theories which have been hitherto considered.

Drechsel (1878) showed that calcium carbamate,

$$Ca\,(O\,.\,CO\,.\,NH_2)_2\,.\,H_2O,$$

was extremely unstable in aqueous solution, whilst the solid at the ordinary temperature soon developed an ammoniacal odour, being decomposed (hydrolysed) by its own water of crystallisation. The chances of calcium carbamate remaining unchanged in solution in a large volume of water at the temperature of the body are therefore extremely remote.

Calcium cyanate, on the other hand, is much more resistant to hydrolysis, and the writer has not been able to find any tests used to recognise the carbamate which would distinguish it from the cyanate.

Whilst there can be no hesitation in turning down the theory of the formation of urea by the dehydration of ammonium carbamate, it is no harm to point out that a carbamate may be formed in urine as an intermediate product of the hydrolysis of a cyanate ; thus—

$$Ca''(OCN)_2 + 2H_2O = Ca(O\,.\,CO\,.\,NH_2)_2.$$

Even this change is rendered doubtful from what we know of the mechanism of the hydrolysis of the cyanates of the divalent metals (see Chapter V.). Admitting it did occur, it would no doubt be confined to voided urine after it had been kept for some time. As it is difficult to see how either the presence, or absence, of carbamic acid in normal urine could be proved once the presence of a cyanate is admitted, it follows that the evidence on this point must be accepted with full reserve.

The Relation of Cyanic Acid to Other Nitrogenous Compounds in Urine.

In round numbers 90 per cent of the total nitrogen normally excreted by the kidneys is found in the urine as urea, together with a small proportion of combined ammonia.[1]

The remaining 10 per cent is distributed amongst several substances, the chief of which are uric acid, creatinine, hippuric acid, xanthine, and hypoxanthine.

Uric acid is commonly considered as a diureide, and to be built up of two urea residues— ·· HN—CO—NH ·· —presumably derived from the "carbamide" formula—united by the tri-carbon nucleus

$$\overset{\vdots}{-\,C} = \overset{:}{C} - CO$$

---

[1] Since urine is normally acid in its reaction, it is not surprising that a certain proportion of nitrogen should be present as "saline" ammonia. This would result from cyanic acid in accordance with the normal realisation to a small extent of equation (3).

the molecular constitution being represented thus—

$$CO\left\langle \begin{array}{c} NH—C—NH \\ \quad \overset{\|}{C—NH} \\ NH—\overset{|}{C}O \end{array} \right\rangle CO, \quad \begin{array}{c} \text{or in the} \\ \text{tautomeric} \\ \text{form} \end{array} HO . C\left\langle \begin{array}{c} N—C——N \\ \quad \overset{\|}{C—NH} \\ N=\overset{|}{C}(OH) \end{array} \right\rangle C . OH.$$

Uric acid may be equally well considered as the product of the condensation of three molecules of cyanic acid with the di-carbon-nitrogen nucleus

$$- \overset{\displaystyle :}{C} = \overset{\displaystyle :}{C} - NH \cdots.$$

Considered from this point of view, Horbaczewski's (1882) synthesis of uric acid by heating a mixture of urea and glycine at 220°-230° can be easily explained, since the former yields cyanic acid, whilst the latter contains the above di-carbon-nitrogen nucleus.

We know, in the first place, that urea dissociates readily into cyanic acid and ammonia above its melting-point (132°), and that it changes into the reactive form

$$HN : C\left\langle \begin{array}{c} NH_2 \\ OH \end{array} \right.$$

in the presence of acids. Nevertheless, in all experiments in which it is heated to a high temperature with organic acids, or their amino-derivatives, the urea molecule is commonly assumed to react as "carbamide" throughout the entire change. This view is, of course, quite erroneous. The active agents derived from the decomposition of urea in all these experiments are cyanic acid and "nascent" cyanamide, resulting from a dehydration of the unstable "iso-urea" molecule.

The reason for drawing attention to this fact here is obvious. We have seen that free urea is by no means a reactive substance, and it is in this form that urea is produced in the body. It is therefore highly improbable that it should enter into "condensation reactions" to give rise to the purine bodies, or any of the other complex nitrogenous compounds which accompany it in the urine.

Once we recognise the formation of the very reactive cyanic acid as the end product of protein oxidation, the production of small quantities of other nitrogenous compounds, independent of preformed urea, appears quite intelligible. The formation of more or less urea from a source other than cyanic acid is of course not precluded by the present theory. For example, the enzymic decomposition of arginine

9

—a-amino-δ-guanido-valeric acid—which is believed to yield urea as a result of the hydrolysis of the guanidine residue, is a change which may be quite independent of the formation of cyanic acid.

The simplest nitrogenous product of protein metabolism is ammonia. Its formation in the body has been generally considered by physiologists as an essential precursor of urea. This we have seen is based entirely on the acceptance of the theory that urea is formed from ammonium carbonate, or carbamate.

In addition to the view that ammonia may be formed by the hydrolysis of amino-acids, it is also maintained that it can be formed by their oxidation,[1] thus—

$$R . CH_2 . CHNH_2 . COOH + O_2 = R . CH_2 . COOH + CO_2 + NH_3$$

and

$$\frac{CH_3}{CH_3}{>}CH . CH_2 . CHNH_2 . COOH + O_2$$

Leucine.

$$= \frac{CH_3}{CH_3}{>}CH . CH_2 . COOH + CO_2 + NH_3.$$

Isovaleric acid.

It is obvious, in view of the numerous experiments by Fosse, which have been fully referred to, that the formation of ammonia in these oxidations must be reconsidered. Ammonia, in the writer's opinion, cannot be a *direct* product of oxidation.

Fosse has proved the formation of cyanic acid in the oxidation of various amino-compounds, and there can be little doubt that the carbon dioxide and ammonia shown in the above equations are derived from cyanic acid produced by the oxidation of the group, $\cdot\cdot CH - NH_2$.

Whilst the "cyanic-acid-precursor" theory of the formation of urea does not preclude the formation of ammonia in the body from a source other than the hydrolysis of cyanic acid, it seems very probable that much of it (perhaps all) originates in this way.

The formation of ammonia in the body by the hydrolysis of amino-acids is also very doubtful. Folin and Denis (1912) found no increase in the ammonia in the portal blood, or in the mesenteric vein after injecting glycine and asparagine respectively into the small intestine of cats. They also showed that amino-acids were absorbed as such from the intestine, and were transported unchanged to all the different tissues of the body.

[1] "Oxidations and Reductions in the Animal Body," Dakin, 1922, chapter iii., p. 65.

The resistance of amino-acids to hydrolysis *in vitro* in accordance with the equation

$$R . CH . NH_2 . COOH + HOH = R . CHOH . COOH + NH_3$$

is well known.   In fact such a change is only brought about under exceptionally severe conditions, as, for example, in the well-known Kjeldahl process,[1] i.e. so far as obtaining ammonia is concerned.

If amino-acids showed a tendency to be hydrolytically de-aminated, they could not be obtained in quantity as the result of the hydrolysis of proteins by strong hydrochloric acid.   It may be argued that changes are effected in the animal organism under conditions which are not capable of being imitated *in vitro*.

Such an argument is based on our ignorance of the *mechanism* of the vast majority of the chemical changes which take place *in viva*, and not on our knowledge of the mechanism of any one.

The formation of urea in the body is an interesting case in point. The dehydration of ammonium carbonate, or carbamate—it does not matter which—has been the favourite theory of the origin of urea.[2] Since ammonium carbonate is not normally present in urine, urea must be assumed to be quantitatively formed from it *by dehydration* at the low temperature of 36°-37°.   Now, in order to imitate this seemingly simple change *in vitro* a high temperature and a high pressure are necessary, and even then the yield of urea is small.   If the *mechanism* of the change is the same *in viva*, and *in vitro*, we have no explanation for this difference.

When the true origin of the formation of urea *in viva* is brought to light, we find no difference in the conditions under which the change can be effected outside the body, for the simple reason that the formation of natural and of artificial urea in the free state is similar in mechanism.

Most of the chemical changes taking place in plants and in animals are effected through the agency of enzymes.   It is interesting to note that in every case where an enzyme, or the preparation containing the active elements which we call an enzyme, responsible for any definite chemical change has been isolated from its natural source, it is found

[1] Or by heating to a high temperature with fuming hydriodic acid.

[2] In considering the theory that urea may be formed in the animal body from carbonate of ammonia, it must be remembered that this is an endothermic reaction.   This is true no matter which view be taken of the mechanism of the change.   It is therefore not a reaction likely to be selected by the animal organism for the elimination of excess nitrogen when this can be accomplished by an exothermic change, namely, the union of ammonia with cyanic acid, the latter being also the product of an exothermic reaction in the oxidation of protein matter (see Appendix II.).

to reproduce the particular change *in vitro* under conditions no different as regards temperature, pressure, and nature of solvent, and on the same lines as in the living organism.

Fosse and Rouchelman (1921) found that during the aseptic autolysis of fresh liver there was marked formation of urea, but no urea was formed after the liver had been previously immersed for some time in boiling water.

Whilst the formation of cyanic acid as the end product of protein oxidation in the body is probably the result of an enzyme action,[1] hydrolysis of the acid with production of urea is quite independent of such an agent.

Now certain enzyme actions can be imitated by artificial means, and the production of cyanic acid by the oxidation of proteins is one. By the oxidation of blood to which dextrose had been added Fosse (1919) obtained a considerable yield of urea; thus, under the most favourable conditions the amount of urea formed was equal to 40 grams per litre of blood.

Is it not likely that every one of the chemical changes in the body could be imitated *in vitro* if the full mechanism of each was known?

It may be of interest to draw attention to the following analogy :—

The reciprocal action of animal and plant life in relation to carbonic acid and carbon assimilation is well recognised. From carbon dioxide and water plants build up complex carbohydrates from which animals derive energy in oxidising them to the two simple substances from which they were formed. Similarly, plants absorb ammonia, which is oxidised in the presence of carbohydrates to cyanic acid, which is used in the building up of protein matter. Animals, by hydrolytic and oxidation changes, break down proteins to cyanic acid and ammonia, which are excreted as urea, from which plants again derive the necessary material to continue the cycle of changes.

The chemical analogy between the simple compounds concerned in the respective changes is also of much interest, thus—

O : C : O and H . O . H (in carbohydrate formation).

NH : C : O and H . (NH) . H . (in protein formation).

The analogy which is represented here between the oxygen atom and the imino-group (NH) is well illustrated by the series of compounds compared in the succeeding chapter.

---

[1] Richet (1894) found that the liver continued to produce urea after its removal from the body and while the vitality of its cells lasted. A ferment (or enzyme) was precipitated by alcohol from extract of liver, which gave an increased production of urea when added to liver extracts. The activity of the ferment was destroyed by boiling.

The Formation of Urea from Proteins by Hydrolysis in the Presence of Alkalis.

Whilst urea can be readily obtained from proteins by oxidation in alkaline solution, it can also be obtained by their "alkaline hydrolysis" in the absence of any oxidising agent.

Fosse (1916) showed that urea was formed in quite appreciable quantity when egg-albumen, serum-albumen, gelatin, casein, and peptone respectively were boiled under reflux for twenty minutes with a 10 per cent solution of potassium hydroxide. Weaker alkalis, such as sodium carbonate, barium hydroxide, and calcium hydroxide, were also effective, though the decomposition required a longer time.

The hydrolysis of the guanidine nucleus of arginine (a cleavage product of several of the proteins) has been assumed to be exclusively responsible for the origin of urea in this decomposition of proteins by alkalis alone.

Now, if cyanic acid is an active agent in the building up of the proteins, as suggested by the writer, it follows that the group —NH—CO— must form a prominent part of the various protein molecules. The formation of a cyanate would be a natural consequence of their direct decomposition by alkalis in this case, and we have seen that urea is generated when alkali cyanates are hydrolysed.

Hence urea may arise from this source as well as from the decomposition of the guanidine nucleus of the protein molecule. Quantitative experiments with reference to the yields of urea from the different proteins in relation to their arginine content would help materially to test this suggestion.

Whilst the production of urea from arginine during "alkaline hydrolysis" appears to be well established, the mechanism of the process has yet to be investigated. It would appear that whilst *free* guanidine is easily hydrolysed to urea, a salt of the base is not hydrolysed to a salt of urea. This is another point which is of interest in connection with the structural relation between the two compounds.

Is Urea Formed when Proteins are Hydrolysed or Oxidised in the Presence of Free Acid?

Jolles (1901) claimed to have obtained urea in quantity by the combined hydrolysis and oxidation of a number of proteins by potassium permanganate in the presence of sulphuric acid. The formation of urea under such conditions has been denied by Falta (1901), by Schulz (1901), and by Abderhalden (1903). Lanzer (1903), on the other hand, confirms the results obtained by Jolles.

On the supposition that urea is carbamide (and this was assumed), and that it may be formed from CO_2 and NH_3, or from the group —CO—NH_2— and NH_3, there seems no reason why it should not be formed just as well in the presence of free acid, as in the presence of free alkali.

Salts of urea are not hydrolysed, whilst free urea is the form which gives rise, as we have seen, to what has been commonly called the "hydrolysis" of urea. Hence, if urea is directly generated from the breaking down of the protein molecule, it should survive to a greater extent during hydrolysis in an acid solution than in an alkaline one.

When we recognise that cyanic acid is the precursor of urea in the decomposition of the protein, the result claimed by Jolles appears very doubtful, since cyanic acid could not give rise to urea in the presence of an excess of free mineral acid.

The possible formation of urea from a guanidine nucleus in Jolles' experiments must not, in the writer's opinion, be overlooked.

CHAPTER XIII.

REFLECTIONS ON THE CONSTITUTION OF SALTS OF AMMONIA IN CONNECTION WITH THEIR RELATION TO UREA.

AMMONIA possesses a residual affinity which enables it to combine with acids to form compounds which are commonly called " ammonium salts." The reaction $NH_3 + HX' = NH_4X'$ is accepted as the simple expression of the change. The existence of the ammonium group NH_4' is purely hypothetical since all attempts to isolate it have proved futile.

The same is true of its substituted derivatives, " NH_3R," " NH_2R_2," and " NHR_3." Even attempts to obtain $N(CH_3)_4$, Palmaer (1903), and $N(C_2H_5)_4$, Schulbach (1920), have not given direct evidence of their existence.

So far as the existence of a compound *in the free state* is concerned, the affinity of nitrogen for hydrogen (or for an electro-positive radicle) is exhausted when it has combined with three atoms of the element. Can it unite directly with a fourth atom of hydrogen when an electro-negative radicle is also present in the molecule, such as is implied by the formula NH_4X'? It is the answer to this question which has given rise to so much discussion on the constitution of salts of ammonia during the last twenty years.

In the days of the dualistic theory of salts, chemists were content to express the constitution of sal-ammoniac by the formula $NH_3 . HCl$. This is a simple expression of a fact, and is bound only by the theory of the existence of atoms and molecules. It conveyed the idea that the salt was a " molecular " compound.

A. Werner (1902), in considering the constitution of ammonium compounds, suggested the existence of two kinds of valency—a primary or " principal " valency as represented by the union of nitrogen with hydrogen in NH_3, and a secondary or " auxiliary " valency to explain the union of NH_3 with HCl. Thus it was proposed to write ammonium chloride as H_3N . . . $H \cdot Cl$, the H of HCl being assumed to be in direct union with the nitrogen atom, while still combined with chlorine. Obviously an auxiliary valency is also assumed for the hydrogen atom. The maximum valency of the nitrogen atom would therefore be four.

135

The occurrence of compounds of the type NR_4X', much more stable than derivatives of ammonia, let it be noted, and particularly the existence of physically isomeric forms of the type $NR^aR^bR^cR^d . X'$, has led to the general belief that in ammonium chloride—and in all other ammonium salts—it is unlikely that one of the hydrogen atoms is united to nitrogen with a different degree of affinity from the other three.   Hence A. Werner (1905) proposed the formula

$$\left\{ \begin{matrix} H \\ H \end{matrix} \!\!>\!\! N \!\!<\!\! \begin{matrix} H \\ H \end{matrix} \right\} \; \ldots \; X'$$

to represent the structure of an ammonium salt.

Langmuir (1920) has applied the interesting octet theory[1] of valency (Lewis 1916, Langmuir 1919) to explain the constitution of various nitrogen compounds.   According to this theory, the nitrogen atom is considered to be "quadricovalent," and the formula of ammonium chloride is represented thus—

$$\left[\begin{matrix} H \\ H \end{matrix} \!\!>\!\! N \!\!<\!\! \begin{matrix} H \\ H \end{matrix} \right]^{+}_{Cl^{-}}$$

an expression in agreement with that suggested by A. Werner, with the difference that no additional assumptions are made as regards " extra " valencies.

In all attempts to represent the constitution of ammonium salts, the great difficulty has been to give an intelligible explanation of the part played by the electro-negative element, or radicle, in the molecule. We know that in the consideration of the physically isomeric quaternary bases, $NR^aR^bR^cR^d . X'$ the electro-negative radicle is left out of account, since it has apparently no influence on the occurrence of the phenomenon.

Whilst the constitution of compounds of the type $NR_4 . X'$ can be satisfactorily explained by a formula such as

$$\left(\begin{matrix} R \\ R \end{matrix} \!\!>\!\! N \!\!<\!\! \begin{matrix} R \\ R \end{matrix} \right)^{+}_{X^{-}}$$

it does not follow that the constitution of $NH_4 . X'$ nor of any of the intermediate types, $NH_3R . X'$, $NH_2R_2 . X'$, and $NHR_3 . X'$, can be satisfactorily represented by a similar expression.   The presence of

---

[1] The original papers must be consulted for an explanation of this theory.

hydrogen atoms in direct union with nitrogen makes all the difference, as we shall see presently, when we come to compare the properties of such compounds with those of the type $NR_4 . X'$.

The undoubted existence of true carbamides of the types $CO\begin{smallmatrix}NR_2\\NR_2\end{smallmatrix}$

and $CO\begin{smallmatrix}NR_2\\NHR\end{smallmatrix}$, for example, is no evidence, as we have clearly seen,

that urea is $CO\begin{smallmatrix}NH_2\\NH_2\end{smallmatrix}$, though the compounds can be formed by

reactions which are *apparently* analogous to those which yield urea. Reasoning from analogy is very useful in indicating lines of research, but it leads just as often as not to erroneous theoretical conclusions. The constitution of the salts of ammonia and of the amines is, in the writer's opinion, a case in point.

Before dealing with this digression from the main subject, the following suggestion put forward by Langmuir with reference to the cyclic formula of urea requires consideration. In applying the octet theory to explain the structure of a cyclic ammonia compound, it is suggested, since the covalence of nitrogen is 4, the formula,

(a) $R\diamondsuit\begin{smallmatrix}CO\\NH_3\end{smallmatrix}O$ [1], may be written (b) $R\diamondsuit\begin{smallmatrix}CO\\NH_3^+\end{smallmatrix}O^-$

whilst in the case of urea the formula would be,

(c) $HN:C\begin{smallmatrix}NH_3^+\\O^-\end{smallmatrix}$ derived from $HN:C\begin{smallmatrix}NH_2\\OH\end{smallmatrix}$

The following explanation given by Langmuir refers to (a) and (b), but since it is stated that similar considerations apply to the structure of urea proposed by E. A. Werner (1915), it can be taken here in this connection : " It is evident that the normally electrically neutral ammonia must become positively charged when it shares a pair of electrons with the carbon atom. Similarly the oxygen atom must be negatively charged because it has lost the positive charge which the NH_2 group has acquired (in being converted to NH_3). Under these conditions, in the absence of an ionising solvent, it is natural that the

---

[1] The cyclic formula derived from an amino-acid $R''\begin{smallmatrix}COOH\\NH_2\end{smallmatrix}$

positive and negative groups should be held together electrostatically as indicated by the dotted line. Since in this case the oxygen and nitrogen cannot hold a pair of electrons in common, it seems desirable not to connect them by a valence bond in the formula."

Whilst this modified expression of the cyclic formula of urea does not imply any difference in molecular configuration from that suggested by the writer, its acceptance must depend upon one's views of the constitution of salts of ammonia.

Apart from the question of molecular structure, the difference between cyanate of ammonia and urea lies in the combination of ammonia with each form of cyanic acid, $HO.C:N$ and $HN:C:O$. respectively.

We have seen that the ionic theory fails to explain the simple relation between the two isomerides, and whilst the formula $NH_3.HOCN$ is sufficient to explain all the properties of cyanate of ammonia, the expression $NH_3.HNCO$ does not suffice to explain all those of urea (see p. 156.)

Now, the reactions of ammonia with other molecules may be broadly divided into two kinds: (1) those in which the original ammonia molecule remains unchanged, as in the formation of salts—this is true whether we represent " ammonium " chloride, for example, as $NH_3.HCl$ or as $(\overset{+-}{NH_4})Cl$; (2) those in which the ammonia is decomposed by a transference of hydrogen to some other atom before the new compound is formed. Whether urea is produced from ammonia and cyanic acid in the keto-form, by direct combination of the two, or through the medium of the latter type of reaction, thus—

$$HN:CO + NH_3 = HN:C\begin{array}{c}NH_2\\OH\end{array} \rightarrow HN:C\begin{array}{c}NH_3\\O\end{array}$$

it is not possible to say.

The cyclic formula is put forward to explain the properties of urea in the free state, as distinct from urea when present as a salt, in either an acid or an alkaline solution. So long as the constitution of the simple salts of ammonia remains unsolved, no formula[1] which explains the facts any better appears to present itself.

[1] An alternative cyclic formula

$$O:C\begin{array}{c}NH_3\\NH\end{array}$$

which obviously suggests itself, fails to explain the formation of the salts of urea, as well as many of the reactions which have been considered.

The sharp dissociation into ammonia and cyanic acid is one of the most characteristic properties of urea in the free state, and in this respect it resembles its prototype, namely, a salt of ammonia. Since an analogy in structure is indicated by this fact, we must give some consideration here to the prevailing views regarding the constitution of "ammonium" salts.

Reflections on the Theory of the Constitution of Ammonium Salts.

The expression $[NH_4]^+_{Cl}$ precludes a *principal* pentavalence of the nitrogen atom. This break-away from an old-standing view appears to have met with general acceptance. It is not quite so easy, however, to concede a principal tetravalence, or quadricovalence, of the nitrogen atom towards hydrogen, as indicated by such a formula. Whilst the ionic theory has been the guiding principle in considering the constitution of all "ammonium" salts, it is doubtful whether this has been accompanied by a sufficiently careful regard to their properties.

In presenting the formula

$$\begin{bmatrix} H & & H \\ & N & \\ H & & H \end{bmatrix}^+_{Cl^-}$$

Langmuir says "the structure of the ammonium ion is thus exactly like that of the methane molecule, except for the difference in the charge on the nucleus." Further, "according to this (the octet) theory, the substituted ammonium compounds should show isomerism exactly like that of carbon compounds, since the nitrogen is quadricovalent. This is in full accord with all the experimental data."

So far as tetra-substituted ammonium compounds are concerned, the analogy to methane appears to hold good, since we have physical somerides, $(NR^aR^bR^cR^d).X'$ corresponding to, $CR^aR^bR^cR^d$. In the writer's opinion the analogy goes no further.

In the case of carbon we have numerous physical isomerides of the type $CR^aR^bR^cH$, and the isomerism is independent of the electro-chemical nature of the radicles $R^aR^bR^c$ respectively. All attempts to obtain physical isomerides derived from nitrogen of the type

$$\begin{bmatrix} R^b & & R^c \\ & N & \\ R^a & & H \end{bmatrix}^+_{X^-}$$

have proved futile, yet the existence of such isomerides appears to be clearly indicated by the above expression. It is evident that the presence of one or more atoms of hydrogen in the molecule makes all the difference in the case of the "ammonium" compounds.

When we come to consider the basicity, or relative strengths, of the substituted derivatives of ammonia, the difficulty in accepting the above structure for "ammonium" salts, other than those of the type $(NR_4)X$, is even greater. It has been generally assumed that the successive introduction of alkyl groups (R) into ammonia is accompanied by an increase in the basicity, or strength, of the amine formed. Granting, for the moment, that this is true, it is well known that the increased strength of a quaternary base, NR_4OH, is still out of all proportion to what would be normally expected from the introduction of the fourth alkyl group into the molecule. Assuming the existence of $N(C_2H_5)_3H . OH$, its strength as a base is insignificant as compared with $N(C_2H_5)_4 : OH$, the existence of which we know is beyond question. As a matter of fact, the strength of the substituted [1] derivatives of ammonia are in the inverse order of that commonly accepted.

The following results, which were pointed out by the writer (1918, 1919), can lead to no other conclusion :—

1. Ethylamine $(C_2H_5)NH_2$ quantitatively displaced diethylamine $(C_2H_5)_2NH$ from a solution of diethylammonium chloride, whilst triethylamine $(C_2H_5)_3N$ was quantitatively displaced from its hydrochloride by diethylamine.

2. A solution of triethylammonium-, diethylammonium-, and ethylammonium chlorides in approximately equal molecular proportions was fractionally treated with sodium hydroxide. The tertiary amine was liberated first, the secondary next, and the primary amine last.

3. By partial neutralisation, with hydrochloric acid, of a solution of a primary and a secondary amine, the bulk of the latter remained in the free state, whilst in the case of a mixture of a secondary and a tertiary amine, the weaker tertiary base was left free.

The results of a considerable number of experiments which have not yet been published go to show that the strength of an amine is determined by the ratio of hydrogen to carbon in the molecule, that is, so far as open chain compounds are concerned. Methylammonia

---

[1] Of course only those derivatives in which hydrogen is replaced by an electro-positive radicle are considered here. In the case of phenyl derivatives the fact has been long since recognised.

CH_3NH_2, in which we have the highest possible ratio of 5 to 1, is apparently the strongest of the amines.

Müller (1885) determined the heats of neutralisation of the three methylammonias by hydrochloric acid, and arrived at the conclusion that trimethylamine was a weaker base than the other two, whilst dimethylamine was weaker than monomethylamine.

It is obvious there must be a radical difference in constitution between the salts of the quaternary bases and those derived from ammonia, and from its mono-, di-, and tri-substituted derivatives.

The theory of the existence of a tetra-substituted ammonium ion is probably quite sound, and can be quite satisfactorily explained on the basis of a principal tetravalence, or quadricovalence, of the nitrogen atom. The existence of the ammonium ion, and of partially substituted ammonium ions is open to much doubt, and it cannot be claimed that the structure of the salts of ammonia and of the amines has been explained by any of the theories which have been suggested.

The electrical conductivity of " ammonium " salts is assumed to be solely due to their ionisation, thus—

$$NH_4Cl \rightarrow NH_4{}^{\cdot} + Cl', \quad N(CH_3)H_3Cl \rightarrow N(CH_3)H_3{}^{\cdot} + Cl'.$$

Whilst this explanation is purely hypothetical, it leaves out of account a property common to all such salts, namely, their hydrolytic dissociation, according to the change

$$NH_4X' \rightarrow NH_3 + HX', \quad \text{and} \quad NRH_3X' \rightarrow NRH_2 + HX'.$$

We have abundant evidence of this phenomenon [1] where a salt of ammonia or of an amine is dissolved in water or in a non-ionising solvent.

The formation of urea from cyanate of ammonia is a typical example. Urea—an ammonia compound—undergoes dissociation, but is not ionised. The recognition of this fact has made it possible to give a simple explanation of the relations of the two isomerides, where the ionic theory has failed.

It must not be assumed that the writer is opposed to the ionic theory, far from it. At the same time it is well to recognise that ionisation is not the overruling factor in explaining the properties of salts of ammonia, as is so generally supposed. To surrender all to one theory is not wise, and it certainly has not been fruitful of the best results.

[1] The mechanism of the interaction of formaldehyde and ammonium salts is readily explained on the basis of this dissociation.—Werner (1917).

In view of all the facts, the writer ventures to suggest that the electrical conductivity, for example, of salts of ammonia may be explained in accordance with the changes—

$$NH_3 . HX' = NH_3 + H\cdot X' \rightarrow H\cdot + X'$$
$$NRH_2 . HX' = NRH_2 + H\cdot X' \rightarrow H\cdot + X'$$

and so on for salts up to the type NR_3HX.

According to this suggestion, we have a certain amount of hydrolytic dissociation accompanied by ionic dissociation of the acid no longer held in union by the "extra" or "auxiliary" valence of the nitrogen atom, or of the amine group as a whole.

Conductivity experiments have led to the conclusion—assuming direct ionisation only—that the strengths of the aliphatic amines are in the inverse order of that deduced from their chemical properties, and from their heats of neutralisation by acids.

The different conclusions, it will be seen, can be reconciled in the light of the above explanation.

All other conditions being equal, a salt of a weak base is hydrolytically dissociated to a larger extent than one derived from a strong base; hence a higher concentration of H and X' ions must result in the former case. In other words, the electrical conductivity of a salt of a tertiary amine—the weaker base—must be greater than that of a primary amine, the stronger base. This view of the behaviour of salts of ammonia and of the amines in solution would appear to merit attention in considering their properties as electrolytes. It seems to offer a plausible explanation of the observed facts.

The almost complete hydrolytic dissociation of such salts as acetamide hydrochloride, $CH_3CONH_2 . HCl$, and glycine hydrochloride,

$$CH_2 \Big\langle \begin{array}{l} NH_2 . HCl \\ COOH \end{array} ,$$

when dissolved in water is freely recognised, and the electrical conductivity of their solutions is, according to the ionic theory, due to the ionisation of the hydrochloric acid liberated. A similar result obtains in the case of urea hydrochloride

$$HN : C(OH) . NH_2 . HCl$$

which we have seen is largely dissociated in solution.

Granting these facts, is it sound to assume that hydrolytic dissociation may be ignored in considering the electrical conductivity of a salt of ammonia, or of those derived from it by the substitution of one, two, or three atoms of hydrogen by electro-positive radicles ?   A theory which attributes the effect to the existence of "ammonium" and of partially substituted "ammonium" ions is certainly not in agreement with the chemical properties of either the free bases or their salts.

The Decomposition of Salts of Ammonia by Heat.

Dissociation is the first step in the decomposition by heat of all salts of ammonia, and the various results can be easily explained on the basis of this fact.

The production of nitrous oxide from nitrate of ammonia, for example, is commonly represented as though it were the result of the direct decomposition of the molten salt, thus—

$$H_4N . O . NO_2 \rightarrow 2H_2O + N_2O.$$

The generation of more or less ammonia, nitric oxide, and nitrite of ammonia, as by-products, according to the rate of heating, as shown by Berthelot (1876), is clearly indicative of dissociation into ammonia and nitric acid as the first step in the change.   The mechanism of the main reaction, according to this view, is as follows :—

$$
\begin{array}{ccc}
H & & HO \\
| & & | \\
N & + & N-O \rightarrow 2H_2O + N \equiv N = O \\
\| & & | \quad / \\
H_2 & & O
\end{array}
$$

oxidation of ammonia by nitric acid at the temperature (about 210°) of dissociation of the salt being the cause of the final result.

Langmuir (1920) has applied the octet theory to explain the constitution, and the decomposition of molten nitrate of ammonia. On considering the merits of the following possible arrangements :—

(a) $\overset{+}{NH_4}\left(\begin{array}{c} O \\ | \\ O-N=O \end{array}\right)^-,$ (b) $NH_3 + O = \overset{O}{\overset{|}{N}} - OH,$

(c) $\begin{array}{c} H \quad OH \\ HN - O - N - O, \\ H \end{array}$ or   (d) $\begin{array}{c} H \quad OH \\ HN - N - O, \\ H \quad O \end{array}$

he divides his choice between (c) and (d).   These two structures suggested by the octet theory are admitted to be quite inconsistent with the ordinary valence theory.   It is pointed out that whilst (c) on heating should give $2H_2O$ and $N = O = N$, (d) should give $2H_2O$ and $N = N = O$, the formation of nitrous oxide being thus explained by these constitutional formulae for the molten salt.

The constitution of nitrous oxide is a question outside the present discussion, which is concerned solely with the structure of salts of ammonia in relation to the constitution of urea. Whilst Langmuir does not contemplate dissociation of the salt into nitric acid and ammonia as the likely preliminary step in the change, it will be seen that formulae (c) and (d) differ from (b) merely as regards the nature of the union between ammonia and nitric acid. All three conform to the expression $NH_3 . HNO_3$.

If solid "ammonium" nitrate is to be viewed as $[NH_4]^+ \overset{-}{NO_3}$, the mechanism by which molecules having the structures (c) and (d) respectively are produced in the molten salt, as suggested by Langmuir, is not easy to understand. That such changes are not likely to be true seems to be sustained by the difficulty in explaining them.

The explanation based on dissociation is simple, and in agreement with all the facts, and, moreover, it has the merit of not passing beyond the bounds which are limited by the present state of our knowledge. Applying his theory to the decomposition by heat of an organic salt of ammonia, Langmuir proposes to explain the change in the following manner. Taking ammonium formate, as an example, it is suggested that the molten salt may contain molecules having the structure

$$(e) \quad H . \overset{H}{\underset{\dot{H}}{\dot{N}}} - \overset{OH}{\underset{\dot{H}}{\dot{C}}} - O$$

in which one of the oxygen atoms is unicovalent. Water, it is pointed out, can be readily split off from such a molecule with production of formamide $H_2N . CHO$. Whilst the nitrogen atom of ammonia is assumed to be in union with carbon, through the medium of a principal valency of the respective atoms, the structure is, nevertheless, that of a salt of ammonia, conforming to the type $NH_3 . HX$. It is thus a radical departure from the commonly accepted structural formula $H . CO . O . NH_4$, which apparently is assumed by Langmuir to still hold good for the salt in the solid state.

Now, when ammonium formate is decomposed by heat, under normal pressure, the yield of formamide falls far short of that required by theory on the assumption that water is directly split off from the group —$O . NH_4$, the reason being that the main change is dissociation into ammonia and formic acid. The mode of formation of the amide, as suggested by Langmuir, gives a more plausible explanation of the mechanism of the reaction than that commonly accepted, particularly when more attention is given to the part played by the oxygen atom represented as unicovalent in the above formula (e).

A consideration of the reverse phenomenon, namely, the production of a salt of ammonia by the hydrolysis of a nitrile, helps to throw further light on the mechanism of the changes under discussion and on the probable constitution of salts of ammonia derived from organic acids. Hydrogen and hydroxyl ions are no doubt active agents in the changes which are represented as follows:—

$$HCN + H^{\cdot}.OH' \rightarrow \begin{array}{c} H.CO.NH_2 \\ \downarrow \quad \uparrow \\ H.C{\Large\diagup}^{NH}_{\diagdown OH} \\ \text{(Formamide.)} \end{array} + H^{\cdot}.OH' \rightleftarrows H.C{\diagup}^{NH_2}_{\diagdown OH}^{\diagup OH} \rightleftarrows H.C{\diagup}^{NH_3}_{\diagdown OH}{\diagup}^{O} \\ \qquad\qquad\qquad\qquad\qquad\quad (f) \qquad\qquad (g) \\ \qquad\qquad\qquad\qquad\qquad\qquad\qquad\quad \text{(Formate of ammonia.)}$$

It will be seen that formula (g) is similar in constitution to the cyclic formula of urea, so far as the union of ammonia with the rest of the molecule is concerned. It differs from the formula (e) put forward by Langmuir to represent *molten* ammonium formate, merely as regards the function assigned to the " unicovalent" oxygen atom. For want of a better explanation, it may be assumed that the NH_3 group is united to oxygen through the medium of a mutual "subsidiary" valence, a suggestion similar to that applied by Langmuir to the cyclic formula of urea, and which is obviously equally applicable to formula (g) as a representation of "ammonium" formate. The weakest point in the molecule must therefore lie in the union between the oxygen atom and NH_3, a conclusion which helps at once to explain why the salt is decomposed by heat in two ways. Whilst dissociation into ammonia and formic acid is the major effect, a simultaneous change of (g) to configuration (f) would give rise to formamide by loss of water from the very unstable system $>C(OH)_2$.

It is well known that the yield of the amide is greatly promoted by heating the ammonium salt under pressure, a fact which is quite in agreement with the foregoing explanation, since whilst dissociation would be thereby checked, the change from (g) to (f) would still continue. This view of the mechanism of the formation of an amide from a salt of ammonia, though it differs but little from the explanation suggested by Langmuir, appears to be in better agreement with the facts.

Whether we accept the structure (e) or (g) to represent the molecule of formate of ammonia at the moment of its decomposition, is it

10

to be assumed that either is derived from a molecule having the structure $[\overset{+}{N}H_4]\overset{-}{H}CO_2$, i.e. ammonium formate in the solid state, or below the temperature of its decomposition? If so, this implies that ammonia can unite with formic acid in two, or possibly three, different ways, a conclusion which seems highly improbable, and which few will admit.

The idea that the nitrogen atom has a principal tetra-valence, or "quadricovalence," as indicated by the octet theory, does not solve the problem of the constitution of salts of ammonia. In conjunction with the ionic theory, it may give a satisfactory explanation of the constitution of compounds of the type NR_4X, but it must be borne in mind that a reaction such as $N(CH_3)_3 + CH_3Cl = N(CH_3)_4Cl$ does not necessarily lead to the formation of molecules having a constitution similar to those produced from the union of $NH_3 + HCl$ (nor even from the union of $N(CH_3)_3$ and HCl). Compounds of the type $N(R)_4 . OH$ are numerous ; they are very strong bases, easily isolated and stable, yet all attempts to isolate a single base of the type $N(R)_3H . OH$, to say nothing of the lower substituted derivatives, have proved fruitless. The isolation by Rupert (1909) of two crystalline hydrates of ammonia, namely, $NH_3 . H_2O$ and $2(NH_3) . H_2O$ by cooling a very strong solution of ammonia to $-80°$, does not prove that the former hydrate is $NH_4 . OH$.

According to the electronic theory, valency is exerted through a discharge, or exchange, of electrons between the reacting atoms or radicles. In order that a discharge of electrons, which will enable the nitrogen atom to exert a principal tetra-valence, can take effect, it is evidently necessary that four electro-positive radicles should be brought within the range of attraction of the nitrogen atom.

If the union of $N(CH_3)_3$ and HCl gives rise to a salt of the type $[NH(CH_3)_3] . Cl$, it is difficult to understand why the base $[NH(CH_3)_3] . OH$ should be so elusive.

Derivatives of trivalent nitrogen show a great variation in constitution as regards the electro-chemical nature of the elements or radicles united to the nitrogen atom. If the fourth principal valence of nitrogen is of the same order as the other three, why should it always require the simultaneous display of a subsidiary valence in order to exert its effect? This is certainly the case so far as the production of a molecule sufficiently stable to exist in the free state is concerned.[1] If the existence of the NH_4 ion was an established fact, based on sound experimental evidence, it could scarcely lay claim to a more

[1] This refers solely to compounds where the nitrogen atom is assumed to be in direct union by principal valence with four electro-positive radicles.

widespread recognition than it has received as a theoretical conception. Yet, when we stop to think and consider the facts, may we not after all be "hugging a delusion"—like the carbamide formula—the result of a deduction from analogy pushed beyond its legitimate limitations.

What properties of a salt of ammonia are explained by the formula NH_4X that are not equally well explained by the symbol NH_3 . HX?

Urea in the free state is an ammonia compound, the properties of which go to prove that the union of NH_3 and HNCO is completed without any change in the order of arrangement of the atoms in the respective groups. The compound cannot be represented by the expression $[NH_4]NCO$. When urea is brought into contact with an acid —stronger than HNCO, such as HCl—a substituted ammonia salt is formed, namely $(HN:C . OH)NH_2$. HCl, as the result of migration of an atom of hydrogen from nitrogen to oxygen in the original urea molecule. Such electrostatic equilibrium as is necessary to enable urea hydrochloride to exist in the free state is thereby established. What reason have we to suspect that in the formation of the urea salt there is also a separation of hydrogen from chlorine with production of an "ammonium" salt of the type $[HN:C(OH) . NH_3]$. Cl? In other words, is it likely that an atom of hydrogen is transferred from nitrogen to oxygen, in order that the same nitrogen atom may attract to itself another atom of hydrogen from such a stable compound as hydrogen chloride?

It is curious, assuming the carbamide formula, that it has always been the practice to represent a salt of urea as CON_2H_4 . HX, never as (CON_2H_5) . X, and similarly we speak, for example, of pyridine hydrochloride $(C_5H_5N . HCl)$, rather than of pyridonium chloride (C_5H_6NH) . Cl, and so on in the case of the salts derived from nearly all of the more or less complex nitrogen bases. This is suggestive of an underlying suspicion that they are additive compounds, in which the molecule HX remains intact. Most of these salts are known to be largely dissociated into the base and free acid in solution, and it has not been found possible to isolate any of the corresponding hydroxyl derivatives, or "ammonium" bases; this seems to lend strong support to the conclusion that the suspicion is well founded.

Chemical Analogy between Water and Ammonia, and between the Oxygen Atom and the Imino-Group (NH).

Since evidence from analogy has been largely relied on in considering the constitution of "ammonium" salts, and the existence of the "ammonium" ion, $NH_4^{\cdot}$, it is permissible to pursue evidence of this nature in another direction.

In drawing a comparison between water and ammonia, Angeli (1910, 1915) and Ciamician (1918) have directed attention to the remarkable chemical analogy of the oxygen atom and the imino-group (NH). Whilst this has been lightly touched upon in Chapter X. in comparing the systems

$$>C(OH)_2, \quad >C(OH).NH_2, \text{ and } >C(NH_2)_2,$$

an inspection of the following analogous compounds will help to bring out the striking relations under consideration :—

(Oxygen Derivatives.)	(Corresponding Imino-derivatives.)
1. H.O.H	H.(NH).H'. Ammonia.
2. HO – OH	HO.(NH).H $\}$ Hydroxylamine.
	H(NH)—(NH)H $\}$ Hydrazine.
3. :C:O.	:C(NH). Hydrogen cyanide.
4. O:C:O	O:C:(NH) $\}$ Cyanic acid.
	(NH):C:(NH) $\}$ Cyanamide.

$$\begin{array}{cc} O & NH \\ 5.\ HO - \overset{..}{C}.OH & HO - \overset{..}{C} - OH \end{array}$$

$$\left.\begin{array}{c} O \\ H(NH).\overset{..}{C}.OH \\ O \\ H(NH).\overset{..}{C}-(NH)H \end{array}\right\} \text{Not known in free state.}$$

$$\begin{array}{c} NH \\ H(NH).\overset{..}{C}.(NH)H. \quad \text{Guanidine (?).} \end{array}$$

6. $CH_3.O.H$ . . $CH_3.(NH)H$. Methylammonia.

7. $CH_3CO.OH$. $CH_3CO(NH)H$. Acetamide.
   $CH_3C(NH).(NH)H$. Acetamidine.
   $CH_3C(NH).OH$. Acetamide (imino-form).

8. $H_2:C:O$ . . $H_2C:NH$. Known only as a polymeride.

9. $CH_2:C:O$ (keten) $CH_2:C(NH)$. As yet unknown.

The idea of looking on ammonia as $(NH)H_2$, or water in which oxygen has been replaced by the imino-group, is not so far fetched as perhaps it might appear. For example the change

$$CO + (NH)H_2 = HN:CO + H_2$$

which has been referred to in Chapter VIII., and was studied by Jackson and Northall-Laurie (1905), is strictly analogous to the reaction

$$CO + OH_2 = O : CO + H_2$$

which is known to be effected under similar conditions.

Whilst the foregoing comparison is just one of special interest in connection with the chemistry of urea, many other analogous reactions and properties suggest themselves. For a full account of these the reader should consult the work of Cady (1897), and more particularly the comprehensive researches of Franklin and Kraus (1900), Franklin and Stafford (1902), and Franklin (1905), in which the striking resemblance between the physical properties of water and liquid ammonia is fully discussed, together with several analogous chemical reactions in the respective solvents.

The Catalytic Action of Water in Promoting the Formation and Decomposition of Salts of Ammonia.

The simple expression

$$(1) \quad NH_3 + HCl \underset{(b)}{\overset{(a)}{\rightleftarrows}} NH_4Cl$$

is not a true representation of the facts, since we know that the presence of water is necessary to enable the change to take effect in either direction. The catalytic function of the water, whereby it initiates either a discharge in one direction, or a mutual exchange of electrons—Lewis-Langmuir theory—between NH_3 and HCl, still remains without a convincing explanation. Whatever may be its function, it seems likely that it must affect both molecules in a similar manner. Whilst the change in direction (a) can take place up to 350°, it is generally assumed that the inverse change is only brought about, under normal pressure, at about the temperature mentioned. The writer, for one, is not prepared to accept this view, since it is maintained that the salt is hydrolytically dissociated to a certain extent in aqueous solution even at the ordinary temperature.

The attraction of HCl for water is much greater than the attraction of NH_3 for water. According to Thomson, HCl . Aq = 17·314, whilst NH_3 . Aq = 8·430 calories. The readiness with which ammonia may be expelled from its aqueous solution by heat, or by a current of air, is further proof of this.

Since " ammonium " chloride is a stable substance, the attraction between NH_3 and HCl must be greater than the attraction of either for water, or, to put it in another way, the force which holds NH_3 and HCl in combination, when once they have united, must be greater than that which holds either of the compounds in union with water.

This being so, and we have no reason to doubt it, what, then, is the function of water in promoting a reaction between NH_3 and HCl?

The following tentative explanation appears as good as any of those which have hitherto been put forward.

Liquid water is composed of associated molecules, the least complex of which may be represented by the formula $H_2 = O : O = H_2$, i.e. dihydrol. These molecules would be rapidly depolymerised by HCl and NH_3 respectively, on account of the great affinity of both for simple molecules of water (hydrol). As a result, the compounds

$$HCl : OH_2, \text{ and } H_2O : NH_3 \text{ or } \begin{matrix} H \\ H \end{matrix} \hspace{-4pt} >\hspace{-4pt} O : (NH) \hspace{-4pt} <\hspace{-4pt} \begin{matrix} H \\ H \end{matrix}$$

would be simultaneously formed. Their existence would be ephemeral, since they may be assumed to interact at once with regeneration of dihydrol and production of $HCl : (NH) \hspace{-2pt} <\hspace{-2pt} \begin{matrix} H \\ H \end{matrix}$. How, or whether, the latter becomes NH_4Cl is a matter for further consideration.

Since water promotes dissociation of the "ammonium" salts, the changes may be expressed thus—

$$(2) \ HCl : O \hspace{-4pt} <\hspace{-4pt} \begin{matrix} H \\ H \end{matrix} + \begin{matrix} H \\ H \end{matrix} \hspace{-4pt} >\hspace{-4pt} O : NH_3 \rightleftharpoons HCl : NH_3 + \begin{matrix} H \\ H \end{matrix} \hspace{-4pt} >\hspace{-4pt} O : O \hspace{-4pt} <\hspace{-4pt} \begin{matrix} H \\ H \end{matrix}$$

In discussing the catalytic action of water in promoting the formation of "ammonium" salts, Falk (1920) represents the change thus [1]—

$$(3) \ HCl . H_2O + NH_3 . H_2O = NH_3 . HCl + 2H_2O,$$

in which, let it be clearly understood, the hydrates are treated as double molecules. In this respect it differs from the view suggested by equation [2] (2). Further, the reaction is dealt with on the basis of the theory that a catalyst—water, in this case—is incapable of starting a reaction and can only modify its velocity.

[1] "Chemical Reactions" (Falk), 1920, chapter v., pp. 80-83.

[2] The suggestion that "nascent" hydrol molecules may be the active catalytic agents in promoting the union of NH_3 and HCl is a feature of the "hydrate-formation" theory, which, so far as the writer is aware, does not appear to have been considered in previous discussions of the subject. Whilst it may be said to throw additional light on the phenomenon, it still leaves one wondering why NH_3 and HCl do not combine with considerable velocity even in the absence of water. At the same time it is well to bear in mind that we know little of the properties of mono-molecular water in the liquid state.

Whether we accept equations (2) or (3), or ignore entirely the influence of water, as in the common expression equation (1), we arrive at the one important conclusion, namely, that the hydrogen atom of HCl forms part of the molecule of the "ammonium" salt.

In considering reaction (3) in greater detail, Falk suggests that the hydrate $H_3N . OH_2$ may, and probably does, tautomerise to ammonium hydroxide, $NH_4 . OH$. If we accept this assumption, it will be seen after careful consideration that it leads to rather unexpected conclusions. In fact it demands a radical change in our conception of the mechanism of the formation of ammonium salts, when NH_3 and HX' are brought together under ordinary conditions, i.e. moisture being present.

Obviously the compound $HCl . H_2O$, really more stable than $NH_3 . H_2O$, must also be considered in this connection. Whilst the structural formula

$$\begin{matrix} H \\ \\ H \end{matrix} \!\!\!\searrow\!\!\! O \!\!\!\swarrow\!\!\! \begin{matrix} H \\ \\ Cl \end{matrix}$$

has been suggested, it has not received the same recognition which has been so freely accorded to the formula NH_4OH. The reason is clear. The idea that hydrogen chloride dissolved in water is largely decomposed into hydrogen and chlorine ions has proved sufficient to meet the requirements of the ionic theory, and to explain all the properties of the compound so far as salt formation in its reaction with bases is concerned. The formula suggested being consistent with the ionic theory, the change may be represented thus—

$$(4) \quad \begin{matrix} H \\ \\ H \end{matrix}\!\!\searrow\!\! O\!\!\swarrow\!\!\begin{matrix} H^+ \\ \\ Cl \end{matrix} + \left[\begin{matrix} H \\ \\ H \end{matrix}\!\!\searrow\!\! N\!\!\swarrow\!\!\begin{matrix} H \\ \\ H \end{matrix} \right]^+_{.\overline{OH}} \rightleftarrows N\overset{+}{H}_4\overline{Cl} + 2H_2O.$$

Let us consider now the conclusions which must be inferred from this expression of the reaction from the ionic point of view.

1. The decomposition of hydrogen chloride into H and Cl ions, each carrying their electrical charges, is apparently preceded by a separation of the two atoms in combining with the oxygen of a hydrol molecule. They must obviously be easily released from this combination.

2. Ammonia does not become a base until the nitrogen atom has combined with a fourth atom of hydrogen—derived from water to produce the ammonium ion $N\overset{..}{H}_4$. Consequently the ammonium

chloride formed from the union of $NH_4{}^{\cdot}$ and Cl' *does not contain the hydrogen atom originally present in the hydrogen chloride.*[1]

3. If it is necessary to produce the NH_4 ion, and since a hydrol molecule is decomposed in producing it, then it must be admitted that water starts the reaction. Hence it does not act as a catalyst in accordance with the theory already referred to. It is difficult to see how we can arrive at any other conclusion.

Now, the theory of the existence of an NH_4 radicle is much older than the theory of the existence of an NH_4 ion. It is true that they are practically similar in conception, and whilst the arguments which have given rise to their origin are too well known to be referred to here, attention must be drawn to the following point. In assuming the formation of NH_4—radicle or ion, it does not matter which—as the prefinal stage in the completion of equation (4) in direction left to right, we anticipate a result which has always been assumed to take effect only after HCl and NH_3 have combined, as indicated by equations (1), (2), and (3).

The idea that $NH_3 : HCl$ changes to NH_4Cl rests *apparently* on a much better foundation than the supposed change

$$NH_3 : H_2O \rightarrow NH_4 . OH.$$

Much heat is developed when ammonia is dissolved in water. This is an indication of the formation of a compound of some type, nevertheless the chemical properties of the aqueous solution do not differ from those of a solution of ammonia in a non-ionising solvent. The ammonia, in fact, appears to be all in the free state.

Heat is also developed when ammonia is dissolved in pure ethyl alcohol. The product certainly does not contain $(NH_3C_2H_5) . OH$, and unless we allow the belief in the existence of the NH_4 group to prevail, there is no evidence to show that $NH_4 . OC_2H_5$ is produced. The compound $CH_3OH . NH_3$, obtained by Baume (1914) from ammonia and methyl alcohol at low temperature, is considered by Falk to belong to this type. The writer is more inclined to the belief that the compound is one conforming to the type

$$\begin{matrix} R \\ {}^{\diagdown}\!\!\diagup \\ H \end{matrix} O : NH_3 \text{ analogous to } \begin{matrix} H \\ {}^{\diagdown}\!\!\diagup \\ H \end{matrix} O : NH_3.$$

[1] It appears to have been shown that the vapour of benzene can bring about the union of dry ammonia and hydrogen chloride. It has never been suggested that a hydrogen atom of benzene takes part in the formation of the resulting salt. Is there any reason to suppose that the salt is formed in a different manner when a trace of moisture effects a union of the two gases?

If the heat developed when ammonia is dissolved in water is due to the formation of $NH_4 . OH$, it is difficult to understand why the evidence deduced from the ionic theory should lend such feeble support to the existence of the compound.   Is the solution rich in $NH_4 . OH$ molecules, only a small proportion of which are ionised, or is the low concentration of $NH^{\cdot}_4$ and OH' ions a measure of the amount of $NH_4 . OH$ formed? The latter view is generally accepted, since it complies with the chemical properties of the solution, or rather these properties are considered to be best interpreted on this assumption.

According to Langmuir, the weakness of ammonia as a base is not due to a lack of ionisation of ammonium hydroxide, since this substance, according to his theory, can only exist in the completely ionised condition.   There are, therefore, no NH_4OH molecules, but only $NH_4^{\cdot}$ and OH' ions in an aqueous solution of ammonia.   The writer ventures to suggest that the heat of solution of ammonia in water is due to the formation of $H_3N : OH_2$ molecules, only a very small proportion of which may possibly give rise to $NH^{\cdot}_4$ and OH' ions.

An objection to the formula $[NH_4]^+Cl^-$ has been raised by Rhodes (1921), on the ground that it suggests an unstable structure, on account of the ill-defined part played by the chlorine atom as regards its union with the complex (NH_4).   Briggs (1921) apparently refuses to recognise such an objection, and contends that the stability of " ammonium " chloride is not difficult to understand, when it is remembered that the ammonium radicle and the chloride ion possess equal and opposite electrical charges.

Assuming the existence of the ammonium radicle, the opposite nature of the electrical charges becomes an essential part of the theoretical conception.

The statement that the charges are equal in their opposite signs is another matter.   How do we know these charges are equal?   So far as one can see, the neutrality of ammonium chloride supplies the only evidence for this assumption, and if we accept this it soon leads us into difficulties.

The constitution of NH_4Cl is assumed to be similar to $N(CH_3)_4Cl$. The stability (and neutrality) of the latter salt must evidently be attributed to the same cause.   Hence it is to be supposed that the electrical charges possessed by the tetra-methylammonium radicle and the chloride ion are also equal in their opposite signs.   The charges possessed by (NH_4) and $N(CH_3)_4$ respectively must, therefore, be equal, since each is equal in opposite sign to the charge possessed by the chloride ion.   This being so, it is difficult to understand why

$(NH_4)OH$ and $N(CH_3)_4OH$ are not equally stable. Whilst no doubt the electrical charges possessed by (NH_4) and OH, and by $(N(CH_3)_4)$ and OH respectively are not equal in the opposite signs, the relative difference in their values should be the same.

The difficulty in explaining the constitution and relative stability of "ammonium" and of partially substituted "ammonium" salts, in agreement with the structure $(NH_4)X$ is also apparent when we come to consider their dissociation, whether hydrolytic or by heat.

Dissociation of Salts of Ammonia.

In promoting the union of NH_3 and HX', the action of water is assumed to be purely catalytic.[1] For this reason it is believed not to have any influence on the atomic structure of the "ammonium" salt formed, and is therefore commonly left out of consideration in dealing with this problem. Consequently the role played by water need not be considered in discussing the dissociation of ammonium salts.

The expression

$$\left[\begin{matrix} H \\ H \end{matrix} \!\!\! \diagdown \!\! N \!\! \diagup \!\!\! \begin{matrix} H \\ H \end{matrix} \right] Cl$$

clearly implies that the forces of attraction between the nitrogen atom and each of the hydrogen atoms are equal. In putting forward this formula A. Werner suggested so much, and Langmuir, we have seen, has recently gone so far as to maintain that the NH_4 radicle is exactly like the methane (CH_4) molecule in structure. Now ammonia is a very stable substance (i.e. towards heat); the force or attraction which holds the three atoms of hydrogen in union with nitrogen must therefore be considerable. According to the formula $(NH_4)X$, it follows that the force which binds the fourth atom of hydrogen to nitrogen must also be considerable, since it is assumed to be equal to each of the others, and this is apparently independent of the nature of the electro-negative element, or radicle X.

The weaker the acid with which ammonia unites, the more readily is the resulting salt dissociated by heat into NH_3 and HX. Ammonium cyanate may be taken as a typical case in connection with the views which have been developed in this, and in the preceding chapters.

Cyanic acid is a weak acid. The attraction between hydrogen and

---

[1] The truth of this assumption depends altogether on the view taken of the function, or mode of action of a catalyst. If depolymerisation of $(H_2O)_2$, as suggested in equation (2), is a necessary effect before the main reaction can take place, it follows that the hydrol molecules start the change. If so, the water is not a catalyst according to a prevalent theory.

chlorine must be very much greater than the attraction between hydrogen and the —OCN radicle. Ammonium cyanate dissociates with considerable velocity above 25°, whilst ammonium chloride requires to be heated above 300° before it commences to dissociate into ammonia and hydrogen chloride. Comparing the formula [NH_4].OCN and [NH_4].Cl, it is difficult to understand this apparent anomaly. The separation of an atom of hydrogen from its "firm" union with nitrogen is readily effected by the —OCN radicle, but with difficulty by the chlorine atom, in spite of its much greater affinity for hydrogen.

If we assume all salts of ammonia to be represented by the structural formula [NH_4]$^+$X$_-$ or NH_4X, i.e. pentavalent nitrogen, with X also in direct union with the nitrogen atom, we must also accept the following conclusion : " the weaker the attraction of X for hydrogen the more readily does the change $(NH_4)X \rightarrow NH_3 + HX$ take place." This conclusion, let it be remembered, is merely the statement of an experimental fact. So long as it is maintained that the fourth atom of hydrogen (previously in union with X) in (NH_4) is held by the nitrogen atom with the same force as the other three, neither hydrolytic dissociation, $NH_4.X + 2H_2O \rightleftarrows NH_3.H_2O + HX.H_2O$, nor ionic dissociation, $NH_4X \rightarrow NH_4 \cdot + X'$, seems to offer an explanation of the fact.

Acids, according to Langmuir, are substances from whose molecules hydrogen ions are readily detached, and the more easily these ions are given up, the stronger the acid which results. Bases are substances whose molecules can easily take up hydrogen ions, and the greater the tendency to take up these ions the stronger the base. Therefore ammonia can take up a hydrogen ion to form NH_4 more readily from the strong acid HCl than from the weak acid HOCN. This would explain one of the apparent difficulties referred to in the foregoing. But the tendency of ammonia to take up a fourth hydrogen ion is assumed to be also due to the fact that the four hydrogen ions enable it to assume a particularly stable form. Why, then, should this stable (NH_4) complex give up again with consummate ease a hydrogen ion to —OCN, but with difficulty to the chloride ion? Unless we admit that —OCN has a *much greater* attraction for hydrogen than chlorine has, it is not easy to understand the facts on the basis of the formula [NH_4]$^+$X$^-$.

An "ammonium" salt is formed from the union of NH_3 + HX' and afterwards dissociated by heat. Does HX contain the same atom of hydrogen as was originally in union with X before the salt was formed? We have no means of deciding this important question by experiment. According to the formula $[NH_4]_+ X^-$ it may be any one of the four hydrogen atoms. The formula [1] $H_3N : HX'$ gives a straight answer to the question, since it indicates that H and X have not been separated in the formation of the salt. The facts and arguments which have been discussed appear more in favour of this conclusion than against it.

The phenomenon of degree of molecular stability, the result apparently of differences in degree of combining power, is well illustrated by the various compounds of ammonia. The relation between "ammonium" cyanate and urea is an interesting case in connection with this question.

A desire to dispense with the idea of residual affinity as implied by the terms "auxiliary," "subsidiary," or "extra" valence is shown by the formula $[NH_4]^+ X^-$, which, it is maintained, disposes of any additional assumption regarding valence. The term "residual affinity" may have a vague meaning, yet we cannot brush aside the definite phenomenon which it seeks to explain.

Since Langmuir assumes that all "ammonium" salts are completely ionised even in the solid state, and are of course completely ionised in solution, the idea of a higher combining power than quadricovalence for the nitrogen atom becomes superfluous. Molecules of an "ammonium" salt, such as chemists have been led to understand, do not exist, and no "bond" of union is required to illustrate the attraction between $NH_4^{\cdot}$ and the ion X'. Is the idea of a pentavalent nitrogen atom, which was originally introduced to explain the constitution of salts of ammonia, to be dismissed once and for all? In the light of Langmuir's interesting "octet-covalence" theory, apparently that is so, but this does not demand at the same time the acceptance of the formula $[NH_4]^+X^-$, as we shall see presently.

Urea is an ammonia compound which is not ionised in solution. Whilst it cannot therefore be represented as an "ammonium" derivative, the expression $H_3N . HNCO$ is sufficient to account for the properties of "free" urea either in the solid or fused state, or in a neutral solution. Is it a derivative of tetravalent nitrogen, to be represented thus

$$HN : C {\overset{\displaystyle NH_3^+}{\underset{\displaystyle O...}{\Big<}}}_{-}$$

[1] This formula is meant to convey the same idea as that suggested by the formula put forward by Abegg (1904), Cain (1904), and Friend (1908), so far as the union of HX as a whole to the NH_3 molecule is concerned.

in which stability is maintained through electrostatic attraction between NH_3 and the oxygen atom? It is immaterial whether we represent NH_3 and O joined by a dotted line, as suggested by Langmuir, or as above. The attraction implied is the same, and of course it is also similar to the attraction supposed to exist between NH_4 and ...:...OCN, in representing "ammonium" cyanate by the formula

$$\left[NH_4 \right]^+ \overset{-}{OCN}.$$

The wide difference in stability between the two isomerides is not indicated by the respective formulæ, the more so when (NH_4) is assumed to be a particularly stable complex.

A salt of urea, in accordance with the views under discussion, must be considered an " ammonium " salt, and is apparently completely ionised. Here again the attraction between $\overset{-}{X}$, and the complex " urea-ion," as shown in the formula

$$\left[HN : C \underset{OH}{\overset{NH_3}{<}} \right]^+ \overset{-}{X}$$

is similar to that between NH_3 and the oxygen atom in " free " urea. On this assumption a salt of urea resembles " free " urea in containing the NH_3 group, the relation of which to the rest of the molecule appears to be much the same in the two formulæ. If so, how can we explain the marked difference between urea and its salts in their behaviour, say, towards nitrous acid? Why should the NH_3 group, if present in a salt of urea, be rapidly attacked (oxidised) by nitrous acid, and yet remain indifferent to this reagent in the case of " free " urea.

In a strong alkaline solution of urea we have presumably ionised " molecules " represented by the expression

$$\left(HN : \underset{O}{\overset{NH_2}{<}} \right)^- \overset{+}{Na}.$$

In such a solution urea, or rather the complex electro-negative ion derived from it, is readily oxidised, for example, by sodium hypobromite. In a neutral, or in a faintly alkaline, solution urea is not attacked by the oxidising agent (see next chapter). The presence of the amino-group supplies the vulnerable point for attack, as we have already seen, and there is good reason to conclude that this group is also present in salts of urea, which are therefore more correctly represented by the formula $HN : C(OH) . NH_2 : HX'$ than by one of the "ammonium" type.

Urea being an additive ammonia compound as distinct from a substitution derivative as required by the "carbamide" formula, the evidence which supports its constitution, and its properties would appear then to demand principal pentavalence of the nitrogen atom. The following considerations show that this is not necessarily the case.

In the majority of its compounds nitrogen is trivalent. We may consider this its normal combining power. When the valence is raised from the normal to a *maximum* of four, as in the formation of "ammonium" compounds, a radicle (or ion) is consequently generated which can exist in equilibrium with X' only by electrostatic attraction. This is apparently a condition inseparably connected with the manifestation of tetravalence by nitrogen. In the union of NH_3 with HX', the valency of X', whether an element or a radicle, must be duly considered. Its influence on the constitution of the resulting compound may be just as important as that of the nitrogen atom.

Oxygen is normally divalent. It is assumed to be tetravalent in the so-called "oxonium" compounds. This is wrong if the derivatives are supposed to be analogous to "ammonium" compounds. The compound $R_2O . HCl$ must be expressed by the formula

$$\left(\begin{matrix} R \\ R \end{matrix} \!\!>\!\! O \!\!\diagup\!\! {}^H \right)^{+} \bar{Cl} \, ,$$

with electrostatic attraction between the radicle and the chloride ion, if it is an "oxonium" salt. The expression

$$\begin{matrix} R \\ R \end{matrix} \!\!>\!\! O \!\!<\!\! \begin{matrix} H \\ Cl \end{matrix}$$

is not comparable to an "ammonium" salt. Thus, when the normal valency of oxygen is increased from two to three, a condition may be assumed to exist similar to that which is manifested when the valency of nitrogen is increased from three to four.

Principal tetravalence of nitrogen has therefore its counterpart in a principal trivalence of oxygen, with apparently analogous effects. According to this view the constitution of cyanate of ammonia may be represented by the formula

$$H_3 \overset{+}{\equiv} N \text{------} \bar{O} \!\!<\!\! \begin{matrix} H \\ CN \end{matrix} {}' $$

electrostatic attraction being indicated for convenience by the dotted line, whilst a bond of co-valence is illustrated by the continuous line between H_3N and oxygen. The nitrogen is tetravalent, or quadri-covalent, without assuming an "ammonium" radicle. Any effect, such as heat, which will destroy the electrostatic attraction must also overcome the particular bond of co-valence, since the existence of the latter is dependent on the duration of the former. This will explain the easy dissociation of the salt.

When ammonia combines with $HN : CO$, we have good reason to believe that union between carbon and the nitrogen of ammonia is effected. There is no evidence that the normal valency of carbon is ever exceeded, hence in the formula

$$H_3 \overset{+}{\equiv} N \cdots \overset{\overset{\bar{O}}{|}}{C} = NH,$$

the co-valent bond between H_3N and the carbon atom is not strictly analogous to that between H_3N and oxygen in cyanate of ammonia.

Urea is an electrically neutral compound, and much more stable than its isomeride. This indicates a superior degree of electrostatic equilibrium than appears to be suggested by the expression of the cyclic formula as proposed by Langmuir. Whilst the stability of urea is explained by the fact that the bond between H_3N and carbon is not affected when the electrostatic attraction between H_3N and O is overcome, the representation of the latter as uni-co-valent is difficult to accept.

In spite of the interesting and ingenious theories which have been put forward to explain the constitution of "ammonium" salts, a subject with which the chemistry of urea is obviously intimately connected, it must be admitted that there are several points which still await a satisfactory interpretation.

The structural formula for cyanate of ammonia given above represents an attempt to combine the suggestion that nitrogen is quadrico-valent with the view, which has been maintained throughout this discussion, that HX' is not decomposed when it unites with ammonia.

The expression is clearly applicable to salts of ammonia generally, and also to the so-called "oxonium" compounds. The combination of HCl with mono-molecular water is better explained by the formula

$$H - \bar{Cl} \cdots \overset{+}{O} \overset{\displaystyle H}{\underset{\displaystyle H}{<}}$$

than by the expressions

$$H \diagdown O \diagup Cl \atop H \diagup \diagdown H \quad, \text{ or } \left(H_3O\right)^+ \overline{Cl}.$$

When HCl combines with NH_3, the constitution of the product must not, in the writer's opinion, be considered solely from the point of view of the valency of the nitrogen atom. Whilst the valency of the latter is assumed to be raised from three to four, the valency of chlorine is simultaneously raised from one to two—a co-valent effect in fact. The constitution of the salt may be represented by the expression

$$H_3 \overset{+}{\equiv} N \cdots\cdots \overset{-}{Cl} - H.[1]$$

This formula, the writer ventures to maintain, can explain the properties of the salt in a satisfactory manner; and whilst a principal tetravalence or quadrico-valence of the nitrogen atom is upheld, it is not necessary to assume a change to the form $(NH_4)^+ \overset{-}{Cl}$.

The fact that many salts of ammonia are isomorphous with the corresponding salts of potassium is one of the original reasons for assuming the existence of the ammonium radicle. Modern researches on crystal structures, as revealed by the aid of X-rays, appear to support this view. Whilst no opinion is offered on the evidence from this source, it is no harm to point out that the interpretation of the results is based on the assumption that the existence of the ammonium radicle (or ion) is beyond question. In connection with this interesting point the reader is referred to a recent contribution by Wyckoff (1922) on the crystallographic and atomic symmetries of ammonium chloride. Wyckoff arrives at the conclusion, " not only is the symmetry of the structure that has been assigned to ammonium chloride in conflict with its observed symmetry, but that there is no other possible structure which will possess the requisite symmetry." If this be true the significance of the conclusion is obvious.

---

[1] Since liquid water (dihydrol) may be viewed as an oxonium compound, its constitution may be represented by the expression

$$H \diagdown \overset{+}{O} \cdots\cdots \overset{-}{O} \diagup H \atop H \diagup \diagdown H$$

The electrostatic attraction between the two oxygen atoms would no doubt be of a low order and easily overcome.

CHAPTER XIV.

THE DECOMPOSITION OF UREA IN ALKALINE SOLUTION BY HYPO-CHLORITES AND HYPOBROMITES RESPECTIVELY.

IN their comprehensive study of impure urea Fourcroy and Vauquelin (1799) did not omit to examine its decomposition by chlorine in alkaline solution. Their observations were recorded in the following words: " La décomposition de l'urée par l'acide muriatique oxygénée [1] est d'une manière singulière et très rémarquable, . . . dans cette de-composition l'urée nous a fourni un volume de gaz composés de parties égales en volume de gaz acide carbonique et d'azote." Considering the accuracy of this observation made so early in the history of urea, it is surprising that over half a century passed before the reaction was again studied.

In 1854 E. Davy proposed a simple and rapid method for the gasometric estimation of urea, dependent on its decomposition by a solution of sodium hypochlorite in accordance with the equation

$$CON_2H_4 + 3NaOCl = CO_2 + N_2 + 3NaCl + 2H_2O.$$

The carbon dioxide was absorbed by the excess of the alkaline solution used.

Knop and Hüfner (1870) proposed the use of a strongly alkaline solution of sodium hypobromite, since this reagent was found to de-compose urea more rapidly than the hypochlorite. The reaction is commonly represented thus—

$$CON_2H_4 + 3NaOBr + 2NaOH = N_2 + 3NaBr + Na_2CO_3 + 3H_2O,$$

the alkali being supposed to function merely as an absorbent for the carbon dioxide produced by the oxidising action of the hypobromite.

It was soon found, when pure urea was decomposed by the re-agent, that the volume of nitrogen evolved was decidedly less than that required by the above equation. For solutions of urea, varying in concentration from 1 to 10 per cent, the deficiency of nitrogen amounts to about 8 per cent of the theoretical. According to Russell

---

[1] This was the name given to chlorine by Berthollet, who believed it to be a compound of " muriatic " acid and oxygen. Its elementary character was proved by Sir H. Davy in 1810.

and West (1874), the volume of nitrogen set free was much the same whether sodium hypochlorite or hypobromite was used as the reagent.

In the case of urine the other nitrogenous constituents present yield a small proportion of their nitrogen during the decomposition. The amount, however, is not sufficient to interfere with the value of the reaction for the estimation of urea where a high degree of accuracy is not required. Consequently the "hypobromite" method has been largely used for clinical purposes, since it undoubtedly supplies us with the most rapid means for the estimation of urea. On account of its practical importance, this particular decomposition of urea has been the subject of quite an exceptional number of investigations. Those concerned with the invention of apparatus for simplifying the technique of the process need not be considered here. The mechanism of the decomposition is the question of chief interest.

According to the equations usually given, the decomposition of urea by hypobromite, or by hypochlorite of sodium, is apparently a simple case of direct oxidation. Whilst the velocity of the reaction is much greater when the former salt is used, the mechanism of the main change must be similar in both cases. On the basis of the "carbamide" formula there appears no reason why the volume of nitrogen evolved should show a deviation from the theoretical value, but the main reaction is accompanied by several secondary changes. These will be briefly summarised in the order in which they were first noticed, before an attempt is made to explain their origin.

Secondary Changes in the Decomposition of Urea by Hypochlorites and by Hypobromites Respectively.

Fenton (1878) showed that when urea is decomposed by sodium hypochlorite in the presence of an excess of sodium hydroxide, only about half of the theoretical volume of nitrogen is evolved, the remaining half being "fixed" as sodium cyanate. Foster (1878, 1879) showed that the formation of alkali cyanate was also responsible for the deficiency of nitrogen evolved in the decomposition of urea by alkaline hypobromite.

Fauconnier (1880) drew attention to the formation of a small quantity of nitric acid during the decomposition of urea in this reaction. This observation was confirmed by Luther (1889), who claims to have shown that when urea was decomposed by an excess of barium hypobromite, from 3 to 4 per cent of the nitrogen was oxidised to nitric acid. It is certain that this amount of nitric acid is not formed when the decomposition is effected by alkaline sodium hypobromite.

Lord Rayleigh (1898) found traces of what was apparently nitrous oxide as an impurity in the nitrogen prepared from urea by the action of sodium hypochlorite or hypobromite.

Schestakoff (1905) showed that hydrazine was formed when urea was treated with an alkaline solution of sodium hypochlorite at a low temperature and under special conditions. This interesting fact is of no practical importance so far as the volume of gas evolved is concerned. Its theoretical bearing is considered later.

Krogh (1913) found small quantities of carbon monoxide in the gas liberated from urea by sodium hypobromite. This was confirmed by Canti and Hurtley (1916), and later Hurtley (1921) showed that the nitrogen evolved from a 2 per cent solution of urea, when acted upon by hypobromite of the usual strength, contained on an average 0·7 per cent of carbon monoxide. This gas was shown to be also present, though in smaller amount, with the nitrogen evolved from urea by a hypochlorite.

Several observers have drawn attention to the occasional presence of a trace of oxygen in the gas evolved, as a result of decomposition by heat of a small portion of the alkali hypobromite.

The secondary changes which combine to influence the volume of gas evolved when urea is decomposed by " hypobromite " in the usual manner are, therefore, (*a*) evolution of traces of carbon monoxide, oxygen, and nitrous oxide—the effect of the last could only be due to its greater solubility in the solution ; (*b*) fixation of nitrogen as alkali cyanate, and as nitrate, the former being by far the chief disturbing cause of all.

Conditions Affecting the Volume of Gas (Nitrogen) Evolved.

The numerous attempts which have been made to cause urea to yield the whole of its *nitrogen* in a gaseous form when decomposed by hypobromite, *in a single operation*, have not been successful. Several investigators claim to have " practically " obtained the desired result. These claims are based on a false conclusion.

The formation of alkali cyanate cannot be completely suppressed in this reaction, and Fenton (1878) showed that cyanates are not attacked by the reagent.

Now cyanates are readily hydrolysed in the presence of acids, according to the equation

$$NaOCN + H_2O + 2HX = NH_3 . HX + NaX + CO_2 ;$$

and ammonia is readily oxidised by alkaline hypobromite thus—

$$2NH_3 + 3NaOBr = N_2 + 3NaBr + 3H_2O.$$

The following procedure which has been adopted by the writer (1922), has been found to give nearly the whole of the nitrogen from urea after decomposition by alkaline hypobromite. Two operations are necessary, and hence a nitrometer is the most convenient form of apparatus to use. A small excess of alkaline hypobromite is introduced into the nitrometer. The urea solution is then added, and the decomposition is allowed to proceed in the usual manner. After about twenty minutes the volume of gas evolved is carefully recorded. It is then expelled from the nitrometer. Sulphuric acid (1 in 5 of water) is now added to the residual liquid, until the latter, after careful mixing, shows the *permanent* presence of free bromine. The carbon dioxide liberated from the solution by this treatment must *not* be expelled from the nitrometer. After fifteen minutes, to allow for hydrolysis of the cyanic acid set free, sodium hydroxide solution (30 per cent) is added in excess. Whilst this regenerates hypobromite from the free bromine present, it is nevertheless advisable to add a small amount of the reagent to the residual solution. After complete absorption of the carbon dioxide, the volume of the remaining gas is noted. This is added to the volume of nitrogen recorded in the first stage.

The results of experiments carried out in this way are given below. The two stages are referred to as (*a*) and (*b*) respectively. In each case 0·06 gram of urea, equal to 22·4 c.c. N_2 at N.T.P. was used.

Expt.	Urea.	Volume of Gas at N.T.P.			Per Cent of Total N_2 in Urea.
		(*a*).	(*b*).	Total.	
1	1 per cent.	20·44 c.c.	1·84 c.c.	22·28 c.c.	99·46
2	2 ,, ,,	20·48 ,,	2·09 ,,	22·48 ,,	100·35
3	3 ,, ,,	20·52 ,,	1·82 ,,	22·34 ,,	99·75
4	6 ,, ,,	20·10 ,,	2·30 ,,	22·40 ,,	100·00

Variations in the velocity of the reaction, due to differences in the rate of mixing, influence the proportion of cyanate formed. This, of course, does not affect the final result, since the deficiency of nitrogen (*a*) due to this cause is made up by a corresponding increase in the volume of nitrogen set free in the second stage of the experiment. Nevertheless *all* of the nitrogen is not evolved. The close agreement with theory is the result of a compensating effect between the small quantity of carbon monoxide generated and the small quantity of nitrogen permanently fixed as nitrate.

We have now to consider the value of the results which have been set forth in attempts to obtain the whole of the nitrogen from urea in this reaction in a single operation.

Méhu (1879), by mixing glucose, or cane sugar, with a solution of urea before adding the hypobromite, claimed to have obtained evolution of the whole of the nitrogen. Several investigators have verified these results with regard to the increased volume of gas evolved in the presence of either of the sugars. Supported by the fact that dextrose alone does not evolve any gas when mixed with alkaline hypobromite, the procedure proposed by Méhu has been adopted in certain quarters on the assumption that the dextrose enhances the evolution of nitrogen from urea. In order to effect this the sugar must obviously suppress the formation of cyanate.

The following results show clearly that it does nothing of the kind. The experiments were made in two stages (*a*) and (*b*), as already described. Pure dextrose was added to 0·06 gram of urea in 3 c.c. of water, after which an excess of alkaline hypobromite[1] was added.

Theoretical yield of N_2 = 22·4 c.c. at N.T.P.

Expt.	Urea.	Dextrose.	Volume of Gas at N.T.P.			Per Cent of Total N_2 in Urea.
			(*a*).	(*b*).	Total.	
			c.c.	c.c.	c.c.	
1	0·06	nil	20·42	1·89	22·26	99·37
2	0·06	0·06 gram	20·88	1·96	22·84	101·96
3	0·06	0·12 ,,	21·34	1·93	23·27	103·88
4	0·06	0·18 ,,	21·92	1·97	23·89	106·65
5	0·06	0·24 ,,	22·34	1·92	24·26	108·30

It will be seen from the above results that whilst the addition of dextrose leads to a proportionate increase in the volume of gas set free in the first stage, its presence has practically no effect on the volume of gas liberated in the second stage. In other words, dextrose does not prevent the formation of alkali cyanate, and hence cannot enhance evolution of nitrogen, which is fixed from this cause during the primary reaction.

It is true that no gas is evolved when alkaline hypobromite is added to plain solution of dextrose, at all events within a reasonable lapse of time. It is equally true, however, that when alkaline

[1] Since oxidation of the sugar gives rise to more CO_2 than under normal conditions excess of alkali is necessary to ensure its complete absorption.

hypobromite is added to a solution of a salt of ammonia and dextrose, the nitrogen evolved will always be found to contain quite an appreciable quantity of carbon monoxide. The marked and gradual increase in the volumes of gas under (a) in experiments 2, 3, 4, and 5 was due to carbon monoxide, the presence of which was readily proved by the usual tests for this substance.

This is an interesting point, since more or less cyanic acid is formed, as a result of the reaction

$$CO + NH_3 + O = NH:CO + H_2O.$$

By means of the method adopted for stage (b), the amount of cyanic acid generated in this way was easily determined.

The results given below were obtained by adding an excess of alkaline hypobromite to 0·0535 gram of ammonium chloride, and the stated amounts of dextrose, dissolved in 3 c.c. of water. A control experiment with the ammonium salt alone was made for comparison, since the theoretical yield of nitrogen was not evolved, on account of the fixation of a portion as nitrate. Theoretical yield of $N_2 = 11·2$ c.c. at N.T.P.

Expt.	NH₄Cl.	Dextrose.	C.c. of gas at N.T.P.			Calculated on percentage of nitrogen in NH₄Cl.
			(a).	(b).	Total.	
I	0·0535	nil	10·95	no gas	10·95	97·76
2	,,	0·03	10·58	0·80	11·38	101·60
3	,,	0·06	10·35	1·29	11·64	103·96
4	,,	0·09	10·22	1·87	12·09	107·94
5	,,	0·12	10·11	2·13	12·24	109·28

When compared with the results given in the previous table, it will be seen that in spite of the fact that the gas evolved in stage (a) contained carbon monoxide (except experiment 1), the volume of gas diminished as the proportion of dextrose was increased. The results of stage (b) prove that this was due to the relatively large proportion of nitrogen fixed as cyanate.

In the case of experiment 5, for example, 18·99 per cent of the theoretical yield of cyanic acid was generated during the decomposition of the ammonium salt in the presence of the stated amount of dextrose. If the reaction under consideration is essentially an oxidation change, this result goes to show that a strong tendency must exist towards the realisation of the equation given above. On the other hand, since alkaline hypobromite must act as a brominating agent as well, the formation of cyanic acid in the manner

$$CO + NH_2Br + NaOH \rightarrow CO : NH + NaBr + H_2O$$

must not be overlooked.

Any easily oxidisable carbon compound in the presence of urea is liable to give more or less carbon monoxide during decomposition by hypobromite. The discordant results which have been obtained by different observers in the estimation of urea in urine are in a large measure due to this effect.

The composition of the hypobromite solution, as regards concentration of NaOBr, degree of alkalinity, etc., has also an important influence on the volume of nitrogen evolved. Considering all the facts, it is not surprising to find that the history of the decomposition of urea by hypobromites is largely a history of contradictions.

Duggan (1882) showed that by generating the hypobromite *in situ* with urea, by first mixing the urea solution with sodium hydroxide, and then adding the bromine, a nearly theoretical yield of nitrogen was obtained. Thus with solutions containing 1, 2, and 3 per cent respectively of urea, volumes of nitrogen varying from 99·02 to 99·91 per cent of the theoretical were evolved. The last result was obtained from a 2 per cent solution of urea. Le Comte (1903), adopting a similar procedure, claims to have obtained all the nitrogen in this manner. Garnier (1904) maintains that whilst the method succeeds with a 1 per cent solution of urea, it fails to give complete evolution of nitrogen with solutions containing 2 per cent of urea.

The following results were obtained when the procedure proposed by Duggan was completed by the addition of the second stage.

In each experiment 0·06 of urea was dissolved in 20 per cent sodium hydroxide solution, as recommended by Duggan.

Expt.	Urea.	Volume of Gas at N.T.P.			Per Cent of Total N$_2$ in Urea.
		(a).	(b).	Total.	
1	0·5 per cent.	21·81 c.c.	0·82 c·c.	22·63 c.c.	101·0
2	1·0 ,, ,,	21·54 ,,	0·89 ,,	22·43 ,,	100·1
3	2·0 ,, ,,	21·63 ,,	0·95 ,,	22·58 ,,	100·8
4	3·0 ,, ,,	21·87 ,,	0·66 ,,	22·53 ,,	100·5

There can be no doubt that the formation of cyanate is considerably suppressed when the hypobromite is generated in the alkaline solution of urea. The reaction is particularly energetic under such condition, yet this does not prevent the formation of a small quantity of carbon monoxide. This is responsible for the excess of gas over the theoretical value for nitrogen only.

All observers appear to agree on the point that excess of alkali facilitates the decomposition of urea by hypobromite. Krogh (1913) showed that the amount of carbon monoxide evolved also increased with the alkalinity of the hypobromite.

Fenton (1879) examined the behaviour towards the "hypohalogenites" of a few substances more or less allied to urea in constitution, namely, biuret, guanidine, ammonium carbamate, and other salts of ammonia. A comparison of the results obtained, as regards the quantities of nitrogen evolved, is given by Fenton as follows :—

Alkaline.	Urea.	Ammonium Carbamate.	Guanidine.	Biuret.	Ammonium Salts	Cyanates.
NaOCl	$\frac{1}{2}$	$\frac{1}{2}$	$\frac{2}{3}$	$\frac{1}{3}$	all	none
NaOBr	all	all	$\frac{2}{3}$	$\frac{2}{3}$	all	none

In using the word "all" no doubt "nearly all" was intended, since Fenton states, "there appears to be a mean loss of about 2·5 per cent of the evolved nitrogen in all hypochlorite reactions, whether from urea or ammonium salts, and of about 8 per cent in hypobromite reactions." The evolution of only half of the nitrogen from urea, shown in the above comparisons, refers to the use of a hypochlorite solution containing an excess of alkali. It was shown that the "suppressed" nitrogen was present in the residue in each case as a cyanate.

Considering the early proof that was given by Fenton and by Foster of the formation of cyanate from urea in the decomposition under consideration, it is curious that it should have been overlooked by many of those who have studied the reactions. Krogh (1913) assumes that when urea is decomposed with sodium hypobromite the nitrogen which is not set free is wholly converted into oxides of nitrogen, whilst the carbon is, in part, oxidised only to carbon monoxide, the chief portion being oxidised to carbon dioxide.

Now when we consider the constitution of urea, it is quite evident that neither a cyanate, nor carbon monoxide need be viewed as products of direct oxidation.

What is the Mechanism of the Decomposition of Urea by a Hypohalogenite?

The several secondary products formed in this reaction indicate that the main decomposition must be the result of a series of changes. With a hypochlorite we have a chlorination, hydrolysis, and oxidation taking place, either simultaneously, or following each other with considerable velocity. Similar effects must take place with a hypobromite with still greater velocity. Schestakoff's discovery (1905) that hydrazine can be obtained by the action of alkaline hypochlorite on urea at a low temperature has confirmed the belief in the complexity of the reaction. The discovery is considered to throw much light on the mechanism of the whole change, since it is assumed that the evolution of nitrogen from urea by the action of a hypochlorite (or hypobromite) is dependent on the decomposition of the hydrazine derivative, $H_2N . NHCOONa$. The formation and decomposition of the latter is explained by Schestakoff as follows :—

$$H_2N . C = O \atop | \quad NH_2 \qquad (1)$$

$$+ NaOCl = H_2O +$$

$$H_2N - C - O . Na \atop || \quad Cl . N \qquad (2)$$

$$\rightarrow$$

$$Cl . C - O . Na \atop || \quad H_2N . N$$

$$Cl - C - O . Na \atop || \quad H_2N . N \qquad (3)$$

$$+ NaOH = NaCl +$$

$$O : C - O . Na \atop | \quad H_2N . NH \qquad (4)$$

$$\xrightarrow[\text{hydrolysis}]{+ H_2O}$$

$$NaHCO_3 \atop + \quad H_2N . NH_2$$

(5) $H_2N . NH_2 + 2NaOCl = N_2 + 2H_2O + 2NaCl.$

According to the above mechanism of the reaction, we have (1) chlorination, (2) an isomeric change, (3) a peculiar attack by sodium hydroxide, (4) hydrolysis, and (5) oxidation following each other in the order noted. It cannot be said that the explanation is convincing. The remarkable isomeric change assumed to take place in the second reaction is a pure speculation devised to bring the two nitrogen atoms in union.

It is obvious that the explanation of the formation of hydrazine cannot be reconciled with the fact that a considerable amount of alkali cyanate is formed when urea is attacked by a hypochlorite in the presence of alkali. The claim put forward by Schestakoff as regards the *quantity* of hydrazine formed from urea has never been confirmed.

In the writer's experience the amount formed is very small,[1] and others appear to have arrived at the same conclusion.

[1] Schestakoff used benzaldehyde to isolate the hydrazine as benzalazine $C_6H_5 . CH : N - N : CH . C_6H_5.$

Armstrong and Robertson (1905) are inclined to attribute Schesta-koff's result to a reaction taking place in the following stages :—

$$CO\begin{cases}NH_2 \\ NHCl\end{cases} \xrightarrow{-HCl} CO\begin{cases}NH \\ | \\ NH\end{cases} \xrightarrow{+H_2O} \begin{matrix}NH_2 \\ | \\ NH.CO_2H\end{matrix} \longrightarrow \begin{matrix}NH_2 \\ | \\ NH_2\end{matrix} + CO_2.$$

There is a good reason for concluding that the formation of hydrazine, in the reaction in question, is the result of a secondary, rather than of a primary, change.

When we consider the tendency of urea to yield ammonia and cyanic acid as the first step in all its decompositions, the formation of more or less hydrazine, in accordance with the simple change $NH_2Cl + NH_3 = H_2N.NH_2.HCl$, must not be overlooked. There is good evidence to support this simple explanation.

Chattaway (1908) showed that dichloro-urea $CON_2H_2Cl_2$ is hydrolysed by water at the ordinary temperature with evolution of nitrogen and carbon dioxide, whilst ammonium chloride is formed in the solution. The decomposition is greatly accelerated by alkalis. The change, which is violent, under this condition, is represented by Chattaway as follows :—

$$3CON_2H_2Cl_2 + 12KOH = 3K_2CO_3 + 2NH_3 + 6KCl + 2N_2 + 6H_2O.$$

The writer has not been able to confirm this equation as regards the evolution of ammonia. As a matter of fact the formation of a considerable proportion of alkali cyanate can be readily proved.

Monochloro-urea prepared by Béhal and Detoeuf (1911) is also hydrolysed by water with evolution of nitrogen and formation of biuret, and of chloramine.

It is interesting to note that this chloro-derivative of urea inter-acts with potassium iodide in an acid solution, according to the equation

$$CON_2H_3Cl + 2KI + CH_3COOH = CON_2H_4 + I_2 + KCl \\ + CH_3COOK.$$

The chlorine is therefore separated as hypochlorous acid, since two atoms of iodine are set free. A similar change occurs with dichloro-urea. Chlorination is undoubtedly the first stage in the reaction when urea is attacked by a hypochlorite.

By hydrolysis of this with dilute sulphuric acid, hydrazine sulphate is formed; from one litre of urine he claims to have obtained from 30-40 grams of the sulphate. The yield is said to be equal to 60 per cent of that required by theory. (Compare Fenton, "Ann. Reports Chem. Soc.," 1905, 2, 96.)

Whilst the constitution of neither of the chloro-ureas has been definitely established, the products of their hydrolytic decomposition clearly indicate that under the conditions of Schestakoff's experiments, hydrazine may be easily formed in the simple manner suggested above. Indeed the decomposition of the hypothetical compound

$$\begin{array}{c} H_2N.C.O.Na \\ \parallel \qquad \text{into } H_2N.Cl, \text{ and NaOCN} \\ Cl.N \end{array}$$

is much more likely than the remarkable isomeric change (2) suggested by Schestakoff, in the foregoing scheme.

Urea in the Cyclic Form is not Attacked by a Hypohalogenite.

It does not appear to be generally recognised that alkalinity of the solution is essential in order that urea may be decomposed by either a hypochlorite or a hypobromite. In a neutral, or even faintly alkaline, solution urea remains indifferent to the reagent, so far as the evolution of gas is concerned. The case is comparable to the behaviour of urea towards nitrous acid. We have seen that with the latter a change in the configuration of the urea molecule is necessary before oxidation can take place.

A similar change apparently occurs before urea can be decomposed by a hypohalogenite. The excess of alkali commonly present may be assumed to bring about the required condition. The following results obtained with hypobromite solutions prove the fact mentioned above, and a few others which it may be useful to record. When bromine is added to a solution of sodium hydroxide in proportions required by the equation

$$2NaOH + Br_2 = NaOBr + NaBr + H_2O,$$

the amount of hypobromite formed is very small.

Sixteen grams of bromine were added to 50 c.c. of $4N.-NaOH$ solution cooled to $0°$; 15 c.c. of the resulting solution were added to 0·06 gram of urea in 2 c.c. of water contained in a nitrometer. After fifteen minutes nothing more than a few bubbles of gas were evolved. On addition of 2 c.c. of sodium hydroxide solution (20 per cent) there was an immediate brisk evolution of gas, equal to 12·1 c.c. at N.T.P., whilst the hypobromite solution was decolorised. Excess of urea remained. If hypobromite were formed in theoretical amount according to the above equation, 1·5 c.c. of the solution, after addition of alkali, would have been sufficient to decompose the amount of urea taken, thus only a little more than 5 per cent of the theoretical quantity of hypobromite was formed.

When 16 grams of bromine were added to 50 c.c. of 8N – NaOH solution, i.e. to produce NaOBr. 2NaOH, 2 c.c. of the resulting solution were more than sufficient to decompose 0·06 gram of urea. The results were (a) gas evolved = 19·9 c.c., (b) 2·45 c.c., equal to 99·77 per cent of the theoretical. Excess of alkali is therefore necessary to promote the formation of hypobromite and also to enable it to decompose urea. No bromo-derivatives of urea corresponding to the chloro-compounds have been isolated. They are evidently very unstable; nevertheless the formation of such a derivative is no doubt the first step in the hypobromite decomposition of urea.

When alkaline hypochlorite is added to a solution of urea, a period of quiescence can be easily distinguished before evolution of gas suddenly starts, and then it continues with increasing velocity. With alkaline hypobromite the action is vigorous at the moment of mixing, and, as we know, the proportion of cyanate formed is small and fairly constant. Since the velocity of the decomposition in this case is always very great under the usual conditions of working, it may be assumed that the velocity is nearly always the same, and hence the approximately constant results obtained.

When the reaction is slowed down the proportion of cyanate formed is considerably increased as shown by the following result.

An excess of neutral hypobromite was added to 0·06 gram of urea in 2 c.c. of water. After fifteen minutes, no gas having been evolved, sodium hydroxide solution was added gradually until no more gas was liberated. Volume obtained (a) = 15·74 c.c. at N.T.P. The gas was expelled from the nitrometer, and the residual solution treated for the second stage as previously described. Volume obtained (b) = 6·92 c.c. at N.T.P. Total = 22·66 c.c. or 101·1 per cent of the total nitrogen of urea. Approximately 30 per cent of the nitrogen of urea was fixed as cyanate during the decomposition under the above conditions. Carbon monoxide was here again responsible for the excess of gas evolved.

It has been noticed by most observers that in the decomposition of urea by hypobromite, evolution of nitrogen is enhanced by increasing the concentration of alkali. The result is no doubt due to the fact that the velocity of the reaction is considerably increased by this means. Since excess of alkali would favour the change

$$HN:C \underset{O}{\overset{NH_3}{<}} + NaOH = HN:C \underset{O.Na}{\overset{NH_2}{<}} + H_2O,$$

it might be expected that this would promote the formation of alkali cyanate, and so lead to a decrease in the evolution of nitrogen. Fenton's (1878) observations on the decomposition of urea by alkaline hypochlorite are in agreement with this view. Hurtley (1921), on the other hand, has shown that a concentrated alkaline hypochlorite gave much less nitrogen than a hypochlorite of one-fifth the strength but containing far more alkali.

Both the chloro-ureas are violently decomposed by alkalis with evolution of nitrogen. Their formation, constitution, and decomposition must be intimately concerned with the mechanism of the reaction under consideration. A bromo-urea may be assumed to have an ephemeral existence in the decomposition of urea by a hypobromite, and so the reaction can be considered from a similar point of view.

Now in an alkaline solution urea is very largely " free," i.e. it is in the cyclic form. This is an important point to bear in mind.

Chloro-urea, according to Béhal and Detoeuf (1922), is formed in accordance with the equation

$$2CON_2H_4 + Cl_2 = CON_2H_3Cl + CON_2H_4.HCl,$$

whilst Datta (1912) has pointed out that in the formation of dichloro-urea a similar reaction takes place. Urea as hydrochloride cannot be converted into either a mono- or a dichloro-derivative, and hence it is free urea only which is chlorinated. The conditions are therefore favourable for the immediate formation of a chloro-derivative when an ordinary hypochlorite solution is added to urea.

Chloro-urea may be represented by the formulæ

$$HN:C \begin{matrix} NH_2Cl \\ | \\ O \end{matrix} \quad or \quad HN:C \begin{matrix} NHCl \\ \\ OH \end{matrix}$$

Simultaneous hydrolysis and oxidation would complete its decomposition, without any secondary changes, according to the equation

$$HN:C \begin{matrix} NH_2Cl \\ | \\ O \end{matrix} + O_2 + NaOH = N_2 + CO_2 + NaCl + 2H_2O.$$

It is conceivable that during the violent disruption of such a compound by-products may arise as the result of its direct decomposition in two different directions, thus—

$$(1) \quad HN:C \begin{matrix} NH_2Cl \\ | \\ O \end{matrix} \rightarrow HN:CO + NH_2Cl.$$

$$(2) \quad HN:C \begin{matrix} NH_2Cl \\ | \\ O \end{matrix} \rightarrow HCl + ... HN - CO - NH ...$$

Hydrolysis of . . $HN - CO - NH$ . . at the moment of its liberation could give rise to CO_2 and $H_2N - NH_2$, whilst incomplete oxidation would be represented by the change

$$. . . HN.CO.NH . . . + O = N_2 + CO + H_2O.$$

The union of two . . . $HN.CO.NH$ . . . groups would give p-urazine, which is rapidly decomposed by alkaline hypochlorite, with evolution of CO_2 and nitrogen.

It is during a violent reaction that one would expect the : CO group to escape oxidation to CO_2. The facts support this conclusion. Krogh found that hypobromite rich in alkali produced a greater evolution of carbon monoxide than when less alkali was present. Hurtley found that there was much less carbon monoxide present in the gas evolved from the decomposition of urea by a hypochlorite than by a hypobromite. Finally, Hurtley showed that there was a mean of 1·24 per cent of carbon monoxide in the gas (N_2) evolved when dichloro-urea was decomposed by alkali alone.

This is not surprising since the dichloro-derivative evidently does not give rise to sufficient hypochlorous acid to effect the complete oxidation of its decomposition products. It seems, therefore, more reasonable to explain the origin of the secondary products in the manner suggested than to assume that the products in question indicate that the main reaction is the result of a series of complex changes.

CHAPTER XV.

SIMPLE LECTURE EXPERIMENTS TO DEMONSTRATE THE CHIEF PRO-
PERTIES OF UREA, AND TO SHOW EVIDENCE OF ITS CONSTITU-
TION, AND THE MODES OF ITS FORMATION.

THE experiments which are commonly described in text-books on organic chemistry to illustrate the chief properties of urea fail entirely to make clear the true properties of the compound. Most of the experiments are of a very superficial kind, and as a result are misleading in the information which they convey to the student.

They are made, in fact, to "fit in" with the "carbamide" formula. The following series of simple experiments have been selected to demonstrate the chief reactions of urea, and to bring out the main facts which illustrate its properties and supply evidence of its constitution.

Experiment 1.—*The Dissociation of Urea by Heat.*

About a gram of urea is heated in an ordinary test-tube, until gas, chiefly ammonia, is freely evolved for about two minutes. Attention is drawn to the white vapour which accompanies the ammonia, and to the copious sublimate which forms on the sides of the tube. Three tubes are prepared and, after cooling, tested as follows:—

(*a*) A few drops of a solution of cobalt nitrate, or acetate, are allowed to trickle down the side of the tube. On contact with the sublimate an intense blue colour is developed.

(*b*) The sublimate is dissolved in about 2 c.c. of water, one or two small crystals of hydroxylamine hydrochloride are introduced, and after a few moments an excess of ferric chloride solution is added. An intense purple-blue colour is produced.

These are two very delicate colour reactions for cyanic acid.

(*c*) To a solution of the sublimate add silver nitrate solution. A copious white precipitate of silver cyanate is formed.

To save time in making the last test, it is advisable to make two small nicks with a file, or glass cutter, on opposite sides of the test tube about two centimetres from the bottom. The tube while hot is plunged into cold water up to the file mark; this causes the tube to fracture at the desired point. The sublimate is then washed into a second tube, and the test applied.

Experiment 2.—*To show that Biuret when heated Dissociates into Urea and Cyanic Acid.*

The tests for cyanic acid are carried out exactly as in the previous experiment, about a gram of biuret (anhydrous) being heated until the melt assumes a pasty consistency. The residue is treated with 4 c.c. of water, the solution filtered, and on addition of nitric acid a precipitate of nitrate of urea is obtained. The presence of urea in the filtrate may also be quickly shown by aid of the xanthydrol test, described under Experiment 11.

Experiment 3.—*To show that Biuret is formed from the Interaction of Urea and Cyanic Acid.*

To 2 grams of urea dissolved in 2 c.c. of strong hydrochloric acid, diluted with 4 c.c. of water, 2 grams of powdered potassium cyanate are gradually added with constant stirring : after a few moments the solution is filtered to separate some cyamelide which has been formed. Attention is drawn to this fact in connection with the polymerisation of cyanic acid. The filtrate when tested in the usual manner with copper sulphate and excess of alkali will be found to give a strong biuret reaction.

These two last experiments show that the decomposition and formation of biuret is a reversible reaction.

Experiment 4.—*To show that Urea, and Biuret in small quantity, are formed when Cyanic Acid is Hydrolysed.*

One gram of pure potassium cyanate is dissolved in 40 c.c. of cold water, and 12·5 c.c. of normal acid (HNO_3 or HCl) added. At this dilution there will be no separation of cyamelide. After about 10 minutes, the solution is divided into two parts, the presence of biuret is shown in one portion by the usual copper test, whilst the presence of urea in the remaining portion is proved by the xanthydrol test—see Experiment 10. If the solution is carefully neutralised, using phenol-red as indicator, the addition of urease will also reveal the presence of urea after a short time.

Experiment 5.—*To show that Sodium Cyanate is first formed when Urea is Hydrolysed by Sodium Hydroxide.*

One gram of urea is dissolved in 25 c.c. of normal *pure* sodium hydroxide solution contained in a small round-bottomed flask. The solution is heated to boiling under reflux for five minutes, after which an excess of barium nitrate solution is added. Attention is drawn to the small amount of barium carbonate precipitated. The solution is filtered. A few drops of phenol-phthalein solution are added to the filtrate, which is then carefully neutralised by dilute nitric acid. On addition of silver nitrate a copious white precipitate of silver cyanate is obtained.

The presence of cyanate in the neutralised filtrate may also be shown by the hydroxylamine – HCl and ferric chloride test.

In order to give a visible demonstration of the two phases of the "hydrolysis" of urea, the above experiment may be varied by replacing the sodium hydroxide by barium hydroxide. By attaching an upright piece of glass tubing about 20 c.m. long to the flask, the evolution of ammonia can be shown to take place for four or five minutes before the appearance of barium carbonate, and if the solution is tested, as described, at this stage, the presence of cyanate can be readily proved.

Experiment 6.—*To show that Ammonia is Formed when Urea is Decomposed by Nitrous Acid.*

A few crystals of urea and of sodium nitrite are dissolved in about 50 c.c. of distilled water (free from ammonia), and five or six drops of strong hydrochloric acid added. After about a minute 2 c.c. of Nessler's reagent are added, when a strong reaction for ammonia will be immediately developed.

Control experiments should be made at the same time with a solution of urea and of nitrous acid separately to show that neither gives any colour reaction with Nessler's solution.

Experiment 7.—*To show that the Ammonia formed in the Previous Experiment is due to the Hydrolysis of Cyanic Acid formed in the First Instance.*

Urea (0·2 gram) and sodium nitrite (0·24 gram) are dissolved in 10 c.c. of water ; 30 c.c. of decinormal silver nitrate solution and 3 c.c. of N-nitric acid are added. The mixture is shaken until the cream-coloured precipitate of silver nitrite has just dissolved. After five minutes, 1 c.c. of N-sodium hydroxide solution is added, and the *pure white* precipitate of silver cyanate is allowed to subside. The supernatant solution is poured off, and the precipitate washed by decantation with about 15 c.c. of water.

12

In order to prove that the precipitate is silver cyanate, a portion is transferred to a porcelain capsule, a small pinch of potassium chloride added, and then a few crystals of cobalt nitrate. A deep blue colour is developed. The remainder of the silver precipitate may be tested by means of the hydroxylamine – HCl and ferric chloride reaction.

A small portion of the silver cyanate may be decomposed by dilute hydrochloric acid, filtered, and the presence of ammonia in the filtrate shown by Nessler's reagent.

Experiment 8.—*To show that the configuration of the Urea Molecule must change on the Addition of a Strong Alkali to the Solution.*

A solution of ammonio-silver nitrate, prepared by adding ammonia to a solution of silver nitrate until the precipitate first formed is *nearly* all dissolved, is added to a solution of urea. Note that nothing happens.

On addition of pure sodium hydroxide solution, a pale yellow precipitate of di-argentic urea is immediately thrown down. Since the silver derivative is formed in this case in the presence of dilute ammonia solution, if there was no change produced in the structure of urea on addition of sodium hydroxide, there seems no reason why the silver derivative should not be directly precipitated on the addition of ammonio-silver nitrate solution to the urea.

Experiment 9.—*To show that Xanthhydrol is not a Test for " Free " Urea, and that a Salt of Urea (i.e. a Change in the Molecular Configuration) must be formed before a Reaction can take place.*

To 10 c.c. of a 1 per cent solution of urea in alcohol 20 c.c. of a 4 per cent solution of xanthhydrol in methyl alcohol are added. No precipitate is formed even when the solution is heated to boiling-point. On the addition of two or three drops of strong hydrochloric acid solution, a crystalline precipitate of di-xanthyl-urea is quickly formed, and after a few minutes the product becomes an almost semi-solid mass.

Experiment 10.—*To illustrate the Delicacy of the Xanthhydrol Test for Urea in a Few Minutes.*

A saturated aqueous solution of xanthhydrol is prepared by adding about 0·15 gram, previously dissolved in 2 c.c. of alcohol, to a litre of boiling water. After a few minutes ebullition the solution is allowed to cool, and, if necessary, filtered.

To 10 c.c. of a 0·01 per cent solution of urea, 90 c.c. of the xanth-hydrol solution are added (1 of urea in 100,000). The addition of five or six drops of strong HCl solution will cause the appearance of a distinct opalescence after two minutes, which will be found to have considerably increased at the end of five minutes. In a similar manner 1 part of urea in 10,000 will be revealed within fifteen seconds.

An aqueous solution of xanthhydrol loses its sensitiveness after a few days on account of gradual oxidation to xanthone. Fosse re-commends the use of glacial acetic acid to promote the formation of the condensation product between urea and xanthhydrol, but then several hours are required in order to detect urea when present in very small quantity.

Experiment 11.—*To show that the Production of Urea by the Hydro-lysis of Cyanamide in the Presence of Strong Nitric Acid is limited to the Amount of Urea Nitrate which can be formed.*

Whilst this experiment cannot be completed at one lecture it can be held over until the following day for the final proof.

To 1 gram of cyanamide dissolved in 20 c.c. of moist ether (which has been well washed to free it from alcohol) contained in a small stoppered bottle, or separating funnel, 0·75 c.c. of strong nitric acid (D = 1·42) is added. After about twelve minutes, small crystals will commence to separate, and at the end of an hour or so a copious precipitate of urea nitrate will have formed.

The ethereal solution, poured off from the crystalline deposit, is shaken with about 30 c.c. of water. The presence of cyanamide in considerable quantity can be shown in the aqueous solution on addi-tion of ammonio-silver nitrate solution.

To prove that all the nitric acid has been removed as urea nitrate, another portion of the aqueous extract is tested with a solution of nitron acetate. No precipitate is formed, but on the addition of one or two drops of dilute nitric acid a crystalline precipitate of nitron nitrate is rapidly thrown down. Attention is drawn to the fact that there was more water present than was necessary to effect the com-plete hydrolysis of all the cyanamide used.

If the experiment is duplicated, but 2 c.c. of strong nitric acid added, then it can be shown that *all* of the cyanamide has been hydrolysed to urea nitrate.

12 *

Experiment 12.—*To show the Formation of Urea during the Oxidation of Glucose (or any Other Sugar) in the Presence of Ammonia.*

Place 0·7 gram of powdered potassium permanganate in a wide-mouthed test tube, add 0·1 gram of glucose dissolved in 4 c.c. of water and 1 c.c. of 2·5 per cent solution of ammonia. The mixture is well shaken, in a few moments considerable heat is developed, and the product solidifies to a dark brown mass. Add 2 c.c. of water, boil for a few seconds, filter. To the filtrate add 4 c.c. of glacial acetic acid and 1 c.c. of a 5 per cent solution of xanthhydrol in methyl alcohol. In about two minutes white flocks of di-xanthylurea will separate.

This experiment, which is described by Fosse, may be modified so as to include the formation of urea from the oxidation of an amino-acid or a protein, and if carried out on a larger scale, the production of cyanic acid (present as KOCN) can be readily demonstrated.

The presence of urea may be shown more rapidly by testing as in Experiment 10.

Experiment 13.—*To show the Formation of Urea when a Protein is Hydrolysed by Alkali in the Absence of an Oxidising Agent (Fosse, 1916).*

A solution of 5 grams of egg-albumen and 5 grams of potassium hydroxide in 50 c.c. of water is boiled under reflux for twenty minutes. The cold solution is treated with 70 c.c. of glacial acetic acid and 20 c.c. of a 5 per cent solution of xanthhydrol in methyl alcohol.

A crystalline precipitate of di-xanthylurea is gradually formed.

The presence of urea may be more rapidly demonstrated by adding 12 c.c. of strong HCl solution to the cold product, after which the solution is added to 300 c.c. of cold saturated aqueous solution of xanthhydrol.

Casein, or gelatin, may be used in place of egg-albumen.

Experiment 14.—*To show the Rapid Decomposition of Urea by Urease at Ordinary Temperature.*

About 4 grams of soy-bean meal are stirred into 200 c.c. of a 2 per cent solution of urea, to which a few drops of neutral phenol-red solution have been added. After about thirty seconds, a marked purple-red colour will have developed.

This reaction is well shown side by side with two similar solutions of urea, one containing a few drops of brom-thymol blue, which has been previously rendered neutral, or very faintly acid, the other containing a few drops of phenol-phthalein solution.

A comparison of the three indicators will illustrate the extreme sensitiveness of the phenol-red.

Experiment 15.—*To show that Urease can Effect the Decomposition of Normal Butylurea at 50°, but has no Action on this Urea at Room Temperature, or at 25°.*

A suitable amount of soy-bean meal is added to a 5 per cent solution of a *pure* n-butylurea $C_4H_9HN . CO . NH_2$ (Werner, 1919), to which phenol-red solution has been added.

The mixture is well stirred and divided into two portions, one of which is placed in a tube immersed in water maintained at 50°-60°, whilst the remaining portion is left at room temperature.

After about ten minutes a distinct purple-red colour will develop in the heated tube, whilst the odour of butylamine will become noticeable. No colour change will appear in the cold solution.

This experiment is interesting, since it shows that urease can decompose a mono-substituted urea if the latter can suffer dissociation below the " maximum " temperature of the enzyme.

Experiments to show the Stability of Urea in Sterilised Water at Room Temperature and its Slow Decomposition when this Condition is not Observed.

A solution of pure urea in distilled water saturated with chloroform, or toluene, is prepared and set aside for a month or more. It will be found to give a negative result when tested with barium hydroxide, or with silver nitrate.

A similar solution of urea in plain distilled water will give a precipitate with both reagents after about fourteen days, and a very marked result after a month. The latter solution will also give a strong reaction for alkalinity with phenol-red, whilst the former will still be neutral.

The point of these simple experiments is to correct the prevalent idea that urea is hydrolysed by water alone, or can revert to ammonium cyanate in aqueous solution at the ordinary temperature.

Micro-organisms are alone responsible for the decomposition of urea in water under such conditions.

Preparations in Connection with the Preceding Experiments.

1. *Preparation of Biuret.*

The following modification of the procedure described by H. Schiff (1896) gives a very good yield :—

Fifty grams of urea are gently heated in a flat-bottomed flask provided with a cork carrying an inlet and an outlet tube and a thermometer, the bulb of which is immersed in the molten urea. A current of dry hydrogen chloride is passed over the surface of the urea, while the temperature is gradually raised to 145°, and maintained at about this point for eighty minutes. The outlet tube is connected to an ordinary tap pump, and a gentle aspiration is kept up during the heating. The contents of the flask should be given an occasional rotary motion, to prevent caking on the surface. The cold product is digested, and extracted, with not more than 80 c.c. of water in all, to remove ammonium chloride and unchanged urea. The residue is treated with 200 c.c. of water and sufficient sodium hydroxide to effect complete solution at a gentle heat. A current of carbon dioxide is passed through the cold solution, when biuret will be precipitated in the form of thin needle-like crystals. As soon as a granular precipitate appears (sodium dihydrogen cyanurate), the current of carbon dioxide is stopped. The product is collected and re-crystallised from solution in hot water, or may be purified by re-solution in sodium hydroxide and precipitation by carbon dioxide. The yield is about 9 grams of the pure substance. More may be recovered from the first mother liquor after precipitation of the cyanuric acid.

2. *Preparation of Pure Potassium Cyanate. K.O.C.N.*

The methods commonly described for the preparation of potassium cyanate are very tedious.

The decomposition of urethane by potassium hydroxide in alcoholic solution, in accordance with the equation

$$CO {\overset{\displaystyle NH_2}{\underset{\displaystyle OEt}{\Big<}}} + KOH = KOCN + EtOH + H_2O,$$

as pointed out by Mulder (1888), supplies an elegant method for the rapid preparation of the pure salt in nearly theoretical yield.

Urethane is dissolved in the minimum amount of absolute alcohol required ; potassium hydroxide dissolved in 90 per cent alcohol is added in amount required by the above equation. The solution is heated on the water bath at 100°, for about half an hour, and then allowed to cool. Pure potassium cyanate is precipitated as a fine granular powder. If the solution of urethane and potassium hydroxide is allowed to remain in the cold for twenty-four hours, potassium cyanate separates in large crystals. When the alcohol mother liquor is concentrated by distillation, a further crop of the cyanate can be collected. There is no difficulty in obtaining a 90-95 per cent yield of the pure salt.

When urethane is heated with sodium hydroxide under similar conditions, a mixture of sodium cyanate with more or less of the sodium derivative of urethane is obtained. No intermediate compound appears to be formed when potassium hydroxide is used to decompose urethane.

3. *Preparation of Xanthhydrol.*

$$C_6H_4{\overset{\displaystyle -\,O\,-}{\underset{\displaystyle CHOH}{\big<}}}\!\!\!\!\!\!\!>\,C_6H_4.$$

Meyer and Saul (1893) prepared xanthhydrol by the reduction of xanthone (2·5 per cent in alcohol) with zinc dust and sodium hydroxide. Curiously enough, they recommended that the mixture should be heated on the water bath at 100° for one day.

They also prepared the compound by the reduction of xanthone in alcoholic solution with sodium amalgam. Fosse (1916) recommends the use of the latter agent for the rapid preparation of xanthhydrol.

The writer has found the following procedure to work admirably :—

Ten grams of xanthone

$$\left(C_6H_4{\overset{\displaystyle O}{\underset{\displaystyle CO}{\big<}}}\!\!\!\!\!\!\!>\,C_6H_4\right)$$

in fine powder are dissolved by the aid of heat in 150 c.c. of pure alcohol contained in a conical flask. Zinc dust (about 15 grams) and 10 grams of pure sodium hydroxide dissolved in 20 c.c. of hot water are added. A purple-red colour is developed on the addition of the alkali. The mixture is heated over an Argand burner, at about 70°, for not more than twenty minutes, when the solution will have become nearly colourless. The liquid, filtered while hot, is poured into 1200 c.c. of cold water, which has been previously boiled to expel dissolved air. Xanthhydrol is precipitated as a voluminous mass of white microscopic needles. The yield of the dry product is nearly theoretical, allowing for the small quantity which is retained in the mother liquor. The latter may be used to prepare a specimen of di-xanthylurea as described under Experiment 10.

4. *Preparation of Cyanamide from Calcium Cyanamide.*

One gram of calcium cyanamide mixed with about 25 c.c. of water is titrated with normal acid, using phenol-phthalein as indicator. The neutralising power of the sample, in terms of acetic acid, is then calculated from the result obtained.

In order to prepare a few grams of cyanamide, about 30 grams of the sample of calcium cyanamide are added gradually and with constant stirring to the calculated amount of pure acetic acid diluted with an equal weight of water, contained in a glass mortar of suitable size. When about four-fifths of the calcium cyanamide has been added, the product will be a rather thick pasty mass. At this stage a pestle should be used in order to secure thorough mixing when the last portions of the calcium cyanamide are added. After the pasty material has been well kneaded, it is transferred to a flat-bottomed dish, and heated at 70°, when it will soon become a friable and easily pulverisable solid.

If time is not material, the mass may be left exposed to dry air at the ordinary temperature for twenty-four hours. The coarsely powdered product is transferred to a Soxhlet apparatus, and extracted with ether in the usual manner. The ether extract, which should be almost colourless, is concentrated to a small bulk by distillation at a gentle heat, and finally evaporated to dryness in a desiccator, preferably over sodium hydroxide. The yield is over 90 per cent of the theoretical, and a good sample of calcium cyanamide should contain from 25-28 per cent of available cyanamide.

Cyanamide being very stable in the presence of acetic acid (see Chapter IX.), a slight excess of the latter over the theoretical amount should be taken in order to ensure that the product, before extraction with ether, shall be faintly acid throughout (Werner, 1916). A very good yield of cyanamide may also be obtained from sodium cyanamide by a similar procedure.

5. *Preparation of Normal Butylurea* $CON_2H_3(C_4H_9)$. M.P. 86°.

A nearly theoretical yield of the urea is readily obtained by evaporating, at 100°, an aqueous solution of n-butylamine hydrochloride and potassium cyanate (Werner, 1919).

N-butylurea is easily soluble in alcohol, from which it crystallises in thin flexible needles.   It is best purified by re-crystallisation from benzene.

Since the urea is formed as a result of the dissociation of n-butyl-amine cyanate, a small amount of urea is formed from the hydrolysis of cyanic acid.   Hence the product when separated from alcohol after the first crystallisation will be found to give a positive reaction with urease at room temperature.   This is due to the presence of ordinary urea as an impurity.   It may be removed by leaving n-butylurea in contact with urease until the latter ceases to give a positive reaction. It is well to test the compound in this way before using it for de-monstrating the fact referred to under Experiment 15.

APPENDIX I.

SUMMARY OF THE SEVERAL METHODS FOR THE DETECTION AND
ESTIMATION OF UREA.

(A) Detection of Urea.

(1) *Precipitation of urea by nitric acid, as urea nitrate* $CON_2H_4 . HNO_3$.—
This rather crude test depends on the fact that whilst urea nitrate is readily
soluble in water, it is sparingly soluble in an excess of nitric acid.

Normal urine contains over 2 per cent. of urea—approximately 2·15
per cent.—yet, as is well known, it gives no precipitate after the addition
of an equal volume of strong nitric acid, even when the product is cooled
to 0°, or is allowed to remain for twenty-four hours at the ordinary temperature.
The following results show that the colloidal matter present in urine is
responsible for the effect.

An equal volume of *colourless* nitric acid (D = 1·42) was added to 10 c.c.
of a 2 per cent. aqueous solution of urea. The liquid was cooled under
tap-water. Urea nitrate commenced to separate after about three minutes;
at the end of twenty minutes the precipitate was collected, well washed
with ether, after which it was titrated with N/10—NaOH. The weight
of urea precipitated as nitrate was 0·1182 gram, equal to 59·1 per cent. of
the total present.

A similar experiment was made with a solution of urea to which 0·5
per cent. of gelatin had been added. Only 28·5 per cent. of the urea
was precipitated as nitrate.

After the addition of 10 c.c. of strong nitric acid to an equal volume
of a 4 per cent. solution of urea, 0·292 gram of the latter was precipitated
as nitrate, i.e. 73·73 per cent. of the total present. On the other hand,
when 2 grams of urea were dissolved in 100 c.c. of urine, containing 2·01
per cent. of urea (determined by the hypobromite method), the weight precipitated as nitrate from 10 c.c. of the solution was 0·18 gram, as the
mean result of three experiments. This equals only 44·8 per cent. of the
theoretical amount present. Compared with the result of the preceding
experiment, it will be seen that in the presence of the colloidal[1] matter

---

[1] The phenomenon in question is no doubt connected with the property of urea of
combining with colloids, to which attention was drawn by Ramsden (1902), who showed
that various proteins swell up and dissolve in saturated solutions of urea. In such

of the urine, the amount of urea precipitated was nearly 29 per cent. less ($73\cdot73 - 44\cdot8 = 28\cdot93$) than in the plain aqueous solution.

The writer is not aware that attention has ever been drawn to this peculiar property of urine of hindering the precipitation of urea by nitric acid.

The preparation of urea from urine is carried out as follows: The urine is concentrated by evaporation on a water-bath to about one-sixth of the original volume. The liquid is cooled to $0°$, and an equal volume of cold strong *colourless* nitric acid is added. After about fifteen minutes the crystalline precipitate of urea nitrate is collected, and well drained by the aid of the filter-pump. The crude salt is transferred to a porcelain dish; barium carbonate, mixed with water in the form of a thick cream, is carefully added until its addition no longer produces effervescence. The reaction

$$2CON_2H_4HNO_3 + BaCO_3 = 2CON_2H_4 + Ba(NO_3)_2 + CO_2 + H_2O,$$

is then completed. The product is evaporated to dryness on a water-bath at $80°$-$90°$, after which the residue is transferred to a flask and extracted with hot alcohol. The alcoholic solution, having been transferred to another flask, is warmed with animal charcoal until an almost colourless solution is obtained. The filtered solution is finally concentrated by evaporation, and set aside to crystallise.

(2) *Precipitation of Urea by Ortho-nitrobenzaldehyde* (Lüdy, 1889).— This test, which depends on the formation of the very sparingly soluble nitrobenzodiureide $NO_2 . C_6H_4 . CH(CON_2H_3)_2$. m.p. $200°$, is carried out as follows: A slight excess of o-nitrobenzaldehyde is added to the alcoholic solution supposed to contain urea, the mixture is heated for some time on the water-bath, and allowed to cool. If urea is present, a white precipitate is formed. This is washed once with alcohol, water acidified with sulphuric acid is then added to the residue, and the whole boiled; if in the resulting solution a few drops of a solution of phenylhydrazine produce a red colour, this shows the presence of nitrobenzaldehyde, and consequently of urea. It is obvious that the test is vitiated by the presence of any other substance capable of forming a sparingly soluble condensation product with the aldehyde.

(3) *Xanthhydrol Test. Precipitation of Di-Xanthylurea* (*Ureine*).—This test, discovered by Fosse (1913), is by far the most valuable for the detection of urea by precipitation. In testing for urea at dilutions up to 1 in 20,000, Fosse recommends the addition of $3\cdot5$ parts of glacial acetic acid to 1 part of the solution, and then $0\cdot5$ part of a 10 per cent. solution of xanthhydrol in methyl alcohol. The precipitate of di-xanthylurea appears under the

solutions the proteins are not coagulated by heat. Attention was also drawn to the value of urea in histology, its action on connective tissues facilitating the separation of a tissue into its individual elements. The writer takes this opportunity of confirming the value of this property of urea, which certainly seems to merit further investigation.

microscope in the form of radiating filaments ; when dried in the oven the precipitate assumes a pale rose colour.

The solubility of "ureine" in absolute alcohol is approximately 0·009 in 100 c.c. at 15°, hence the test is available in alcoholic solution at high dilution. Di-xanthylurea melts at 260°-261°. The procedure mentioned in the previous chapter can be recommended for the rapid detection of urea in an aqueous solution containing less than 1 part in 100,000.

It must be remembered that mono-substituted ureas, thiourea, biuret, and urethane also yield sparingly soluble condensation products with xanthhydrol.

Colour Tests for Urea.

(4) *The Biuret Reaction.*—This well-known test depends on the formation of biuret, which is produced when urea is heated for a short time above its melting-point. On addition of copper sulphate and sodium hydroxide solution to the residue dissolved in water, a deep violet or reddish-violet colour is obtained. It is interesting to note that the colour reaction is not given with a copper solution and ammonia, but is immediately developed on the addition of either sodium or potassium hydroxide to the latter. This indicates that biuret must assume the enol-form in giving the colour test. Copper hydroxide is insoluble in a solution of biuret, the addition of alkali hydroxide causes it to enter rapidly into solution. Schiff (1896) concludes that the coloured compound responsible for the test has the composition $Cu(OH)_2 . 2KOH, 2C_2H_5N_3O_2$, the biuret molecule being assumed to remain intact. The writer finds the expression

$$(C_2H_3N_3O_2)_2CuK_2 . 4H_2O$$

more correct, since the water of crystallisation is all expelled at 100°-110° without much change in colour, and without decomposition of the compound. The anhydrous salt dissolves readily in water to give the characteristic colour.

(5) *Furfurol Colour Test* (Schiff, 1877).—A crystal of urea is treated with one or two drops of concentrated freshly prepared aqueous solution of furfurol, and then *immediately* with a drop of hydrochloric acid (D = 1·10). A play of colours is noticed passing rapidly from yellow through green-blue to a rich violet.

In the writer's experience this test is not very reliable ; with pure furfurol it fails altogether. According to Ganassini (1919), acetone is the active constituent of an efficient sample of furfurol. A reaction is obtained with certainty with a reagent of the following composition : furfurol (5 drops), acetone (2 c.c.), water (2 c.c.), and concentrated HCl (1 c.c.). When this reagent is added to a crystal of urea, a pink coloration is gradually developed, which soon becomes intensely purple.

(6) *Methyl-Furil Test* (Fenton, 1903, 1911).—Minute quantities of the reagent ($C_{11}H_8O_4$) and of urea are mixed on a filter paper and treated with a drop of fuming hydrochloric acid. An intense deep blue colour is developed

after a few seconds. Whilst the test is a very delicate one, the fact that the reagent is not easily accessible detracts from its value for general use. The reaction is also given by several mono-substituted ureas, and by biuret.

A colour test for urea recently proposed by Arreguine and Garcia (1921) consists in adding resorcinol and hydrochloric acid to the substance under examination and boiling for about one minute. After cooling and dilution with water the liquid is shaken with ether. The latter is coloured pink to red, according to the amount of urea present. It is stated that ·001 gram of urea may be detected by this test. Considering that a salt of ammonia gives a similar colour reaction under exactly similar conditions, the reaction, in the writer's opinion, is of little value as a test for urea.

The detection of urea by the aid of urease can be made the basis of a delicate colour test; this has been referred to in the last chapter.

(B) Estimation of Urea.

(7) *The Hypobromite Method.*—The reagent, as commonly used, is prepared by adding 25 c.c. of bromine to a solution of 100 grams of sodium hydroxide in 250 c.c. of water. Whilst the excess of alkali is required to absorb the carbon dioxide evolved in the decomposition of urea, its presence promotes the formation of "hypobromite." The solution contains the active substances approximately in the ratio, $NaBrO . 4NaOH$.

In spite of its shortcomings, which have been fully dealt with in Chapter XIV., this method is probably more largely used than any other for the estimation of urea. For a quick result and simple manipulation the process is admirable where plain solutions of urea are concerned and provided that great accuracy is not required.

It is only necessary to refer to the following observations to emphasise the fact that urea cannot be accurately estimated on the basis of the equation

$$CON_2H_4 + 3NaBrO = N_2 + CO_2 + 3NaBr + 2H_2O.$$

It is surprising how many claims to the contrary have been made. According to this equation, three means are offered for the estimation of urea : measurement of the nitrogen evolved, estimation of the carbon dioxide, or determination of the amount of hypobromite required. These have been compared by Dekeuwer and Lescoeur (1919) ; in the case of pure urea a deficit of about the same magnitude was observed when calculated from the nitrogen evolved, or from the hypobromite used, and this was doubled when calculated on the amount of carbon dioxide formed. In the estimation of urea in urine, whilst the results deduced from the amounts of nitrogen and carbon dioxide formed respectively agree fairly well among themselves, the values are too high when calculated from the amount of hypobromite used. When the urine contains sugar the variations in the results are still greater. The reasons are indicated in Chapter XIV.

Brahm (1919) suggests that all methods which are based on the reaction between urea and sodium hypobromite are to be rejected. So far as the estimation of urea in urine, blood, and other organic fluids is concerned, unless the operation is carried out in two stages, and the gas analysed for carbon monoxide content, the writer is inclined to agree with this suggestion.

Stehle (1921) claims to have obtained liberation of the theoretical volume of nitrogen by carrying out the reaction between sodium hypobromite and urea *in vacuo*. The results were found to agree very closely with those obtained by the "urease" method, but it was assumed that the evolved gas was pure nitrogen. Menaul (1922) was unable to confirm Stehle's results, a deficiency of nitrogen being observed.

It is difficult to understand how the formation of alkali cyanate could be completely suppressed by the procedure adopted by Stehle.

The decomposition of a 2 per cent. solution of urea as a standard in checking the estimation of urea in urine by "hypobromite" solution is advocated by Mezger (1921). This does not supply the control intended since, apart from the other nitrogenous compounds in urine attacked by hypobromite, the colloidal matter leads to the evolution of uncertain amounts of carbon monoxide and also affects the proportion of the other secondary reactions.

(8) *Estimation of Urea by Decomposition with Nitrous Acid.*—It has been fully explained in Chapter VI. why this reaction cannot be used for the estimation of urea on the basis of the volume of nitrogen evolved. On the other hand, reliable results can be obtained from the determination of the carbon dioxide evolved, since the ratio $CON_2H_4 \rightarrow CO_2$ is not affected by the secondary reaction, whereby more or less nitrogen is fixed as ammonia. A volumetric method for the estimation of urea by this means has been described by Campani (1887). Concordant results were obtained, using 2 c.c. of urine. Doublet and Lescoeur (1920) have recently revived this method. Urea is decomposed when heated in solution with Millon's reagent with evolution of carbon dioxide and nitrogen.

Riegler (1894) described a method for the estimation of urea based on this decomposition, though it was found that the theoretical volume of nitrogen was not evolved. A corrective factor was suggested. Funcke (1921), in proposing this method, claims to have obtained the theoretical yield of nitrogen from pure urea, but no results are given of the estimation of urea in urine.

(9) *Estimation of Urea by Precipitation with Mercuric Nitrate.*—This method, originally devised by Liebig (1853), was for many years a standard process for the estimation of urea in urine. It depends on the fact that urea is completely precipitated by a solution of mercuric nitrate, which must be as nearly neutral as possible. The white compound formed is commonly assumed to have the composition

$$(CON_2H_4)_2 \cdot Hg(NO_3)_2 \cdot 3HgO.$$

In practised hands the method is capable of giving good results, though it is little used at the present time. For the details of the process the reader is referred to the description given in Sutton's " Volumetric Analysis." Since the older methods for the estimation of urea, dependent on its " hydrolysis " by alkalis and by acids respectively, have been superseded by the simple " urease " method, it is unnecessary to consider them here. At no time were they capable of giving accurate results in the case of the estimation of urea in urine.

Estimation of Urea by Urease.

The complete decomposition of a small quantity of urea by urease is so readily effected that the reaction is largely used for the estimation of urea. The method has one great advantage, that only urea is attacked by the enzyme under the experimental conditions.

Marshall (1913) first published a method for the clinical estimation of urea in urine by this means, but his procedure, which was not very accurate, has been superseded by the following improved processes :—

(10) *Plimmer and Skelton's Method.*—The apparatus required is the same as that for Folin's method of estimating ammonia in urine. 5 c.c. of urine, about 50 c.c. of water, 1 gram of powdered soy bean, and a thin layer of liquid paraffin are put into the tall gas cylinder which is placed in a bath at 40°. A rapid air current is drawn through the cylinder for about an hour, and the ammonia collected in an Allihn wash bottle containing excess of standard acid ; about 1 gram of anhydrous sodium carbonate is then added to the tall cylinder so as to liberate ammonia from ammonium salts and air is drawn through for another half-hour. A separate apparatus can be set up in series for an ammonia determination. Several estimations can be made at the same time if a series of cylinders and receivers be set up. By means of this method the authors also showed that allantoine could be estimated in urine, if Folin's magnesium chloride method for urea were made use of for determination of allantoine, urea, and ammonia together.

(11) *Van Slyke and Cullens' Method* (1914).—In estimating urea in urine, 0·5 c.c. of urine is mixed with 5 c.c. of 0·6 per cent. of potassium dihydrogen phosphate solution and 1 c.c. of a 10 per cent. solution of urease. After twenty minutes at 15°, or three minutes at 50°, 4 to 5 grams of potassium carbonate are added, and the ammonia liberated is aspirated into 25 c.c. of $N/50$. HCl. When the aeration is completed, the excess of acid is titrated with $N/50$. NaOH. Each c.c. of acid neutralised by the ammonia set free is equal to 0·0006 gram of urea.

The urease is prepared by extracting soja-bean meal with water at room temperature, and pouring the clear extract into at least ten times its volume of acetone. The precipitated urease is dried in a vacuum. It is said to maintain its activity for an apparently indefinite period.

(12) *Folin and Denis' Method* (1916).—One c.c. of urine is transferred to a 100 c.c. flask, 0·25 gram of soja-bean meal is added in the form of a 1 per cent. suspension in 20 per cent. alcohol. The flask is stoppered and allowed to remain for 15 minutes in a water-bath at about 50°. Water (25 c.c.) and 1 c.c. of fresh 25 per cent. metaphosphoric acid are added and mixed; about a gram of blood-charcoal and a further 25 c.c. of water are then added, shaken, made up to volume, mixed, and filtered through a dry filter-paper. From 5 to 20 c.c. of the filtrate are then Nesslerised and compared with a standard in the usual manner.

The estimation of urea in blood-serum may be carried out in a similar manner.

(13) *Hahn's Method* (1915).—In the case of blood, 1 c.c. of the serum is placed in a 50 c.c. flask, 20 c.c. of water, a small quantity of urease (or soja-bean meal), and three drops of toluene are added, and the flask closed with a stopper. A similar mixture, but without the enzyme, is prepared in another flask. After ten hours, each mixture is treated with 20 c.c. of N/100 . HCl, 0·5 c.c. of 5 per cent. potassium iodate solution, and a crystal of potassium iodide; 20 c.c. of N/100 . $Na_2S_2O_3$ solution are then added to each mixture, and the excess of thiosulphate titrated with N/100-iodine solution. The difference in the quantity of the iodine solution required for the two titrations multiplied by 0·0003 gives the amount of urea in 1 c.c. of the serum. That is, the ammonia produced from 0·0003 gram of urea will neutralise 1 c.c. of N/100 . HCl, and from the equation

$$5HI + HIO_3 = 3I_2 + 3H_2O$$

the volume of hydrochloric acid neutralised is indirectly recorded, since the amount of iodine liberated will depend on the amount of free acid remaining.

Partos (1920) describes a method for the estimation of urea by determining the carbon dioxide evolved from its decomposition by urease. The original paper should be consulted for a description of the apparatus recommended.

(14) *Estimation of Urea in Urine by Means of Xanthhydrol.*—The following method is due to Fosse (1914). The urine is diluted to ten times its volume with water; 10 c.c. of the liquid are placed in a conical flask, and 35 c.c. of glacial acetic acid added. Five separate portions of 1 c.c. of a 10 per cent. solution of xanthhydrol in methyl alcohol are added at intervals of ten minutes, and the mixture allowed to remain for one hour. The micro-crystalline precipitate is collected, washed with alcohol, dried at 100°, detached from the filter-paper, and weighed. The weight divided by seven equals the weight of urea. The precipitate forms a rigid mat, which can be readily detached from the filter by means of a pair of forceps. Under the conditions given, urea is the only constituent of urine which gives an insoluble xanthhydrol derivative.

(15) *Estimation of Urea in Blood-Serum by Means of Xanthhydrol.*—The following process has been devised by Fosse, Robyn, and François (1914) :—

Ten c.c. of the blood-serum are mixed with 10 c.c. of concentrated

13

Tanret's [1] solution and centrifuged. The clear liquid measures about 17 c.c. Of this 15 c.c. are transferred to a small conical flask. An equal volume of glacial acetic acid is added, and then 1·5 c.c. of a 10 per cent. solution of xanthhydrol in methyl alcohol. After one hour the crystalline precipitate is collected on a filter supported on a perforated porcelain plate, care being taken to keep the precipitate well within the edge of the filter paper. After washing with alcohol the precipitate is dried at 100°, and weighed.

The percentage of urea is calculated from the expression

$$\text{per cent. of urea} = \frac{P}{7} \times \frac{20}{15} \times 10.$$

P = weight of di-xanthylurea, which is equivalent to one-seventh of its weight of urea. Fosse has proposed the name *ureine* for the urea derivative of xanthhydrol.

Nicloux and Welter (1921) have employed this method with success in the estimation of such small quantities as 0·2 to 0·05 milligramme of urea per c.c. of solution. Using 1 c.c., and even less, of blood-serum, remarkably concordant results have been obtained. The original paper should be consulted for the details of this micro-analytical method for the estimation of urea.

Urea and Formaldehyde.

When a mixture of urea and formaldehyde in aqueous solution is acidified a white insoluble condensation product is precipitated after a short time. On the assumption that when an excess of formaldehyde is present the product has the composition $C_5H_{10}O_3N_4$ (i.e. $2CON_2H_4 + 3CH_2O - 2H_2O$), Goldschmidt (1897) proposed to estimate urea gravimetrically by this means. Dixon (1918) has examined the interaction of urea and formaldehyde in considerable detail, and has shown that the composition of the condensation product is liable to much variation according to the proportions in which the two substances may be present. Moreover, when formaldehyde is present in large excess no condensation product is precipitated. Compounds of the composition $C_2H_6O_2N_2$, $C_4H_8O_2N_4$ and $C_5H_{12}O_4N_4$ are described in addition to Goldschmidt's compound. Whilst Dixon admits that from random mixtures of urea and formaldehyde, $C_5H_{10}O_3N_4$ is the product likely to preponderate, it is obvious that the reaction is not one which can be used for the accurate estimation of urea.

It is interesting to note that neutral formaldehyde and "free" urea do not interact to form an insoluble product. The latter is formed within a few minutes, or a few seconds, after acidification depending on the concentration. This clearly indicates that urea must be in the form $HN:C.(NH_2)OH$ in order to react with the aldehyde. Since we may have condensation between formaldehyde and the amino-group of a single molecule of urea and the imino-groups of two molecules of urea, it is not surprising that different condensation products should be formed.

[1] Mercuric chloride (2·71 grams) and potassium iodide (7·2 grams) are dissolved in 66·6 c.c. of glacial acetic acid, and sufficient water to make 100 c.c.

APPENDIX II.

Physico-chemical Constants of Urea.

Urea melts at 132·6° (corr.). It is very easily soluble in water and in methyl alcohol, moderately soluble in ethyl alcohol, sparingly soluble in acetone, and almost insoluble in ether, chloroform, or benzene.

Solubility of Urea.

Grams of urea per 100 grams of solvent.

t.	Water.	Methyl Alcohol.	Ethyl Alcohol.
0°	55·9	13·8	2·5
10	66·0	16·0	3·5
20	79·0	20·0	5·0
30	93·0	24·0	6·5
40	106·0	30·0	8·5
50	120·0	37·0	10·5
60	132·0	47·0	13·0
70	145·0	—	17·5

These results are from values determined by Speyers (1902).

Solubility of Urea in Water. Campetti (1901), Krummacher (1905).

77·9 grams (urea) in 100 grams of water at 5·5° (K)
84·97 „ „ „ 100 „ „ „ „ 9·85° (C)
96·46 „ „ „ 100 „ „ „ „ 14·92° (C)
100·0 „ „ „ 100 „ „ „ „ 17·1° (K)
108·17 „ „ „ 100 „ „ „ „ 19·92° (C)
109·14 „ „ „ 100 „ „ „ „ 20·92° (K)

100 grams absolute methyl alcohol dissolve 21·8 grams urea at 19·5°
100 „ „ ethyl „ „ 5·06 „ „ „ 19·5°
100 „ glycerol „ 50·0 „ „ „ 15·5°

Heat of dissolution of urea in water equals − 3·58 cals. at about 11° C., Berthelot (1890), − 3·769 (Rübner, 1885), − 3·57 (Krummacher, 1905), − 3·628 (Speyers, 1896), − 3·645 at 10°-15° C., − 3·566 at 15°-20° C. (Campetti, 1901) − 3·61 to − 3·66 (Walker and Wood, 1900).

The following determinations are due to Berthelot (1889, 1896, 1897) :—
The heat of combustion of urea for,

$$CON_2H_4 \rightarrow CO_2 \text{ (gas)} + N_2 \text{ (gas)} + 2H_2O \text{ (liquid)} = + 151·8 \text{ cals.}$$

at constant volume, or + 151·5 cals. at constant pressure.

Heat of formation of solid urea from carbon (diamond) liberates + 80·8 cals., and heat of formation in solution in water (or urine) liberates + 77·2 cals. The complete combustion of urea liberates 11·8 cals. less than the

13 *

combustion of its constituents if they were in the free state. The heat absorbed in the dissociation of urea into ammonia and cyanic acid which must accompany the combustion is no doubt mainly responsible for this difference.

It is pointed out by Berthelot and Petit (1889) that the formation of urea from carbonate of ammonia (both in solution) would absorb − 6·4 to − 8·0 cals. This, in the writer's opinion, is a strong argument in itself against the view that urea is formed in the body by a dehydration of carbonate of ammonia. It is not likely that an endothermic reaction is responsible for the final production of urea in the body.

The heat of formation of cyanate of ammonia from its elements = + 68·9 cals. (Urea = + 80·8.) The conversion of the salt into urea liberates about + 7·1 cals., and the heat of neutralisation of cyanic acid by ammonia is about + 10·7 cals.

Walker and Wood (1900) found that the molecular heat of transformation of solid cyanate of ammonia into solid urea is = 49 K (K = 100 gram-cals.), whilst the value for the conversion of the salt into urea in aqueous solution was approximately = 75 K. For the molecular heat of formation of cyanate of ammonia from its elements they found 738 K, and for the heat of formation of urea 787 K. The values are in close agreement with those of Berthelot, considering the sources of error which cannot be avoided in these determinations.

Urea and the Fixation of Nitrogen.

The fixation of atmospheric nitrogen as ammonia is a problem which has now been successfully accomplished by the Haber process. On the other hand, the necessary fixation of ammonia by combining it with an acid (such as H_2SO_4) has a serious drawback from an economic point of view, on account of the relatively large proportion of superfluous material which is thereby introduced. Sulphate of ammonia, for example, contains a maximum of 25·75 per cent. of available NH_3, and upon this depends its value as a fertiliser.

Urea supplies an ideal source of nitrogen for all forms of plant life. It is capable of yielding 56·66 per cent. of its weight of ammonia, whilst it is not unlikely that its carbon content may be also available to a certain extent in the form of nascent cyanic acid. The fixation of nitrogen in the form of urea is therefore a problem of considerable importance. It is one which has attracted much attention in recent times, and that the efforts to solve it have met with some success may be judged from the following brief extracts :—

1. A melt of 10 parts of ammonium carbamate, or of the product of the interaction of carbon dioxide and ammonia, and 1 part of water prepared at 90° under a pressure of 15 atmospheres is passed through a heated pressure-proof spiral pipe heated at 135°-140°. If the time occupied

in passing through the spiral pipe is from two to three hours, then on relieving the pressure 25 per cent. of the carbamate will have been converted into urea. (Badische Anilin und Soda Fabrik. G.P., 332,679.)

2. A mixture of 2 vols. of ammonia and 1 vol. of carbon dioxide is forced into an autoclave heated at 135°-150° for about two hours under a pressure of 50°-100° atmospheres. The product is slowly blown out through the bottom of the apparatus into a distillation column, whence the uncombined gases are returned together with a fresh supply of the mixed gases to an autoclave. The yield of urea is said to be better than by the previous procedure. (B. Anilin u. Soda Fabrik. E.P., 145,060.)

This manufacture of urea is based on the erroneous view that carbamate of ammonia is directly dehydrated to urea in accordance with the change

$$CO {\Large\langle} {{NH_2} \atop {O . NH_4}} \rightleftarrows CON_2H_4 + H_2O.$$

It is of course a synthesis of urea on the lines suggested in Chapters VII. and VIII., namely, $CO_2 + NH_3 \rightleftarrows H_2O + HN : CO$, and

$$HN : CO + NH_3 \rightarrow CON_2H_4.$$

A catalyst or agent to disturb the equilibrium by removing the water produced in the "critical" reaction between CO_2 and NH_3 is required to make the process a complete success. Matignon and Fréjacques (1922), whilst assuming the formation of urea to be the result of a simple dehydration of carbamate of ammonia, have obtained some very interesting and important results bearing on the point just mentioned.

The yields of urea when equilibrium was reached at different temperatures were as follows :—

Time in hours.	Temperature.	Per cent. of urea.
39	130°	39·2
40	134°	39·92
39	140°	41·4
24	145°	43·3

After four hours' heating at 130°, the yield of urea was only 1 per cent., whilst at 145° the yield was 41 per cent. Thus very little is gained by prolonging the heating at the higher temperature.

The effects of different catalysts in promoting the formation of urea at 130° are shown below :—

	4 Hours. Per cent.	10 Hours. Per cent.	16 Hours. Per cent.
Without a catalyst . . .	1	4·2	13·6
Thoria	1·9	6·3	—
Alumina (Bayer)	2·8	9·8	—
Kaolin (natural) . . .	3·1	11·8	—
Kaolin (artificial) . . .	3·4	15·3	28·6
Alumina (precipitated) . . .	3·4	13·5	26·0
Silica	3·4	14·2	27·2
Ca SO₄	7·2	12·3	—

At a higher temperature, approaching 150°, the catalysts did not exert any beneficial effects.

Krase and Gaddy (1922) obtained a yield of urea equal to 40 per cent. of the ammonia used after heating ammonium carbamate at 150°, in a steel autoclave, for about four hours. Charges of from 10 to 12 lbs. of ammonium carbamate, previously compressed into briquettes, were used in the experiments, and the working pressure was found to be between 80 and 120 atmospheres. For further details, and a description of the experimental plant used, the original paper must be consulted.

Working on the lines suggested by the writer's theory of the origin of urea in this synthesis, Bailey (1922) has obtained very interesting and encouraging results. By passing a current of carbon dioxide and ammonia, the latter being in excess, through a quartz tube heated to 500° C., and under such conditions that the reaction products were subjected to sudden cooling, a yield of over 50 per cent. of urea was obtained, calculated on the amount of carbon dioxide used. This result was obtained under ordinary atmospheric pressure and in the presence of thoria as the catalyst. The cooling was effected by means of a central tube through which a current of cold water was maintained. In this way the equilibrium referred to above was largely overcome, urea being deposited on the cold tube according as cyanic acid was formed.

The possible economic preparation of urea from carbon monoxide and ammonia, in the presence of a catalyst, or oxidising agent on the lines of the reaction $CO + 2NH_3 = CON_2H_4 + H_2$ is a subject which merits investigation.

Processes for the manufacture of urea from calcium cyanamide (Nitrolime) have been the subject of several patents. The fact that cyanamide is not directly hydrolysed to urea, but requires a concentration of acid necessary to produce a salt of urea appears to be a serious drawback to the economic production of urea from this source.

The Purification of Acetone by Means of Urea.

When pure urea was dissolved in commercial " pure " acetone, it was found that the residue left after evaporation of the solvent had a yellow-brown colour, and when added to a solution of potassium permanganate it rapidly destroyed the colour of the latter. Pure urea is not oxidised by permanganate in the cold. Whilst the nature of the impurity in ordinary acetone has not yet been identified, it apparently interacts with urea, or at all events is retained by it in the residue left after distillation.

The following simple procedure was found to yield a product which answered well to the tests for purity when compared with samples of acetone which had been purified by the bisulphite method, and by the sodium iodide method described by Shipsey and the writer (1913).[1] To a litre of ordinary dry acetone, 10 grams of pure urea in fine powder were added.

[1] " T.C.S.," 103, 1255.

The mixture, agitated from time to time to promote solution of the urea, was allowed to remain for forty-eight hours, after which it was distilled from the water-bath until 950 c.c. had been collected. The distillate after remaining for twenty-four hours over anhydrous calcium chloride was redistilled, from a round-bottomed flask, using a *three-section* Young's evaporator still-head. The distillate collected at 56°-56·2° at 760 mm. was almost equal in purity to acetone purified by the other methods. 100 c.c. of a saturated solution of urea in acetone were found to contain at 10°, 0·673 gram, at 15°, 0·792 gram of urea.

BIBLIOGRAPHY.

DATE.   PAGE IN TEXT.

1773.   ROUELLE, F. M.   "L'extrait savonneux de l'urine."   *Journal de Medecine*, November 1, 118

1798-99.   FOURCROY AND VAUQUELIN, M.   "L'Histoire naturelle chimique et medicale de l'urine humaine dans lequel on s'occupe specialement des propriétés de la matiére particuliére."   *Annal. Chimie*, 31, 32, 48, and 80-113 . . . 2, 23, 31, 103, 118, 161

1817.   PROUT, W.   "On the nature of some of the immediate principles of urine."   *Annal. Chimie*, **10**, 369-379 2

1818.   VAUQUELIN, M.   "Sur le cyanogène et sur l'acide Hydrocyanique."   *Annal. Chim. Phys.*, **9**, 113-146 9

1820.   PROUST, M.   "Faits pour la connaissance des urines et des calculs."   *Annal. Chim. Phys.*, 14, 257-288 2

1822.   WÖHLER, F.   "Sur l'acide particulier qui se forme lorsque l'on combine le cyanogène avec les alcalis."   *Annal. Chim. Phys.*, 20, 353-359, and *Annalen der Physik*, **71**, 95 8

1823.   PRÉVOST, J. L., AND DUMAS, J. B.   "L'urée dans le sang."   *Annal. Chim. Phys.*, **2**, 23, 90-104 118

1824.   GAY-LUSSAC, L. J., AND LIEBIG, J. v.   "Analyse du Fulminate d'Argent."   *Annal. Chim. Phys.*, 25, 285-311 15

1824.   WÖHLER, F.   "Recherches analytiques sur l'acide cyanique."   *Annal. Chim. Phys.*, **2**, 27, 196-200 15

1828.   WÖHLER, F.   "La formation artificielle de l'urée."   *Annal. Chim. Phys.*, **37**, 330-334 . . . . 2, 8

1830.   BERZELIUS, J. J.   "Composition de l'acide tartrique et de l'acide racémique, et remarques générales sur les corps qui ont la même composition et possèdent des propriétes differentes."   *Annal. de Chim.*, 1831, 46, 113-137 3

1830.   DUMAS, J. B.   "Sur l'oxamide, matière qui se rapproche de quelques substances animales"   *Annal. Chim. Phys.*, **2**, 44, 129-132 . . . . 3, 59

1830.   DUMAS, J. B.   "Sur la composition de l'urée."   *Annal. Chim. Phys.*, **2**, 44, 273, 278 . . . . 3, 31, 59, 65, 103

1830.   WÖHLER, F.   "Decomposition de l'urée á une temperature élevée."   *Annal. Chim. Phys.*, **2**, 43, 64-74 . . . . 23, 49

1831.   HENRI FILS AND PLISSON, A.   "Les matières organiques azotées dites neutres."   *Annal. Chim. Phys.*, 46, 190-199 4

1831.   LIEBIG, J. v., AND WÖHLER, F.   "Recherches sur l'acide cyanique."   *Annal. Chim. Phys.*, 46, 25-61 . . . . 3, 11, 15, 19

1838.   REGNAULT, V.   "Action du gaz ammoniac sec sur le gaz chloro-carbonique."   *Annal. Chim. Phys.*, 69, 180-183 . . . . 4, 59

1842.   DUMAS, J. B., AND CAHOURS, A.   "Sur les matières azotées neutres de l'organisation."   *C.R.*, 15, 976-984 . . . . 4, 123

1845.   CAHOURS, A.   "Sur une nouvelle production de l'urethane."   *C.R.*, 21, 629-631 . . 62

1846.   LAURENT, A., AND GERHARDT, C.   "Recherches sur les combinaisons melloniques."   *C.R.*, 22, 453-462 24

1847.   LAURENT, A., AND GERHARDT, C.   "Sur le mellon et le melam."   *Annal. Chim. Phys.*, **3**, 19, 93 24

1847.   WILLIAMSON, A.   "Formation of urea from oxamide."   *Mémoires, Congrès scientif de Venise* 5, 72

1848.   WIEDEMANN, G.   "On a new decomposition product of urea."   *Pogg. Annal.*, 74, 67 24

1849.   BUNSEN, R.   "Estimation of urea in urine by decomposition with ammoniacal solution of barium chloride."   *Annalen*, 65, 875 . . . . 31, 45

DATE.		PAGE IN TEXT.

1879.   FOSTER, W.   "The action of alkaline hypobromite on oxamide, urea, and potassium ferrocyanide."   *T.C.S.*, 35, 119-124   162

1879.   MÉHU, C.   "Le dosage de l'urée."   *C.R.*, 89, 175   165

1879.   SCHMIEDEBERG, O.   "Formation of urea in the animal organism."   *Arch. exp. Path. Pharm.*, 8, 1   .   .   .   .   123, 127

1880.   DRECHSEL, E.   "Cyanamide."   *J. pr. Chem.*, 2, 20, 77-79   80

1880.   DRECHSEL, E.   "Formation of urea in the animal organism."   *J. pr. Chem.*, 2, 22, 476-488   .   .   .   .   69, 124

1880.   FAUCONNIER, A.   "Dosage de l'urée."   *Bull. Soc. Chim.*, 2, 33, 103-105   .   .   162

1881.   HOPPE-SEYLER, F.   "Formation of urea in the body."   *Physiol. Chem.*, 808-810   .   123

1881.   HERROUN, E. F.   "On the synthetical production of urea from benzene, ammonia, and air by the action of heated platinum."   *T.C.S.*, 39, 471-474   .   .   73

1882.   FENTON, H. J. H.   "Transformation of urea into cyanamide."   *T.C.S.*, 41, 262-263   90, 112

1882.   GRIESS, P.   "Action of cyanogen on picramic acid."   *Ber.*, 15, 447-452   .   .   6

1882.   HORBACZEWSKI, J.   "Synthesis of uric acid."   *Monatsh. Chem.*, 3, 796   .   .   .   129

1882.   MIXTER, W. G.   "Formation of urea from ammonia and carbon dioxide."   *Amer. C.J.*, 4, 35-38   .   .   .   .   66, 73

1882.   DUGGAN, J. R.   "Estimation of urea by sodium hypobromite."   *Amer. C.J.*, 4, 47-49   167

1883.   ISAMBERT, F.   "Sur les vapeurs de la carbamide."   *C.R.*, 96, 340-341   .   .   29, 30

1884.   HENTSCHEL, W.   "Preparation of carbamide."   *Ber.*, 17, 1286-1287   .   .   6

1885.   LEA, SHERIDAN.   "Some notes on the isolation of a soluble urea-ferment from *Torula ureæ*."   *J. Physiol.*, 6, 136   103

1885.   HOFMANN, A. W.   "The constitution of melamine and of cyanuric acid."   *Ber.*, 18, 2781-2800   6

1885.   MÜLLER, A.   "Chaleurs de formation des sels des amines."   *Bull. Soc. Chim.*, 43, 213-217   141

1885.   MILLOT, A.   "Produits d'oxydation du charbon par l'électrolyse d'une solution ammoniacale."   *C.R.*, 101, 432-433   73

1885.   RÜBNER, M.   "Thermal equivalent of a solution of urea."   *Zeit. f. Biol.*, 20, 414-418   195

1886.   MILLOT, A.   "Electrolyse d'une solution ammoniacale avec des électrodes de charbon."   *C.R.*, 103, 153   73

1886.   EMMERLING, A.   "Action of nitrous acid on urea, uric acid, and ammonium sulphate."   *Landw. Versuchs Stat.*, 440-450   49

1886.   HÄLLER, A.   "Action de la potasse alcoolique sur l'urée, la sulfo-urée et quelques urées substituées.   Reaction inverse de celle de Wöhler."   *C.R.*, 102, 974-976   .   112

1887.   BERTHELOT, M., AND ANDRÉ, G.   "Contributions à l'histoire de la decomposition des amides par l'eau et les acides étendus."   *C.R.*, 103, 1051-1057   .   .   39

1887.   CAMPANI, G.   "Volumetric estimation of urea."   *Gazzetta*, 17, 137-141   .   .   191

1888.   MULDER, E.   "Urethane and some of its derivatives."   *Rec. T.C.*, 6, 169-198   .   182

1889.   BERTHELOT, M., AND PETIT, P.   "La chaleur animale et la chaleur de formation et de combustion de l'urée."   *C.R.*, 109, 759-764   196

1889.   EMICH, F.   "Amides of carbonic acid."   *Monatsh.*, 10, 321-353   .   .   .   91

1889.   LÜDY, E.   "Aldehydic condensation-products of carbamide, and detection of carbamide."   *Monatsh.*, 10, 295-316   188

1889.   LUTHER, R.   "The Knop-Hüfner method of estimating urea."   *Zeit. Physiol. Chem.*, 13, 500-505   162

1889.   SMOLKA, A., AND FRIEDREICH, A.   "Derivatives of cyanamide."   *Monatsh.*, 10, 86-100   29

1890.   BAMBERGER, E.   "Synthesis of ammeline and cyanuric acid."   *Ber.*, 23, 1856-1869   81

1890.   DRECHSEL, E.   "Formation of carbamide from albumen."   *Ber.*, 23, 3096-3102   .   76

1890.   MIQUEL, P.   "Le ferment soluble de l'urée."   *C.R.*, 111, 397-399   .   .   .   103

1891.   ABEL, J. J.   "The presence of carbamic acid in urine after the administration of lime."   *Arch. Anat. Physiol.*, 236   127

1891.   CONRAD, M., AND BRÜCKNER, C.   "Halogen derivatives of malonic acid."   *Ber.*, 24, 2993-3005   95

1893.   MEYER, R., AND SAUL, E.   "Preparation of xanthhydrol."   *Ber.*, 26, 1276-1279   .   183

DATE.		PAGE IN TEXT.

1894. MOUREAU, C. "Conversion de l'urée en cyanamide." *Bull. Soc. Chim.*, 3, 11, 1068-1070 92

1894. RIEGLER, E. "Estimation of urea." *Ziet. anal. Chem.*, 33, 49-53 . . . 191

1894. RICHET, C. "Formation de l'urée dans le foie." *C.R.*, 118, 1125-1128; *C.R. Soc. Biol.*, 525-528 132

1895. WALKER, J., AND HAMBLY, F. J. "Transformation of ammonium cyanate into urea." *T.C.S.*, 67, 746-767 . . . . 9, 39

1896. BERTHELOT, M. "Acid cyanique." *C.R.*, 123, 337-341 195

1896. CAZENEUNE, P. "Sur un nouveau moyen de préparation synthetique de l'urée et des urées composées symetriques." *C.R.*, 122, 999-1000 6

1896. HÖFMEISTER, F. "Formation of urea by oxidation." *Arch. exp. Path. Pharm.*, 37, 426-444 . . . . 70, 76

1896. SCHIFF, H. "Biuret compounds." *L'Orosi*, 19, 109-115 . . . . 182, 189

1896. SPEYERS, C. L. "Heats of solution of some carbon compounds." *Amer. C.J.*, 18, 146, 156 195

1897. BERTHELOT, M. "Chaleurs de formation de l'acide Cyanique et de l'urée." *Ann. Chim. Phys.*, vii., 11, 145-148 195

1897. BOURGEOIS, L. "Le rendement de l'urée des carbonates d'ammoniaque." *Bull. Soc. Chim.*, 3, 17, 474-477 65

1897. CADY, H. P. "Electrolysis and electrolytic conductivity of certain substances dissolved in liquid ammonia." *J. Physic. Chem.*, i., 707-713 149

1897. GOLDSCHMIDT, C. "Action of formaldehyde on carbamide" and "Estimation of urea by means of formaldehyde." *Chem. Zeit.*, 21, 460, 586 194

1897. RUSPAGGIARI, G. "Mercuro-carbamide and its salts." *Gazzetta*, 27, i., 1-13. 113

1897. TAKABAYASHI, S. "Poisonous action of ammonium salts on plants." *B.C. Agric. Imp. U. Tokyo*, 3, 265-274 122

1897. WALKER, J., AND KAY, S. A. "Velocity of urea formation in aqueous alcohol." *T.C.S.*, 71, 489-508 . . . . 9, 10

1898. HALSEY, J. T. "The antecedents of urea." *Zeit. Physiol. Chem.*, 25, 325-336. 70, 77

1898. RAYLEIGH, LORD. "Character of the impurity found in nitrogen gas derived from urea." *Proc. Roy. Soc.*, 64, 95-100 163

1899. JOUVE, AD. "La formation des carbamides." *C.R.*, 128, 114-115 . . . 74

1900. FRANKLIN, E. C., AND KRAUS, C. A. "Electrical conductivity of liquid ammonia solutions." *Amer. C.J.*, 23, 277-313 149

1900. STIEGLITZ, J., AND MCKEE, R. H. "Oxygen ethers of carbamides: methyliso-carbamide." *Ber.*, 33, 807-812 93

1900. WALKER, J., AND WOOD, J. K. "Preparation and properties of solid ammonium cyanate." *T.C.S.*, 77, 21-33 . . . . 9, 21, 195

1901. FALTA, W. "Formation of carbamide by the oxidation of physiological nitrogenous substances by means of permanganate in acid solution." *Ber.*, 34, 2674-2679 133

1901. HUGOUNENQ, L. "Formation de l'urée par oxydation de l'albumin au moyen du persulphate d'ammoniaque." *C.R.*, 132, 1240 76

1901. JOLLES, A. "Carbamide as a product of oxidation of nitrogenous substances." *J. pr. Chem.* ii., 63, 516-522 133

1901. LUTZ, J. "Recerches sur la nutrition des thallophytes à l'aide des amides." *Bull. Soc. Bot.*, 48, 325-334 122

1901. SCHULZ, F. N. "Formation of carbamide by the oxidation of albumen according to Jolles." *Zeit. Physiol. Chem.*, 33, 363-369 133

1902. FAWSITT, C. E. "The decomposition of carbamide by acids and by alkalis." *Zeit. physikal. Chem.*, 41, 601-629 . . . . 32, 34, 40, 109

1902. FRANKLIN, E. C., AND STAFFORD, O. F. "Reactions between acid and basic amides in liquid ammonia." *Amer. C.J.*, 28, 83-107 . . . . . . 112, 149

1902. HOFMEISTER, F. "Constitution of the albumen molecule." *Chem. Centr.*, ii., 1263-1264 124

1902. RAMSDEN, W. "New properties of urea." *J. Physiol.*, 28, 23-26 . . . 187

1902. SENIER, A., AND WALSH, T. "The polymerisation of cyanic acid: cyanuric acid and cyamelide." *T.C.S.*, 81, 290-291 18

1902. WERNER, A. "Principal and supplementary valencies, and the constitution of ammonium compounds." *Annalen*, 322, 261-296 . . . . . 111, 135, 154

DATE.		PAGE IN TEXT

1903. ABDERHALDEN, E. "Formation of carbamide by the oxidation of albumen with permanganate according to Jolles." *Zeit. Physiol. Chem.*, 37, 506; 39, 210-211   133

1903. BAMBERGER, M., AND LANDSIEDL, A. "Occurrence of urea in plants." *Monatsh.*, 24, 218-219 118

1903. CUMMING, A. C. "The formation of urea by the direct hydrolysis of lead cyanate." *T.C.S.*, 83, 1391-1394 46

1903. FENTON, H. J. H. "A reagent for the identification of urea." *T.C.S.*, 83, 187-190 189

1903. LANZER, E. "Oxidation of proteins by Jolles's method." *Zeit. Nahr. Genussm.*, 6, 385-396 133

1903. LE COMTE, O. "La décomposition complète de l'urée et des sels d'ammoniaque au moyen de l'hypobromure de soude naissant dans un milieu alkalin." *J. Pharm. Chim.*, **vi.**, 17, 471-475 167

1903. PALMAER, W. "Preparation of tetramethylammonium." *Zeit. Elektrochem.*, 8, 729-731 135

1904. BRUCE, W. M. "Oxygen ethers of carbamide." *Amer. C.J.*, 26, 449-464 . 25

1904. CAIN, J. C. "The constitution of the ammonium compounds." *Mem. Manchest. Phil. Soc.*, 48, xiv., 1-11 156

1904. FAWSITT, C. E. "The decomposition of methylcarbamide." *T.C.S.*, 85, 1581-1591 108

1904. GARNIER, L. "L'Hypobromure de soude naissant ne libére pas tout l'azote de l'urée." *J. Pharm. Chim.*, **vi.**, 19, 137-139 167

1904. KOSSEL, A., AND DAKIN, H. D. "'Arginase' a urea-forming ferment." *Zeit. Physiol. Chem.*, 41, 321-331 124

1905. ARMSTRONG, H. E., AND ROBERTSON, W. "A contribution to the chemistry of nitrogen, etc." *T.C.S.*, 87, 1272-1297. 170

1905. FRANKLIN, E. C. "Reactions in liquid ammonia." *Amer. C.J.*, 27, 820-851 . 149

1905. GAZE, R. "Urea in fungi." *Arch. Pharm.*, 243, 78-79 . . . 118

1905. HANTZSCH, A. R., AND HOFMANN, F. "Derivatives of cyanuric acid. Tricyanocarbamide." *Ber.*, 38, 1005-1011 29

1905. HANTZSCH, A. R. "Cyamelide." *Ber.*, 38, 1013-1021 . . . 17, 25

1905. HANTZSCH, A. R., AND STUER, B. C. "The action of ammonia on carbonyl chloride." *Ber.*, 38, 1022-1043 60

1905. JACKSON, H., AND NORTHALL-LAURIE, D., "The action of carbon monoxide on Ammonia." *T.C.S.*, 87, 433 . . . . 74, 149

1905. SCHESTAKOFF, P. J. "Action of hypochlorites on urea : New synthesis of hydrazine." *J. Russ. Phys. Chem. Soc.*, 37, 1-7 . . . . 163, 169

1906. PALAZZO, F. C., AND CARAPELLE, E. "Constitution of cyanic acid." *Chem. Centr.*, ii., 1723-24 22

1907. FOSSE, R. "Action de l'urée, de la thiourée, de l'urethane et de quelques amides sur le xanthhydrol." *C.R.*, 145, 813-815 77

1907. PICKARD, R. H., AND KENYON, J. "Contributions to the chemistry of oxygen compounds. II. The compounds of carbamide with acid and salts." *T.C.S.*, 91, 896-905 114

1908. CHATTAWAY, F. D. "Action of chlorine on carbamide." *Proc. Roy. Soc.*, A., 81, 381-388 170

1908. FRIEND, J. A. N. "Valency." *T.C.S.*, 93, 267-270 156

1908 GORIS, A., AND MASCRÉ, M. "Sur la presence de l'urée chez quelques champignons supérieures." *C.R.*, 147, 1488-1489 118

1908. POHL, F. "Dicyanodiamide." *J. pr. Chem.*, ii., 77, 533-548 . . . 95

1909. CARO, N., AND GROSSMANN, H. "The chemical nature of dicyanodiamide." *Chem. Zeit.*, 33, 734 83

1909. CHATTAWAY, F. D. "The preparation of dichloro-carbamide." *T.C.S.*, 95, 464-466   170

1909. MICHAEL, A., AND HIBBERT, H. "Desmotropy and merotropy. VI. Constitution of cyanic acid." *Annalen*, 364, 129-146 21

1909. RUPERT, F. F. "Solid hydrates of ammonia." *Amer. C.J.*, 31, 866-868 . 146

1909. TAKEUCHI, T. "Urease in higher plants. Application of urease to the manufacture of sulphate of ammonia from the urea of the urine." *J. Coll. Agric. Tōkyō*, 1, 1-14, and *Chem. Centralblatt*, II., 635 104

DATE.   PAGE IN TEXT.
1910. ANGELI, A. "Some analogies between derivatives of oxygen and nitrogen." *Atti.*
       R. Accad. Lincei, v., 19, ii., 29-36, and 94-101   148

1910. MASSON, D. O., AND MASSON, J. I. "The decomposition of metallic cyanates by
       water." *Zeit. Physikal. Chem.*, 70, 290-314   46

1911. BÉHAL, A., AND DETOEUF, A. "Nouveau dérivé de l'urée, la chlorurée." *C.R.*,
       153, 681-683   170

1911. ESCALES, R., AND KÖPKE, H. "Ammonium cyanate and carbamide." *Chem. Zeit.*,
       35, 595   30

1911. FENTON, H. J. H., AND WILKS, W. A. R. "Method of characterising certain
       ureides (carbamides)." *Proc. Camb. Phil. Soc.*, 16, 64   189

1911. FICHTER, F., AND BECKER, B. "The formation of carbamide by heating ammonium
       carbamate." *Ber.*, 44, 3473-3480 . . . .   66, 69

1911. FICHTER, F., AND BECKER, B. "The formation of symmetrical dialkyl carbamides
       by heating the corresponding carbamates." *Ber.*, 44, 3481-3485 . . .   69

1912. ARMSTRONG, H. E. AND HORTON, E. "Enzyme action. Urease: a selective
       enzyme." *Proc. Roy. Soc., B.*, 85, 109-127   104

1912. CHATTAWAY, F. D. "The transformation of ammonium cyanate into carbamide."
       T.C.S., 101, 170-173   12

1912. DAKIN, H. D. "Oxidations and reductions in the animal body." *London*, Chap.
       III., 48-81   130

1912. FICHTER, F., STUTZ, K., AND GRIESHABER, F. "The electrolytic formation of
       carbamide and acetamidine nitrate." *Verhand. Naturfors. Ges. Basel.*, 23,
       222-263   70

1912. FOSSE, R. "Production directe de l'urée aux depens des albuminoïdes soit par
       oxydation, soit par hydrolyse"   77

1912. FOSSE, R. "Synthesis de l'urée par oxydation de l'ammoniac et des hydrates de
       carbone, de la glycerine ou de l'aldehyde formique"   77

1912. FOSSE, R. "Sur la production d'urée par l'hydrolyse des albuminoïdes." *C.R.*,
       154, 1187-1188, 1448-1450, 1819-1821 . . . .   77, 180

1912. FOSSE, R. "Researches sur l'urée." *C.R.*, 155, 851-852 . . . .   77, 119

1912. FOLIN, O., AND DENIS, W. "Protein metabolism. III. Further absorption ex-
       periments with especial reference to the behaviour of creatine and creatinine,
       and to the formation of urea." *J. Biol. Chem.*, 12, 141-162   130

1912. WERNER, E. A. "A new structural formula for thiocarbamide." *T.C.S.*, 101,
       2180-2191   101

1912. WHEELER, A. S. "Transformation of ammonium cyanate into carbamide." *Amer.
       C.J.*, 34, 1269-1270   12

1913. ARMSTRONG, H. E., BENJAMIN, M. S., AND HORTON, E. "Enzyme action. XIX.
       Urease. Observations on accelerative and inhibitive agents." *Proc. Roy. Soc.
       B.*, 86, 328-343   105

1913. BONNER, W. D., AND BISHOP, E. S. "The rate of reaction of nitrous acid and
       carbamide in dilute solutions." *J. Ind. Eng. Chem.*, 5, 134-136 . . .   58

1913. ESCALES, R., AND KOEPKE, H. "Distillation and sublimation of ammonium salts
       under diminished pressure." *J. pr. Chem.*, ii., 87, 258-279   30

1913. FOSSE, R. "Formation de l'urée par deux moisissures"   119

1913. FOSSE, R. "Formation de l'urée par les végétaux supérieures." *C.R.*, 156, 263-
       265, 567-568   119

1913. FOSSE, R. "Presence de l'urée chez les invertébrés et dans leurs produits
       d'excretion." *C.R.*, 157, 151-154   119

1913. FOSSE, R. "Sur l'identification de l'urée et sa précipitation de solutions extrême-
       ment diluées." *C.R.*, 157, 948-951   188

1913. KROGH, MARIE. "Estimation of urea in urine by means of sodium hypobromite."
       Zeit. Physiol. Chem., 84, 379-407 . . . .   163, 168

1913. GRUBE, G., AND KRÜGER, J. "Polymerisation of cyanamide to dicyanodiamide in
       aqueous solution." *Zeit. Physikal. Chem.*, 86, 65-105 . . . . .   81, 84

1913. SLYKE, D. D. VAN, AND CULLEN, G. E. "Mode of action of soja-bean urease."
       J. Biol. Chem., 17, 28-29   105

1913. TOIT, D. F. DU. "Combinations of carbamide with acids." *Proc. K. Akad.
       Wetensch. Amsterdam*, 16, 555-556   114

DATE.   PAGE IN TEXT.

1913. WERNER, E. A.   " Mechanism of the transformation of ammonium cyanate into
       carbamide, and of the decomposition of carbamide by heat.   The polymerisation
       of cyanic acid."   T.C.S., 103, 1010-1022 . . . .   7, 17, 82

1913. WERNER, E. A.   " Mechanism of the decomposition of carbamide and biuret by
       heat, and of the formation of ammelide."   T.C.S., 103, 2275-2282 . . .   25, 26, 28

1914. BAUME, G.   " Freezing-point curves of volatile systems."   J. Chim. Phys., 12,
       206-215, 225, 270-275   152

1914. BÉHAL, A.   " Preparation de l'acide cyanurique au moyen de l'urée et du chlore."
       Bull. Soc. Chim., iv., 15, 149-159   29

1914. BURROWS, G. T., AND FAWSITT, C. E.   " The decomposition of carbamide."
       T.C.S., 105, 609-622 . . . .   39, 41

1914. FOSSE, R.   " Présence simultanée de l'urée et de l'urease dans le même végétal."
       C.R., 158, 1374-1376   119

1914. FOSSE, R.   " Analyse quantitative gravimetrique de l'urée."   C.R., 158, 1076-1079   193

1914. FOSSE, R., ROBYN, A., AND FRANÇOIS, F.   " Analyse gravimetrique de l'urée dans
       le sang."   C.R., 159, 367-369   193

1914. KNUDSEN, P.   " Methylene diamine."   Ber., 47, 2698-2701   96

1914. MARSHALL, E. K., JUN.   " Soja-bean urease; the effect of dilution, acids, alkalis,
       and ethyl alcohol."   J. Biol. Chem., 17, 351-362   105

1914. MORRELL, G. F., AND BURGEN, P.   " The polymerisation of cyanamide."   T.C.S.,
       105, 576-590   81

1914. PLIMMER, R. H. A., AND SKELTON, R. F.   " The quantitative estimation of urea, and
       indirectly of allantoin, in urine by means of urease."   Biochem. J., 8, 70-73 .   192

1914. SLYKE, D. D. VAN, AND CULLEN, G. E.   " Mode of action of urease and of
       enzymes in general."   J. Biol. Chem., 19, 141-180   192

1914. SLYKE, D. D. VAN, AND ZACHARIAS, G.   " Effect of hydrogen ion concentration
       and of inhibitory substances on urease."   J. Biol. Chem., 19, 181-210 . .   106

1914. SLYKE, D. D. VAN, AND CULLEN, G. E.   " A permanent preparation of urease, and
       its use in the estimation of urea."   J. Biol. Chem., 19, 211-288 . . .   105

1914. WERNER, E. A.   " The constitution of carbamides.   I. The preparation of iso-
       carbamides by the action of methyl sulphate on urea."   T.C.S., 105, 923-933   93

1914. WERNER, E. A.   " A simple demonstration of the formation of biuret from the inter-
       action of urea and cyanic acid."   Proc. C.S., 262   176

1915. ANGELI, A.   " Decompositions of certain nitrogen compounds."   Atti. R. Accad.
       Lincei, v., 24, i., 1093-1098   148

1915. BAYLISS, W. M.   " The nature of enzyme action.   IV. The action of insoluble
       enzymes."   J. Physiol., 50, 85-94   106

1915. HAHN, A.   " Estimation of urea in small quantities of blood."   Chem. Zentr., i.,
       1230-1231   193

1915. ONODERA, N.   " The urease of the soja bean and its co-enzyme."   Biochem. J.,
       9, 575-590   106

1915. ONODERA, N.   " The effects of electrolytes, non-electrolytes, alkaloids, etc., on the
       urease of soja bean."   Biochem. J., 9, 544-574   106

1915. WERNER, E. A.   " Constitution of carbamides.   II. The relation of cyanamide to
       urea ; Constitution of cyanamide and the mechanism of its polymerisation."
       T.C.S., 107, 715-727 . . . .   82, 86, 89, 137

1916. FOSSE, R.   " Origine et distribution de l'urée dans la nature."   Annal. Chimie,
       6, 13-95, 155-215 . . . .   119, 120, 133

1916. FOLIN, O., AND DENIS, W.   " Estimation of nitrogen by direct Nesslerisation.   Urea
       in urine."   J. Biol. Chem., 26, 501-503   193

1916. MATEER, J. G., AND MARSHALL, E. K., JUN.   " Urease content of certain beans,
       with special reference to the jack bean."   J. Biol. Chem., 297-305 . . .   104

1916. LEWIS, G. N.   " The atom and the molecule."   Amer. C.J., 38, 762 . . .   136

1916. WERNER, E. A.   " Constitution of carbamides.   III. The reaction of urea with acetic
       anhydride."   T.C.S., 109, 1120-1130   94

1916. WERNER, E. A.   " The preparation of cyanamide from calcium cyanamide."   T.C.S.,
       109, 1325-1327   184

1917. RÂY, SIR P. C., DEY, M. H., AND GHOSH, J. C.   " The velocity of decomposition
       and the dissociation constant of nitrous acid."   T.C.S., 111, 413-418 . . .   56, 58

DATE.   PAGE IN TEXT
1917. SCHMIDT, E. "The formation of carbamide from cyanamide." *Arch. Pharm.*,
      255, 351-357   89

1917. WERNER, E. A. "Mechanism of the interaction of formaldehyde and ammonium
      chloride." *T.C.S.*, 111, 844-853   141

1917. WERNER, E. A. "Constitution of carbamides. IV. The mechanism of the interaction
      of urea and nitrous acid." *T.C.S.*, 111, 863-876 . . . . .   50, 56

1918. CIAMICIAN, G. "Comparisons and similarities: Water and ammonia." *Atti. R.
      Accad. Lincei*, **v.**, 27, ii., 141-146 . . . .   81, 148

1918. DIXON, A. E. "Interaction of formaldehyde and carbamide." *T.C.S.*, 113, 238-248   194

1918. FICHTER, F., STEIGER, H., AND STANISCH, T. "Formation of carbamide from
      ammonium carbonate and related substances." *Chem. Zentr.*, ii., 444-446 . .   76

1918. WERNER, E. A. "Constitution of carbamides. V. The mechanism of the de-
      composition of urea when heated in solution with acids and alkalis respectively;
      the hydrolysis of metallic cyanates." *T.C.S.*, 113, 84-99 . . . 34, 42, 45, 47, 104

1918. WERNER, E. A. "Constitution of carbamides. VI. The mechanism of the synthesis
      of urea from urethane." *T.C.S.*, 113, 622-627 . . . .   62, 95

1918. WERNER, E. A. "VII. The mechanism of the synthesis of urea from the interaction
      of carbonyl chloride and ammonia." *T.C.S.*, 113, 694-699 . . . .   60, 95

1918. WERNER, E. A., AND CARPENTER, G. K. "VIII. The formation of urea and of
      biuret from oxamide." *T.C.S.*, 113, 699-701   72

1918. YAMASAKI, E. "Chemical reaction in the system: Urea-urease." *J. Tōkyō Chem.
      Soc.*, 39, 125-184   106

1919. BARENDRECHT, H. P. "Urease and the radiation theory of enzyme action." I.,
      II., and III. *Proc. K. Akad. Wetensch. Amsterdam*, **21**, 1126 and 1307; **22**,
      29-45, and 126-138 . . . .   107, 111

1919. BRAHM, C. "Estimation of carbamide in blood and in urine." *Chem. Zentr.*, iv.,
      442   191

1919. DEKEUWER, E., AND LESCOEUR, L. "Dosage de l'urée au moyen de l'hypo-
      bromure de soude." *C.R. Soc. Biol.*, 82, 445-447   190

1919. FOSSE, R. "Oxydation simultanée du sang et du glucose." *C.R.*, 168, 908-910 70, 78, 121, 132

1919. FOSSE, R. "Formation par oxydation des substances organiques d'un terme
      intermédiare produisant spontanément l'urée." *C.R.*, 169, 320-322 . . .   70, 77

1919. FOSSE, R. "Le mechanisme de la formation artificielle de l'urée par oxydation."
      C.R., 168, 1164-1166 . . . .   70, 77, 121

1919. FOSSE, R. "Formation de l'acide cyanique par l'oxydation des substances
      organiques." *C.R.*, 169, 91-93 . . . .   70, 77, 121

1919. GANASSINI, D. "Schiff's reaction for the detection of carbamide." *Chem. Zentr.*,
      ii., 473   186

1919. LANGMUIR, I. "Isomorphism, isosterism, and co-valence." *Amer. C.J.*, 41, 868,
      1543   136

1919. LESCOEUR, L. "L'urée et l'hypobromure." *J. Pharm. Chim.*, 20, 305, 374 .   190

1919. PRICE, T. W. "The decomposition of carbamide in the presence of nitric acid."
      T.C.S., 115, 1354-1360 . . . .   37, 38

1919. WERNER, E. A. "IX. The interaction of nitrous acid and mono-substituted ureas;
      the preparation of diazomethane, etc." *T.C.S.*, 115, 1093-1102 . . .   102, 115

1919. WERNER, E. A. "X. The behaviour of urea and of thiourea towards diazomethane
      and diazoethane respectively. The oxidation of thiourea by potassium perman-
      ganate." *T.C.S.*, 115, 1168-1174   101

1919. WERNER, E. A. "The separation of aliphatic amines by partial neutralisation."
      T.C.S., 115, 1010-1015 . . . .   140, 181, 184

1919. WESTER, D H. "Examination of the urease-content of indigenous seeds." *Chem.
      Weekblad*, 16, 1548-1551   104

1920. BARENDRECHT, H. P. "The direct synthesis of carbamide by urease." *Rec. Trav.
      Chim.*, 39, 603-605   111

1920. DOUBLET, H., AND LESCOEUR, L. "L'urée et l'acide nitreux." *C.R. Soc. Biol.*,
      83, 1103-1105   191

1920. FOSSE, R. "Synthese d'une deuxiéme diamide, l'oxamide par oxydation du sucre
      et de l'ammoniaque." "Analyse qualitative de l'acide cyanique." *C.R.*, 171,
      398, 635   121

1920. FALK, K. G. "Chemical reactions, their theory and mechanism." Chapter V.,
      80-83   150

DATE.   PAGE IN TEXT.

1920. LANGMUIR, I. "The octet theory of valence and its applications, with special reference to organic nitrogen compounds." *Amer. C.J.*, 42, 274-292 . . . 136, 143

1920. MATTAAR, T. J. F. "Is the direct synthesis of carbamide by urease possible?" *Rec. Trav. Chim.*, 39, 495-498 107

1920. PARTOS, G. "Estimation of urea by means of the carbon dioxide evolved by urease." *Biochem. Zeits.*, 103, 292-299 193

1920. SCHLUBACH, H. H. "Tetra-ethylammonium." *Ber.*, 53, **B**, 1689-1693 . . 135

1920. WERNER, E. A. "XI. The mechanism of the synthesis of urea from ammonium carbamate; the preparation of certain mixed tri-substituted carbamates and dithio-carbamates." *T.C.S.*, 117, 1046-1053 66

1920. WERNER, E. A. "XII. The decomposition of urea when heated in the presence of acids." *T.C.S.*, 117, 1078-1081 38

1920. WERNER, E. A., AND FEARON, W. R. "XIII. The constitution of cyanic acid, and the formation of urea from the interaction of ammonia and cyanic acid at low temperatures." *T.C.S.*, 117, 1356-1362 . . . . 18, 19

1920. YAMASAKI, E. "Chemical kinetics of urease." *Sci. Rep. Tôhoku. Imp. Univ.*, 9, 97, 136 106

1920. YI, P. Y. "Urease of the seeds of *Robinia pseudacacia*." *Ber. deuts. pharm. Ges.*, 30, 178-191 104

1921. ARREGUINE, V., AND GARCÍA, E. D. "A colour reaction for carbamide." *Anal. Asoc. Quím. Argentina*, 9, 183-191 190

1921. BRIGGS, S. H. C. "Valency and co-ordination." *T.C.S.*, 119, 1876-1879 . 153

1921. FUNCKE, Y. "Estimation of urea." *Zeits. Physiol. Chem.*, 114, 72-78 . . 191

1921. FOSSE, R. "Synthése de l'acide cyanique par oxydation de substances organiques." *Bull. Soc. Chim.*, iv., 29, 158-203 78

1921. FOSSE, R., AND ROUCHELMAN, N. "Sur la formation de l'urée dans la foie après la mort." *C.R.*, 172, 771-772 132

1921. HURTLEY, W. H. "The production of carbon monoxide by the action of alkaline hypohalogenites on urea." *Biochem. J.*, xv., 11-18 . . . . 163, 173

1921. MEZGER, F. "Estimation of urea." *Pharm. Zentral.-L.*, 62, 719-721 . . 191

1921. NICLOUX, M., AND WELTER, G. "Micro-analyse quantitative gravimétrique de l'urée. Application au dosage de l'urée dans 1 cm³ de sang." *C.R.*, 173, 1490-1493 194

1921. RHODES, H. T. F. "Theory of auxiliary valencies and water of crystallisation." *Chem. News*, 122, 85, 97-99 153

1921. STEHLE, R. L. "The gasometric determination of urea in urine." *J. Biol. Chem.*, 47, 13-17 191

1921. WERNER, E. A. "Modern investigations on the breaking down of urea by the enzyme urease." *Dublin J. Med. Sci.*, iv., 21, 512-520 . . . . 109, 110

1921. WESTER, D. H. "The specific action of the urease of canavalia." *Rec. Trav. Chim.*, 40, 320-322 104

1922. BAILEY, K. C. "Sur la synthèse directe de l'urée à partir du gaz carbonique et de l'ammoniaque." *C.R.*, 175, 279-281 198

1922. DETOEUF, A. "La monochlorourée." *Bull. Soc. Chim.*, 31, 102-108 . . 173

1922. KRASE, N. W., AND GADDY, V. L. "Synthesis of urea from ammonia and carbon dioxide." *Amer. J. Ind. and Eng. Chem.*, 14, 611-616 198

1922. MATIGNON, C., AND FRÉJACQUES, M. "Sur la transformation de l'ammoniaque en urée." *C.R.*, 174, 455-457 197

1922. MENAUL, P. "The hypobromite reaction on urea." *J. Biol. Chem.*, 51, 87-88 . 191

1922. WERNER, E. A. "The occurrence of urea in nature. Theory of mode of formation of urea in plants and in animals. Cyanic acid in its relation to protein building and protein degradation." *Dublin J. Med. Sci.*, iv., 23, 577-594 . . . 126

1922. WERNER, E. A. "Constitution of carbamides. XIV. The decomposition of urea by sodium hypobromite in alkaline solution, and an improved procedure for the estimation of urea by this means." *T.C.S.*, 121, 2318-2325 . . . 164, 171

1922. WYCKOFF, R. W. G. "The crystallographic and atomic symmetries of ammonium chloride." *Amer. J. Science*, v., 3, 177-183 160

INDEX.